Bt 8.50

MY NAME IS LEGION

The Stirling County Study of Psychiatric

Disorder & Sociocultural Environment

Volume I

MY
NAME IS
LEGION

Foundations for a Theory of

Man in Relation to Culture

Alexander H. Leighton

Basic Books, Inc.   New York

TO   *Gertrude Anne Hamilton and*

Archibald Ogilvie Leighton

A MITE IN RETURN FOR A GIFT

"While I stand on the roadway, or on
the pavement gray,
I hear it in the deep heart's core."

Allister Miles Macmillan

ON AUGUST 13, 1958, Allister died of coronary occlusion
in Wolfville, Nova Scotia. In this event the Stirling County
Study lost not only its Deputy Director but a central figure
in its growth. The field of social psychiatry lost a pioneer.
The blow has been personal and crushing to all his colleagues.

Allister was outstanding for his energy, organizational
abilities, sharpness of criticism, faithfulness to facts, and
keenness in analysis. Of equal note were his tenderness to
those in difficulties and his loyalty to his friends. He saw
these volumes to the edge of their completion; it is in sorrow
that we come now to the end and find that he is not with us.

Table of Contents

List of Figures

And always, night and day, he was in the mountains, and in the tombs, crying, and cutting himself with stones . . . .

And [Jesus] asked him, What is thy name? And he answered, saying, **My name is Legion: for we are many.**

ST. MARK. 5:5,9

A GENERAL INTRODUCTION

to the Stirling County Study

> *This work is under the influence of three central questions: How much psychiatric disorder is there? What are the proportions of different varieties and kinds? How are these distributed in relation to sociocultural factors? In short: How much? Of what kinds? And where?*
>
> *These epidemiological problems are relevant to the desire to increase knowledge about the etiology of*

psychiatric disorder, and because in this connection sociocultural factors are important and worthy of exploration. At the same time, it is apparent that genetic factors and physiological damage from infection, dietary deficiency, and other sources must also be taken into account before substantial conclusions can be reached. Hence the aim is not to "prove"—even in a very loose sense of the word—cause-and-effect relationships between sociocultural factors and psychiatric disorder. The concern is rather to discover certain kinds of association between the two, to define targets for more penetrating investigation, and to consider the nature of the problems inherent in attacking such targets.

These are large questions, and the advance on them in the research reported here is necessarily small. Not only do we move without knowledge of genetic and physiological factors but we also deal with a limited population and touch the problems only at selected points. Volume I of the Stirling County Study is concerned with a frame of reference in terms of which the widely distributed and multifaceted phenomena of our attention can be conceptually organized for study. Some theoretical expectations are outlined regarding the associations between sociocultural environment and psychiatric disorder.

Volume II presents the sociocultural environment as it is relevant to psychiatric disorder in a particular county. The ideas and expectations of the first volume are here put to work in selecting and assessing a number of communities. It has been predicted that these will show contrast in the prevalence of psychiatric disorder due to differences in their sociocultural composition. The fact that the prevalence of disorder is found in some instances to be according to expectation gives reason for analyzing and comparing the communities, for discussing methods, and for a further elaboration of concepts and theory.

Volume III is concerned with analysis of the prevalence data. Since all conclusions hang on what the indices of psychiatric disorder used in the study actually mean, a great deal of attention is given to their assessment. Drawing on the analysis of sociocultural factors presented in the second volume, the various symptom patterns are examined in relation to environmental factors. From these findings conclusions are reached and some generalizations made bearing on the questions of "How much? Of what kinds? And where?" There is, in short, a reassessment of frame of reference and of theory bearing on etiology.

It may be helpful to note that a preceding book, Explorations in Social Psychiatry *(edited by Alexander H. Leighton, John A. Clausen, and Robert N. Wilson and published by Basic Books in 1957) is in many ways an introduction to these three volumes. It was developed as a project of the Social Science Research Council while the Stirling County Study was getting underway.*

Our interest in etiology is connected, of course, with a concern for the treatment of psychiatric disorder, with the hope that greater knowledge will lead to greater effectiveness. Beyond this, however, is a further and more comprehensive interest arising from attention to prevalence and to sociocultural factors: prevention. We look forward to the day when enough will be known about sociocultural factors to allow prevention in a public health sense through deliberate change in the human environment.

The reader may note two limitations in the Study: concern with the effects of environment on psychiatric disorder rather than with the effects of disorder on society and culture; and emphasis on disorder rather than

Introduction to the Stirling County Study

health. The first limitation is a matter of preference. It seemed impracticable to attack all aspects of the inter-relationships between psychiatric disorder and sociocultural factors simultaneously, and hence one alternative was chosen.

The selection of disorder rather than mental health is on a somewhat different basis; it rests on the judgment that we do not as yet have concepts and methods adequate for making a direct advance on the nature of health. Grappling with illness is difficult enough, due to many problems of definition and identification of the phenomena with which one proposes to deal. In the case of mental health the situation appeared even more troublesome and puzzling. We have consequently taken disorder as our point of departure, and for the time being health is treated as a residual category—the absence of disorder. This is not regarded as desirable in any long-range sense, only expedient. It is hoped that through advancing on the problems of disorder a foundation can be laid for the eventual study and understanding of health in positive rather than negative terms.

RESEARCH ORGANIZATION

The Stirling County Study is an ongoing project conducted by Cornell University in collaboration with the Department of Public Health of the Province of Nova Scotia. Within Cornell, the study is attached administratively to the Social Science Research Center and is sponsored by the Department of Sociology and Anthropology of the College of Arts and Sciences and the Department of Psychiatry of the New York Hospital and Cornell Medical College.

The work has passed through five main phases with somewhat different organization of research teams during each. These may be designated as:

I. Pilot study
II. Planning
III. Field operations
IV. Analysis
V. Reporting

The pilot study phase was conducted in Stirling County during the summers of 1948, 1949, and 1950. It was carried out for the most part by graduate students under my supervision. There was some participation by postgraduates interested in having the field experience and a number of senior social scientists gave generously of their time in an advisory capacity.

Intensive planning took place during 1950 and 1951. With the beginning of this phase, the work became a year-round activity and was divided into three main areas of interest: investigation of sociocultural factors, investigation of psychiatric disorder through clinical methods, and investigation of psychiatric disorder through psychological screening devices. The project was organized administratively in terms of these main areas with a Team or "Unit" focused on each. Of major importance in the planning, however, was a faculty level seminar which met during the academic year 1950-1951. This was supplemented by a frequent use of consultants on an individual basis.

The field operations began in 1951, overlapping somewhat with the termination of the planning. In certain respects these have continued to the present. Since 1956, however, the field operations have been related to data-gathering and other specific tasks not reported in these three volumes. The principal features of relevance here were the development and use of a psychological screening device, the establishment of a clinic and an epidemiological survey based on psychiatric method, and the carrying out of anthropological and sociological studies. The clinic had a twofold function—to provide

Introduction to the Stirling County Study

a service to the community and to conduct research as part of the field operations.

The phase of analysis began in 1952 with the completion of the first steps in the field operations. Since 1956 this phase and that of reporting have been the central concern of the Study. Although a number of preliminary articles have appeared (see Appendix D), the main results are the present volumes. There remain, in addition, a number of areas of investigation, particularly with reference to work done since 1956, which, we expect, will eventually appear in print.

From the foregoing it is evident that the Study has lasted more than ten years. During this time it has been carried on the shoulders of many different individuals who have given their help for varying periods of time. They are listed alphabetically in Appendix C, together with indications as to the nature of their work. More particulars with regard to the character and importance of contributions from individual members of the Study will be given at relevant points in the course of the three volumes.

A heavy debt of acknowledgement is also owing to many persons and organizations outside the Study that have helped and made possible the work. These, too, are listed in Appendix C.

INTRODUCTION TO
VOLUME I

MY AIM IN THIS VOLUME is to discuss the possible effects of sociocultural environment on mental health and to suggest a conceptual bridge whereby certain aspects of personality, viewed as a process, and certain aspects of society, viewed as a process, may be related to one another. The work took origin in the need for a frame of reference in a particular research task concerned with the effects of sociocultural environment on the prevalence of psychiatric disorder. Thus, the book is given focus by the requirement of developing a research program and it is intended to serve as an orientation for the succeeding two volumes in which findings are presented and discussed. It may be viewed as an explanation of the kinds of questions our research attempts to ask of nature.

The book is not, however, limited strictly to the ideas in terms of which the research began. Although the greater part of the initial concepts is included, there has been a certain amount of reformulation and considerable amplification as a result both of thinking about the topics over a period of time and of attempting to design and develop the research operations. Since it hardly seems worth while to give a detailed account of these many steps and stumblings toward maturation, the frame of reference is presented in its latest rather than in its earlier or various successive forms. This does not mean, however, that it has been reworked in accordance with the research findings. Modification of this sort remains to be taken up at the end of Volume III. Given here are the essentials of the concepts that guided hypothesis finding and the first waves of observation and analysis.

The ground covered in the frame of reference is more extensive than that strictly required by the research it subsumes. Although an effort is made to keep an eye on central purpose, I have not hesitated to explore avenues that might prove relevant to other research tasks in the same general field.

It is hoped that the results may have several aspects to recommend them. Clinicians, whose daily concern is with the origin, course, and outcome of psychiatric disorders, may be interested to consider the problem of sociocultural components. Students of society and culture, on the other hand, may be interested to consider how shared patterns of human behavior can be related to the mental health of individuals. It is also thought that the work may be useful, at least in terms of background, to those concerned with the broader field of culture and personality.

A conceptual bridge is considered worthy of attention because despite the unity of the phenomenon, man, the tools, both methodological and theoretical, for depicting and predicting individual behavior are different from those which serve the same purpose with regard to societies. These differences comprise contrasting levels and kinds of abstraction. Pathways must be found between them if one is to understand how social and cultural factors may affect the ideas, feelings, unconscious motives, spontaneity, defenses, and other aspects of personality related to mental health. In swinging the point of one's attention back and forth between such concepts as cultural holism and personality holism, or between the function of a cultural pattern and the function of a psychiatric symptom, or between sociocultural organization and personality organization, there is need for some scaffolding of ideas by means of which interconnections may be found and traced.

The form of presentation comprises three parts. The first is an introduction to psychiatric disorder as it occurs in a particular environmental setting and a discussion of main types and main causes. The second part tries to delineate sets of propositions as a means of pulling together some basic characteristics of psychiatric disorder and mental health in relation to some basic characteristics of the sociocultural environment. The final part is concerned with discussing research questions and conceptual tools as a preliminary to actual investigation. The line of thought is carried up to, but not over into, the description of specific operations.

The mode of presentation is the common one of alternation between illustrative example and theoretical discussion. This kind of warp and woof is complicated, however, by the fact that the illustrations involve not only the usual type of excerpt from case-histories but also slices of the sociocultural environment. In order to aid unity in presentation, therefore, and also as a step toward the development of research design, most examples concerned with sociocultural factors will be presented as from a single region and the case material as from a limited number of individuals who are members of its society and carriers of its culture. In the beginning it may appear that a flood of disconnected items are being described, but it is hoped that as the book progresses their relevance will unfold.

The general region utilized as a model for discussion is in the northeastern part of the North American continent. It is selected because of personal familiarity and because the research described later was carried out in one part of this area. The case material is based on life, but is altered under the influence of two considerations. The first is disguise effected to protect privacy and the second is selection of facets to demonstrate particular points. Hence it should be understood as illustrative of ideas and perspectives and as a vehicle for conveying meaning, but not as a report on findings such as will be given in Volumes II and III.

The reader may note a tendency in the writing to rely on illustration and analogy rather than definition for many of the ideas and phenomena that come under discussion. The effort is, in fact, to use descriptions whenever possible that show the heart of the matter and to leave the boundaries and shades of discrimination unstated. In such instances I am in effect saying, "Here is the sort of thing that is meant. You can perhaps supply other examples of your own to match it. Let us not elaborate at this time on the problems of marginal cases or fine distinctions, however important they may be in the long run. Let us first get clear the central point, namely, the order rather than the species of the concept or phenomenon and the general rather than the precise meaning of the term."

The justification for this type of thinking and exposition is that we are necessarily concerned with somewhat broad approximations. The nature of the problem and the severe limitations of current knowledge hardly permit any other foundation on which to begin. Moreover, the ground to be surveyed is extensive and it is necessary to avoid many critical details in order to rough out the main features. It should not, however, be supposed that this is considered the end. Refinement is obviously necessary. *The point is that first approximations set the stage for successive approximations and hence lead to progressive clarification.*

PART ONE

Psychiatric
Disorders

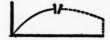

PART ONE

Psychiatric Disorders

Chapter I

Orientations

THERE ARE TWO ORIENTATIONS with which this chapter is concerned, one having to do with the world of thought, and the other with the world of events—of people and the things they do. The first is a particular corner from the expanse of human concepts that has been selected as the starting point for developing the frame of reference. The second consists in the phenomenal base to which the concepts refer, with illustrations couched in terms of a particular place at a particular time.

The reader should be prepared for being addressed in two languages, the one abstract, the other graphic. My desire is to place in the foreground certain concepts and phenomena as points of attention and to give an initial explanation of certain terms. In succeeding chapters the concepts and their terms will be used to develop discussion of the phenomena, which will in turn provide ground for enlargement of the concepts. The frame of reference may thus be thought of as an expanding spiral, getting both more specific and more extensive as it progresses.

I. CONCEPTUAL OUTLOOK

Let us begin with *personality*. This would seem appropriate, since psychiatric disorder can be defined as a disturbance of personality and it is well to get in mind some idea of that which is disturbed.

We should take into account, however, that the psychiatric context implies some limitations and some emphases which are not necessarily present when "personality" is employed in other disciplines, such as psychology and sociology. In psychiatry there is much influence from the demands of diagnosis and treatment, from the problems of evaluating persons while having certain practical decisions in view. It is basically a working concept related to therapy.

Moreover, there are a number of somewhat complicated points in the several usages of the term, and some opportunities for confusion. In the present chapter, the aim is to rough out only one usage, one that has served us in our work. Such mention as will be made of other usages and of origins—including bibliography—will be deferred until Chapter VII.

"Personality" is intended here to designate the acting of a human being as a whole. It is what you mean when you say "Tom" with reference to somebody you know who has this name. The word does not refer to that individual's blood pressure, his basal metabolic rate, his capacity for digesting fats, or to his brain waves. These and other anatomical, physiological, and biochemical dimensions of his being contribute to his personality, but they are aspects, or parts of the processes, rather than personality itself. Similarly, his manual skill, his intelligence, his even temper, his loving disposition, and his nervous mannerisms are not personality but components of this acting whole.

Personality, furthermore, as used here, is not limited to those unique qualities of behavior which Tom and only Tom exhibits, nor on the other hand to those ideas and feelings which he shares with other members of his society, such as patriotism and the custom of wearing a hat. These too are components.

Personality refers to the acting of a person considered as a living, self-integrating unit.

This view rests on thinking of a person as an organism. As such he has a number of different levels of integration, from the biochemical to the psychological. Or, he may be considered as a number of different organs, such as striped muscles, liver, stomach, and brain, interconnected and interdependent so as to form a system.

The point to stress is the idea of system and components (or subsystems); hence, when "personality" is used, the reference is to the net effect of all the components, the system as a whole. Implicit in this are two ideas which greatly affect analysis and theory. One is that the whole is under the influence of its components as well as of events which impinge on it from without. Hence any attempt to understand the acting of the unit must include some consideration of the subsystems as well as factors external to the system. The second is that a component is under the influence of the whole and its acting can only be understood in the context of that whole. To put the matter crudely (and borrowing from Hegel), a man without an eye is blind, but equally an eye without a man cannot see.

The subsystems of a personality system are not generally thought of in terms of physiology and organs, although from the point of view of psychiatry and particularly for some purposes to be made evident in later chapters these levels of integration must not be forgotten. The components receiving most attention are those at the psychological level. Perhaps it would be more explicit to speak of "behavior" in this connection, but it would have to be understood that this includes not only overt and more or less observable action but also that which is covert and has to be inferred—psychic processes.

In considering personality as a system the concept of patterning is useful. Our perceptions of patterning are doubtless based primarily on visible and palpable objects. We distinguish a tree, a man, and a fifty-cent piece because they have characteristic arrangements of shape, size, weight, color, and texture. Something analogous to this is also found with regard to sound. Animals and birds can often be distinguished because of having a characteristic arrangement in the noises they emit. At a more complex level, patterning is seen in the language we speak and has been systematically described in grammars and books on linguistics.

There is an important apparent distinction to be noted between some of the patterns that are seen and all patterns that are heard. Many visible patterns seem to be complete at any given moment during which they are perceived. We take in a friend's face at a glance and so recognize him or her. Sound patterns, on the other hand, extend through time, with beginning, duration, and end. A sentence, a recited poem, and a symphony all illustrate this clearly. They are sequential patterns. Having noted this apparent distinction we may now observe that visible patterns can also be sequential as in waves rolling up a shore, a ballet, the succession of seasonal changes, or the growth of a child. They are multifaceted but sequential.

The point I desire to make is that when one speaks of patterning in personality, the emphasis is on the sequential character of the phenomenon and not on a static arrangement as in a picture or on the study of the arrested patterning of the human body as in anatomy. The personality of an individual flows in sequence through a large number of simultaneous expressions, like a symphony being played by an orchestra, and there is integration somewhat parallel to the integration of wind, strings, and percussion in constituting the total pattern. One may take this analogy a step further and say that personality also has movements in which central themes are repeated with variations—childhood, youth, maturity, and old age.

Like most analogies, however, this comparison with the orchestra and symphony cannot be carried too far. The orchestra, for instance, functions according to a score which exerts a fairly rigid control. Personality may be thought to have a score also, laid down by the genes, but it is much less specific and its patterning is subject to change while in the act of performing. It is as if much of the music were being rewritten as it went along, or improvised in response to circumstances.

Having designated life, organism, wholeness, integration, and patterning with relation to personality, we may now turn to the psychological content of this unit, to illustrations of the component subpatterns of the system. There are, obviously, almost infinite ways in which such aspects of personality could be selected, described, and catalogued. The choice of one method over another depends on intended use as well as on the characteristics of the phenomenon. For some purposes, as for instance picking men of ability for a difficult task, perceptions, skills, and understandings might provide a fruitful breakdown. For the purposes of this chapter I shall turn to a few rather general categories which have been extensively employed in psychiatry. They may have the double usefulness of indicating further what is here meant by personality and at the same time introducing components particularly relevant for the analysis and discussion which comes in later chapters.

The first of these patterned aspects is a characteristic about which man is apt to pride himself, namely, the process of thinking. Perception, comprehension, memory, and reasoning are involved, and the word *cognition* may be used to represent the component.

Another aspect of personality has to do with the emotions—joy, rage, fear, grief, and innumerable blends and mixtures. One may note in this connection two general types: emotions *per se,* which are characteristically short-lived and reactive to situations; and moods, which are more enduring and not so clearly connected with events. In fact, preexisting moods may color immediate events rather than take their coloring from them. For both emotions and moods considered together, the term *affect* is employed.

A third aspect is exemplified in the sexual urge. The potentiality for this is apparently inborn and appears in due course as the personality develops. The urges for food, for sleep, and for action have similar characteristics. Taken together, these four illustrate a component of personality for which the word *instinct* may be used to emphasize the idea of being inborn. There are, it seems probable, other instincts besides those mentioned above, but in considering a total list one soon runs into the difficulty of distinguishing between those urges which are inborn and those which have been in the main acquired. It seems likely that most consistent trends in personality of this character have both inborn and experiential roots. In these pages, *basic urge* will be employed in recognition of this situation. A basic urge is considered to have instinctual tendencies in its origin, but to be differentiated and patterned through experience. A given basic urge, furthermore, may be, or have been, under the influence of more than one instinct.

The three concepts, cognition, affect, and basic urge, are presented as analytic tools at a somewhat rough and perhaps even simple-minded level of approximation. Obviously, when they are elaborated a number of perplexing questions emerge, and there are many differences of opinion among behavioral scientists as to meaning and usefulness of the terms and the nature of the phenomena of reference. The usage here, however, is in harmony with that found practical in designating some of the main aspects of behavior with which clinical psychiatry attempts to deal, and hence appropriate to considering personality in relation to psychiatric disorder. Even so, the terms are not, it must be admitted, always employed by clinicians so as to have clean margins between them; and this is a matter of importance even at this level of approximation.

As conceptual tools in this frame of reference, affect, cognition, and basic urge are mutually exclusive. Affect refers only to emotions and moods and not to the ideas or basic urges that may be a part of the event in the personality system in which the affect occurs. Affect is feeling, but the topics of the feeling are not. On the other hand cognition refers only to the processes of thought and knowing, and not to the satisfactions or apprehensions which may accompany them nor to the basic urges which may have inspired them.

These distinctions are, of course, purely analytic.[1] In the successive patterned events which make up a personality system, affect, cognition, and basic urges are not separate faculties but aspects of the events. In order for discussion to progress, however, and in order to describe and analyze personality, it is necessary to have some terms which have mutually exclusive meanings and which are limited to one or another aspect or component of the phenomenon. This general and in-the-nature-of-language sort of need is enhanced by the fact that, in psychiatric disorder, affect, cognition, and basic urge are often seen in a distorted form.

With this in mind, let us now note that all three of the items designated so far are intersected by the dimension of consciousness. One of the most taken for granted and yet one of the most mysterious of all the innumerable mysteries of existence is the little point in time and space which constitutes each person's awareness that he exists—the center of the pronoun "I." Consciousness may be likened to the field of vision: at any given moment, there is a central focus; around this, a less sharp awareness of other objects; beyond these still more vaguely, others, until imperceptibly the limits of the field are reached. The point of focus in vision can be shifted so as to bring into sharp definition one or another of the vague shapes around the edge which attract attention. It can, of course, also be swung more widely than this to encompass an entirely new field of vision. Not only does one respond to visual stimuli; one seeks things to see as well. Consciousness can be thought of as operating in a similar manner, and when we speak of it we generally mean not only that which is in focus at a particular moment but also the entire range of items that are ordinarily available in memory and imagination.

There are also, however, psychological processes, outside the field readily available to consciousness, which nevertheless affect the acting of a person. Apparently something very similar to cognition can take place without our being aware of it, so that occasionally we find ourselves with answers to intellectual problems while not knowing how they were achieved. There are also grounds for supposing that something analogous to the affect which we feel and the basic urges of which we are aware takès place below the surface of consciousness and determines many aspects of our personality. The word *unconscious* may be applied to these patterns, but it should be understood as having a broader definition here than that often employed in psychoanalytic writings. This point will be taken up again in Chapter V, pages 143-146.

Cognition, affect, and basic urges, together with their unconscious counterparts, serve to illustrate at the psychological level what was meant earlier by unit and integration. They show the kind of components conceived as integrating. Each is, of course, analyzable into innumerable subaspects and hence the integration does not mean a union of neat packages, like volumes in a series stood together on a shelf, but a collection of thousands of interrelated patterns which are only very roughly classifiable under the main terms above. Let me revert again to the analogy of the orchestra to point out that these many subaspects are something like the sounds emitted by the different instruments; the timing and blending of sounds into the form of a symphony is something like what is meant by the kind of unit that constitutes personality.

The reader may wonder why the constituents of the personality system have not been illustrated in terms of *id, ego,* and *superego.* These would convey well the idea of system and components, and they have a major place in psychiatric thinking about the structure of personality. I have preferred aspects which, while not contrary to Freud's trilogy, are at a somewhat more primitive level of conceptualization. These have the advantage of leaving us, at the present stage of presentation, uncommitted to some of the theory which more technical words imply.

We come now to the use of the word "self" in describing personality as a "self-integrating unit" (page 17). This is not a metaphysical concept, but an attempt to designate an attribute which is found in all living things and which is important in grasping the idea of personality. The point is that system A maintains system A. As will be discussed presently, there are durational limits to this (there is beginning and there is end), but within these limits much of the acting of the system is concerned with holding together. It is for this reason that I have not spoken of the unit as "integrated," since this could imply that the integrating forces were mainly outside the system. "Integrated" also has the disadvantage of suggesting that the process is complete, rather than continuous in the duration of the personality.

In conceiving of the system as self-integrating, one is also conceiving struggle and conflict. There is the potential for struggle with forces outside the system that would exert an influence toward radical change or dissolution. There is also the potential conflict between tendencies within the system should one or another component threaten the integration of the whole. This can be visualized in terms of conflict between different sorts of basic urges, and between various kinds of affect, and as taking place both within the area of consciousness and at unconscious levels. Implicit in the idea of self-integration, struggle, and conflict is the idea of dynamic equilibrium and of adaptation to changes within and without the system.

Although one thinks of these tendencies for the most part in psychological terms, it is important to keep in mind that all takes place as biological process. A person is a living organism, and as such is an energy system in the sense in which biologists think of energy. This is to be distinguished from the concept of psychic energy which will be discussed in Chapter V (pages 139-141). An outstanding characteristic of a biological system is that energy is drawn from the environment, becomes part of the system, and is given off again. The total process is called metabolism, with anabolism and katabolism designating the two main aspects.

Cuvier suggested the whirlpool as an analogy for illustrating this sort of concept. The energy of a straight-flowing current enters the spinning vortex, becomes incorporated in that pattern, and then goes out again. Every person has a similar relationship to the world about him. He is, to be sure, an immensely complex energy system with vast elaborations, but every aspect of his existence, conscious and unconscious, inter- and intrapersonal, is movement of energy and is a part in the total process of energy exchange. It is because of this movement that the word "act," as well as "integrating" and "unit," is used to describe what is meant by personality. And it is because of this also that the word "dynamic" can be employed to refer to the interplay within personality of desires, wishes, motives, and motivations, all aspects of energy processes.

Such a viewpoint suggests that it is not desirable to think of personality as a psychological something set on a biological base or as operating in a biological matrix. It is rather an entity which can be conceived as having biological and psychological dimensions but which is, as a phenomenon, a unit.

This matter is of some importance on at least two counts. The biological dimension of personality is relevant for understanding many of those disturbances of its acting which will be described in the chapters dealing with psychiatric disorder. It is also relevant for understanding interdependencies between personalities and the character of sociocultural groups as will be discussed in Parts Two and Three of this book.

Having indicated earlier that sequence is a dimension of the patterning that constitutes personality, it is appropriate now to consider this at more length. The over-all sequence of personality is from conception, through growth and maturity, to decline and death. This obvious fact is represented in Figure 1. Here sequence is depicted on the horizontal dimension while the vertical indicates an heterogeneous category that has been labeled "capacity." At the base there is no life and hence no personality; at the top is the optimum of what we mean when we speak of "prime of life." The physical capabilities and the subpatterns of personality such as cognition, affect, basic urges, and unconscious relationships have achieved a maximum of development and integration.

It is recognized, of course, that different aspects of personality achieve their maximum at different points in the sequence. Aesthetic

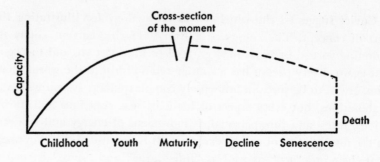

FIGURE 1: *The Life-Arc*

sensitivity and memory for detail in recent events may reach their peak in youth, whereas the maximum of knowledge may come much later. There can be up- and downswings along the curve and there will be variations from one person to another under the influence of constitutional differences, accidents of experience, and the requirements of cultures, subcultures, and roles. The curve shown is, then, a gross approximation, but for the use intended here it is better kept so rather than complicated with multiple lines.

Let us consider now a given personality at a given moment on the life-arc, represented by the bars transecting the curve. The bars are double to show by the space between that a moment, though short, has what Whitehead calls "temporal thickness." As an abstract concept, a moment is often considered to be an instant in time without duration, just as a point is a location in space with no extension. For the purposes here, however, a moment has to be conceived as having sufficient duration to permit the expression of the current patterning. The solid part of the arc to the left and the broken line to the right indicate respectively the actual past and the future (the potential beyond the moment). The selection of the point at which the cross-section has been made is purely arbitrary, but has been placed at the prime of life to be in harmony with the case of Tom to be introduced later in this chapter.

Personality, at any one point on the life-arc, may be considered in terms of two main interlocking dimensions. The first is personality as the precipitate of previous experience in the interplay of heredity and environment, a precipitate which has certain predominant, patterned tendencies that are relatively fixed and hence more or less predictable. The second is the interplay of these "given" precipitates, these patterned tendencies, with the opportunities and limitations of the immediate situation. These two views may be summed up as *life-story* and *cross-section*. They are obviously merely different dimensions of the same phenomena, not rival concepts, although each is sometimes treated to the exclusion of the other.

That the life-story has influence on the nature of the cross-section has already been noted. It should also be underscored that in a sense the reverse is equally true—the cross-section has influence on life-story. This is by virtue of the fact that the cross-section of any particular moment on the arc is part of the life-story for succeeding moments. That is to say, the patterning characteristic of a personality at any one point on the life-arc exerts an influence on the patterning of succeeding points.

A third interacting dimension is the broken portion of the arc—that which lies beyond the cross-section of the moment. One of the functions of a person is the ability to anticipate, and this anticipation, whether accurate or not, exerts a profound and pervasive influence on the patterning of the system as a whole.

In a later Chapter (V, pages 139-141) there will be some further discussion of the concept of energy and equilibrium in relation to the progress of personality along the arc. Suffice it here to make two points: first, the system is considered adaptive to alterations which arise in the environment and which impinge upon it; while holding itself together, the unit changes to accommodate to external events. Second, there is also adaptation to alterations that originate within the system. This is most obvious in the early part of the life-arc with the unit's growth, physiological and psychological development, and pervasive, multiform thrusting out toward new experience, but it seems probable that it continues to some extent over the whole course of the arc. The term "spontaneity" will be used to refer to this aspect of personality and it will be taken up again in discussing some of the main factors concerned in psychiatric disorder (page 60 in Chapter III and 139 in Chapter V).

Having attempted this brief descriptive definition of personality, integration, and pattern, it is necessary to say a few words about another term which has and will occur frequently in these pages, namely, *function*. The word can be used to represent the total process of a unit in the sense in which "act" has been employed in explaining what is meant by personality. Thus, one can say that personality consists in the functioning of a person as a whole.

A second usage refers to the relationship of a part to the performance of the whole in which it participates. A precedent for this meaning is to be found in physiology when one speaks of the "functions of the liver" or "the functions of the nervous system," having in mind their part in the life of the organism. In a similar manner one can speak of the functions of cognition, affect, basic urges, and their unconscious counterparts and by this mean the contribution each is making to the total personality. One can also speak of the function of a person in some larger system of which he is a part, as for instance in a family or a community. This obviously brings the second meaning to a point which is close to, if not identical with, the first noted in the previous paragraph. "Function" is therefore both a relational and a relative term.

The idea of function implies the idea of malfunction which is, obviously, a point of reference for psychiatric disorders. This may take the form of one major aspect of personality which affects the whole system. Faulty cognition as in mental retardation is an example. Or, the personality as a whole may be seen as malfunctioning. In this case the judgment is apt to have a twofold base: one, the person's difficulty in acting as a member of the social system, and, two, inferior performance as estimated against some general standard or model of personality. The psychoses and the psychoneuroses illustrate such malfunction.

Although this is a brief introduction to personality, even this abbreviated and oversimplified description contains the difficulties inherent in the multiplicity of dimensions and relationships. There is need for some concept for pulling them together, and the idea of *sentiments* is suggested as suitable for this purpose.

If Helen were a friend of yours whom I did not know, and if I were to say to you, "Tell me what Helen is like," you would probably try to give me an impression of her age, occupation, whether married or not, her most outstanding abilities, tendencies, opinions, beliefs, and tastes, descriptions of behavior for illustration, and, possibly, some accounts of past experience that might be revealing as to the origins and durability of these characteristics. Central to such a description would be a representation of predominant ideas that are colored with emotion and feeling, that occur and recur more or less consistently, which govern her acts and give you a sense of knowing what to expect. These are what I mean by sentiments.

Looking at sentiments in the light of what has been said previously about the components of personality, one may consider each sentiment as a union, or intersection, of cognitive and affective processes and as having duration along the life-arc. This is again an analytic device, but is coordinate with the mutually exclusive meanings of cognition and affect. With "sentiment" we have a word for these two aspects considered in conjunction.

Thus a personality can be represented economically through a statement of its most outstanding and perduring sentiments, and such a description, when accurate, would be closer to the phenomenon than could be the case if cognitive and affective characteristics were treated independently.

Suppose, however, we are not satisfied with having a shorthand description of Helen. Suppose we want this but, even more, would like to know why she is as she is. Here again the concept of sentiments provides a convenient starting point for exploring not only the kinds of affect and cognition involved but also basic urges and the unconscious processes. To simplify the matter, let us take a particular sentiment such as, "She prefers to live at home rather than go away, get a job, and be on her own." One could approach understanding of a sentiment of this sort through examining the context of other sentiments of her personality in which it occurs and with which it is interdependent, as for instance, "love of mother" and "fear of strangers." There would also be need to examine the sentiments of other people who touch her life—for example, the mother's sense of dependence on Helen and what Helen's friends think is the right thing for a girl to do. In addition to sentiments as such, her whole cognitive and affective capabilities would be relevant for study. Lack of intelligence, or emotional instability, for instance, might play some part in her having such a sentiment. Beyond this, however, there would be need to search out the nature of her particular combination of basic urges and, ultimately, unconscious influences and their origin in the life-story.

Sentiments, therefore, provide a framework in terms of which personalities may be characterized descriptively and then salient points explored and analyzed with reference to origins and determinants. Sentiments are convenient handles with which to grasp the complex system and at the same time constitute crucial aspects of what is meant by personality. Schematically, one may picture personality as a sphere, the surface of which, interacting with the environment, is composed of sentiments. Below this surface and contributing to it are basic urges and unconscious processes. We may conclude and sum up, therefore, by saying that personality is the functioning of a self-integrating unit of sentiments, and the essence of its functioning is resistance to dissolution while moving through sequential changes along a life-arc.

II TIME, PLACE, AND PERSONS [2]

The point in time is the middle of the twentieth century.

Consider the Atlantic watershed, below the St. Lawrence, *fleuve* and *golfe,* from the top of the Bay of Fundy to the Gulf of Maine. This is the heartland of the Northeast—northern New England and Maritime Canada. It is a land of needled forests, humped in hills that send tea-colored water through lakes and rivers to rocky coast and extending sea. The texture of woods and water is interrupted by clearings, settlements, and towns, sometimes a cluster of seasoned brick around a harbor or deep in a valley where rivers meet, more often frame buildings with a temporary look, as if it were still a question whether European civilization had come to stay in North America.

Through all this land are people, concentrated in the towns, dispersed in the isolated farms and fishing coves, a living network of individuals suffused with happiness and misery, moving, meeting, leaving, and meeting again, a network that ever remains while ever replaced by birth, growth, migration, death, and new birth. If one asks what can produce happiness or misery in this multitude of exchanging individuals, he will see at once that there is an infinity of possibilities involving questions of depth and quality as well as numbers. But one gross aggregate of factors is without doubt health. Health makes a difference in whether or not a person enjoys his point in the network and his journey along the life-arc from birth through maturity, to decline and death. Health makes a difference in personality.

Suppose it were possible to reach out and tap these individuals on the shoulder and discover from each his state of health—that man carrying an ax along a lonely timber road, that housewife assembling the Monday wash, that bank manager, that clerk, that diesel mechanic, that deckhand, that union secretary, that schoolteacher, and all the rest. If we could learn the story of their health, it is likely we would find a few who were so well as to be scarcely conscious of their good fortune and a few who were overwhelmed by the disaster of sickness. But what of the rest? Do they lie closer to one rather than the other of these two poles? Where should one draw the line between the tolerable and the intolerable? What is the prevalence of significantly damaging illness? Of this, what part is contributed by disturbance of mind and emotions, sickness of spirit and of feeling?

We may also ask what contributes to the load of illness. Is it, at least in part, in the patterning of the living network? Are there roots in history as well as in present circumstances?

The Northeast is a region of cut-over forests of reduced yield, of thin rocky soil broken by occasional fertile alluvial valleys and ancient lake bottoms. The sea remains rich in fish, but markets are unstable and methods of catching are in the hazards of transition. There is industry in the cities, and some wealth, but the land between—the farms, the settlements, hamlets, and small towns—while often well kept and sufficient, are not on the highway to opulence and new opportunity. The young, for the most part, move away from where they were born, some to the cities of the Northeast itself, many farther south, to the Middle West, and beyond.

The Northeast is pervaded by two great, but different European traditions and languages—British and French. These two groups reach toward each other south and north, spreading over mountains, up and down valleys, each culture interpenetrating the other with peninsulas and islands and fringes of mixing. Each draws continuously from large cultural reservoirs outside the Northeast—the British from English-speaking Canada and the United States, the French from Quebec, that semi-independent nation of the broad St. Lawrence watershed. Sprinkled among the people of these two major traditions are a handful of such others as Negroes, a few surviving Indians, some Chinese, and, mostly in the cities, some representatives of almost every European country.

The distribution of people today, their ethnic unions and divisions, a large part of the sentiments which guide their movements in the network, all these are the result of three centuries of North American struggle and adjustment, first among French, Indians, and British, later among emerging new world countries, and then between the new world and nations in Europe. The Northeast is divided not only along ethnic lines; these are in turn cross-cut by the national boundary between Canada and the United States. There is, on the other hand, union in the common tasks of North American living, in economic ties, in identity with the New World as Americans and Canadians.

The economic situation today has its roots in a preceding way of life that was based on commerce—fur trade, fish trade, lumber trade, and, at times, privateering and slave trade. With the rise of prosperity in Regency England, the world commerce of the Victorian era, and the Civil War boom, the Northeast had a golden age. There was wealth in the production of raw materials, in building and sailing ships, in the carrying trades, in small manufacturing plants such as sawmills, carriage shops, smithies, shoe factories, textile mills (for sails as well as clothes), gun factories, and many more. Water power was a natural resource, and wherever streams dropped steeply through the hills, they were apt to turn wheels for shop or mill. As steam engines developed, they also fitted into this way of life, consuming as they did the readily available wood and relieving the small manufacturer from worry over dry spells.

Then commerce gave place to industry. It was not all at once, but by degrees. Small plants disappeared in favor of large factories; dispersed manufacturing such as shoemaking became centralized for mass production. Individual enterprises were merged or replaced by corporate enterprises. Expansion of railroads, canals, and, later, automotive transportation reduced dependence on ships. Iron and other metals took the place of wood as the basic material in fabrication, and many industries moved closer to the sources of such materials and to coal, and away from woods and water. Agriculture, never very strong in the Northeast as a source of profit, was eclipsed by the burgeoning productivity of the West. At the same time, the natural resources of fur and timber were reduced by years of harvesting at a rate that was faster than growth. Symbolic of the whole transition, the locally made sailing ship, together with her builders, her suppliers, and her crew, gave way to the steamship and motor vessel, built elsewhere.

With all of this, there was movement of population and change in pattern of living. The farm and the farm family decreased in importance as an economic unit. Barter and payment for labor by means of credit were replaced by a cash economy. Whereas commerce and its activities had flourished by coast and harbors, where shipyards and mills stood close to the sea-lanes of trade, industry was drawn toward the center of the continent, toward Appalachian coal fields, toward the gaping markets of the West, toward linking by rails rather than waterways. There was concentration in the cities not only of population but also of capital resources. And existence on the land between grew relatively meager. As this between-land became more and more city-dependent, it also grew city-oriented, dissatisfied with its own way of life. The evolution of automobiles, highways, the metropolitan press, radio, movies and television, all fostered the drift toward cities and the dwindling of small-town newspapers, small-town entertainment, small-town creativity.

The total drift to economic centralization of power in cities, including cities outside the Northeast altogether, such as Montreal, Toronto, New York, Chicago, and London, was paralleled by a centralization of political power. Government remained democratic, or became even more democratic, as far as elected officials were concerned, but control of schools, highways, health, and police passed gradually from local boards into the hands of a professional civil service and into the forms demanded by standards which were set by professionals.

Great as the changes have been within the space of a century, they seem still accelerating rather than tapering or permitting group life to reach equilibrium. Two world wars, with cycles of economic boom and depression, of fear, hope, grief, elation, and disillusionment, have not eased the achievement of stability in the network. With changing economic status, changing distribution of power, with urban-rural shifts, with the proliferation of fast communication, life has become a flotsam and jetsam of conflicting sentiments. Religions fade and then revive, or are displaced by new sects. Older and younger generations live in different worlds. The class system crumbles; unions appear. Seniority takes the place of merit. "Security" replaces "opportunity" as a watchword. Ways of life which seemed to work in the nineteenth century lie in fragments today.

On the other hand, there are advantages and new horizons. In many towns and villages there is still a tradition of "local good," and, at the same time, more education, available and achieved, than ever before. Even remote birch-encircled valleys frequently have the services of a central high school. Vocational training and adult education show parallel expansion. Advances in medicine and surgery now rescue thousands from conditions which previously spelled death. Public health services have helped reduce some of history's worst diseases, such as diphtheria and tuberculosis, to relatively minor significance in the lives of most people. The shorter working hours that have come with industrialization have increased leisure time and hence freedom for self-development and civic contribution. Treasures of the world in art, music, and literature are available to almost everyone. Thus, life-expectancy and life-opportunity have both increased.

These are but a few of the advantages which the mid-twentieth century has for the Northeast as compared to the nineteenth, even in the golden age. But the picture is confused. It is filled with the constant sense of change and more change, a sense of acceleration without a sense of control and direction. It seems a world in which every day new opportunities arise, yet a world also of hydrogen bombs, radio-active fallout, changing climate, hurricanes, flying saucers, rising di-vorce rate, man-made satellites, euthanasia, genocide, increased delinquency, and increased admission to mental hospitals.

On September 20, 1950, an equinoctial gale swept over the North-east. It began in the afternoon and drove hard into the night, bending trees and shuddering the surface of the sea.

At eight o'clock that evening, Tom Young, farmer, settled himself comfortably in his Boston rocker by the kitchen stove and prepared to light his pipe. He listened with appreciation to the rain against the window. The land needed water and, although it was dark outside, he could see, in his mind's eye, the drenched fields, the tossing spruce tops in his woodlot, and the curtains of rain rippling over the hills, across the farmlands, and down across the harbor and the town. His build-ings were sound, his crops were safe, his animals secure. It was good to be thirty-five, good to be a family man, healthy and strong, with all things well in hand.

He lit his pipe and began to rock gently, glancing at low white ceiling and bright yellow walls. He had an hour before it would be his bedtime. He would read the paper presently, but first he would rock and smoke and think a little and enjoy his castle. His eyes traveled about the room and rested for a moment on his rifle, slung on the wall between the green casings of two windows. A month more and the deer season would open. If it got cold early in October, he might open it privately a little in advance.

He thought of his two small children, Robert and Collette, upstairs in bed, and of his wife, Marguerite, gone out to a meeting of the Women's Institute, and hoped she would not get wet on the way. She was prob-ably bundled up good. Most likely she would stop in at her brother

John's on the way back; they would get to talking together, jabbering away in their French, and so she might be late. He glanced again at the rifle and reached for the newspaper.

A moment later his pipe fell to the floor and he sat up clutching his chest. There was a terrible fullness, an awful tightness in it. His heart missed several beats, sputtering like a car engine about to stall, and then picked up speed, raced madly for a while, then missed a stroke again before resuming high speed once more. Sweat stood out on his forehead. His hands trembled and his face became pale and gray in the yellow light of the kitchen. Breathing became more and more difficult and his throat felt drawn together. He could not breathe. He was strangling.

Leaping to his feet, he rushed to a window, fumbled briefly with the catch, and, finding it stuck, put his foot through the glass and thrust his face against the inrush of rain and cold air.

After a few minutes, his breath came more easily, but his heart still pounded and raced and at times missed a beat.

"Gosh," he muttered, "I've had it!"

Taking two or three gulps of air at the window, he ran to the wall telephone and some seconds later said to his brother-in-law:

"John, help! My heart! For God's sake, a doctor, hurry!"

At nine o'clock on the same night, the schooner *Westway,* in trouble with her engine and driven by the gale, ran aground off Cap Aux Anges. She had been on her way up the coast for a cargo of lumber. The officers and crew were able to get ashore without casualty, but the ship herself remained rolling and lurching on the rocks.

"If she breaks up," said the cook to "Goofy" Field, a wet and frightened member of the crew, "it's all your fault for what you done to her engine. She's the last trading schooner on this bay. And one time there must have been thousands. My old man made ten of them himself."

About the time the *Westway* settled on the shore, her owner, Gordon F. Chauncey, died at the age of eighty-seven in his home among the elms along Princess Street in the harbor town near which Tom lived. Had Mr. Chauncey known of the schooner's wreck, he would have regretted it, as he would have regretted losing a pet, but it would have made little difference to him financially. Not only was he wealthy but

Orientations

the core of his wealth lay in conservative bonds in his safe deposit box. He had begun his business career as an assistant to his father, a modest lumber dealer. By a combination of luck and ability to foresee both rising and declining markets, he had made a great deal of money while entering and leaving many different enterprises from timberland, saw-mills, and gold mines, to fishing boats, lobster packing plants, and trading schooners. He often said himself that his career was like Eliza crossing the ice, leaping from one slab to the next. Eventually he had sold out all his local enterprises except for the schooner and one saw-mill he kept as hobbies, and concentrated on investments in the stock market.

His death from a stroke at eighty-seven was the final punctuation mark in a life that had been energetic, full, and rewarding. He left behind him a few people who murmured "pirate" and "exploiter," but a large number of sincere mourners who were well aware of his many contributions to church and community.

On the day of the funeral it was still raining, and the drops that fell on the open grave fell also on open earth near the Chauncey home. The neighboring house had been demolished and in its place was an excavation for a large cellar. Mrs. Chauncey, still vigorous at seventy, noted it as she got into the car and said to her daughter, Helen:

"There is a bigger grave. It's going to bury all that matters. I am glad that your father did not live to see it."

"You mean the apartment house?"

"Yes. The apartments. Common people on Princess Street. This is not the world we struggled for. I shall be glad to rest too."

"Mother, don't be morbid."

Their way led past the Roman Catholic church, its new paint gleam-ing in the wetness. Helen could remember when the Roman church had been a saltbox under the hill, the place Irish and French servants went. Now it faced Princess Street with two square towers, above one of which a gigantic steeple was beginning to rise.

"The French are taking over," her father used to say, not with her mother's bitterness, but with a detached resignation. The Anglican church, whose graveyard contained the headstones of the town's "best" families, would have lost its steeple last year, due to the parish's in-ability to pay for repair, if Gordon Chauncey had not underwritten the cost.

A few days after the funeral, the Chauncey family sold the *Westway* to a salvage company, just as she lay on the rocks of Cap Aux Anges. About the same time, Dr. Auguste Coindreau, a general practitioner and graduate of the University of Montreal Medical School, sat down in his office in the Harbor Town and filled out a form.

REFERRAL FORM
to
THE PSYCHIATRIC CLINIC

Date: *September 26th, 1950*

NAME: *Thomas Young*   AGE: *35*   s ⓜ w Sep D
ADDRESS: *Woodside*

REFERRED FOR:

Diagnosis and Recommendations

COMPLAINTS, HISTORY, MEDICAL FINDINGS:

An acute and circumscribed attack about five days ago of palpitation, tachycardia, dyspnoea, sensations of choking. Marked fear of dying and concern about heart.

DIAGNOSTIC IMPRESSION:

Anxiety attack

OTHER REMARKS:

Except for extra-systoles, a slight systolic murmur, (both of which may be regarded as within the range of normal), examination of the cardiovascular system is negative. This includes teleoroentgenogram and electrocardiogram. General physical condition seems excellent.

No basis for an anxiety attack is known either. He seems to be in good circumstances.

Auguste Coindreau, M.D.

Referring Physician

The rain that came with the equinoctial gale lasted five days, spanning the period from Tom Young's crisis to the sale of the *Westway*. During all that time, Bernie Chiason lay drunk on a bunk in his rented shack in the lea of the Roberts sawmill. Whenever the effects

Orientations

35

of rum wore off to the point that he woke up, he would mutter, "God, I've got to get out of this," and then drink again.

During those same five days his wife, Rose, in another shack in Slashtown, a rural slum at the edge of Woodside, where Tom Young lived, was delivered of their sixth child, a boy. Dr. Coindreau said he was a perfect specimen, but Rose was too tired to take much interest.

The five days were wet days, saturating, cold and autumnal, when men and animals kept to shelter as much as possible. In all the countryside around the Harbor Town, only one person stood deliberately in the rain. This was Willie Smallie, mute and insane beyond any shadow of doubt, standing hour after hour on a clifftop looking at the sea, as he had been doing nearly every day for years. No one told him about the *Westway* because people had long ago given up telling him anything. Yet this time he might have heard, had someone spoken, for decades ago, when his mind had been clear, he had built her.

CHAPTER NOTES

1. The common use of "analytic" and "analysis" as short for "psychoanalytic" and "psychoanalysis" creates some opportunity for confusion. Throughout this book, whenever psychoanalysis is meant the word will be given in full.

2. Suggestions and critical appraisal of this section were given by Louis Gottschalk, Crane Brinton, Milton Friedman, and George Stigler.

Chapter II

What Is the Matter with Him?

TOM YOUNG WAS THE FIRST to ask the question, "What is the matter?" but it was quickly taken up by Marguerite, his wife, when she heard of his illness, by their children, by relatives, by in-laws, and by friends and neighbors. In one way or another, whether they expressed it as, *"Qu'a-t-il?"* or "What's got into Tom?" all wanted an answer to the same basic query, "What *is* the matter with him?"

In asking this question, they were seeking prediction, mainly. Will he die? Will he be disabled? Will he suffer? Will he be all right? Will it happen again? Is there a remedy? Can recurrence be prevented?

An interest in cause is implicit in all of this, but it is an interest in cause as an opportunity to do something in order to rescue Tom from disaster, allay fears, and replace uncertainty with definite expectations.

Dr. Coindreau, as the general practitioner called to help in the crisis, also had rescue in mind, but he visualized a good many intermediate questions between "What is the matter?" and a clear answer. Tom Young's condition was not only an urgent human problem but also a complex puzzle requiring examination and thought. It had layers that must be peeled off one by one in getting to the center. Is it angina? Coronary? Petit mal? Digestive disturbance? Brain lesion? In other words—do the evident *symptoms* and the *signs* discovered on examination form one or another of the patterns recognized and named in the field of medicine? The first question, in short, was one of classification, a step in diagnosis.

Such an approach is possible because, during the centuries physicians have been studying the infinity of symptoms and discoverable signs of illness to which mankind is susceptible, it has been noted that these items appear in patterned clusters, and that they can be described in categories based on similarity. It is as if one had an assortment of many tartans and, after studying size, color, stripes, and texture, he worked out a system of major groupings in terms of which all the fabrics could be arranged in a limited number of heaps, each heap containing fabrics more like one another than like those in another group. There would inevitably be overlap in some dimensions between some heaps, and the patterning of each new fabric that came to hand would have to be studied carefully before a decision could be made as to the category in which it belonged.

In this illustration, the heaps represent disease patterns or syndromes (pneumonia, phlebitis, chickenpox, etc.) and each fabric the particular combination of symptoms and signs displayed by an ailing individual. The value in such classification—identifying the disease type of a patient—lies in the fact that it is a step toward answering the ultimate question, "What is the matter?" At the very least, it eliminates some possibilities from consideration and enables the physician to concentrate on further and deeper exploration of those that remain. If a man who presents himself with a pain in the chest can be placed in the pneumonia category, and not in the heart category or the gall bladder category, then the doctor can devote his attention to assessing the kind, degree, location, and other aspects of the pneumonia that are relevant to predicting its course and planning its treatment. Sometimes the identification of the disease type brings with it partial answers to the question of cause. In a case of measles, for instance, one knows that a virus is an important factor, and one also knows at once the main features of treatment that should be followed. With many other diseases, however, causes and process are not well implied in the classification. In a case of asthma, for example, a great many factors could be implicated, ranging from ragweed to nervous tension, and it is necessary to press the diagnostic inquiry far beyond simple classification.

Hence, when, as a doctor, one says that an individual has signs and symptoms which belong in such and such a disease category, he is not saying that an explanation has been achieved. The classification removes some areas from consideration and opens up others, and tells something about what one may expect; it provides guidance, as a rule, rather than a set of specifications. It is a first approximation leading to other approximations.

Dr. Coindreau, in the course of examining Tom, quickly eliminated brain tumor, petit mal, indigestion, and a number of other disease types as being exceedingly unlikely, and bent his attention to assessing the probability of heart trouble. The more he observed Tom, however —the more he listened to the latter's account of what had happened, the more he tapped Tom's chest with his fingers, and listened with his stethoscope for signs—the more doubtful he became. There was palpitation, certainly, and pallor, breathing difficulty, choking sensations, and occasional extra-systoles—that is, a double beat followed by a pause. But there were no signs of heart failure, no blueness of the skin, no fluid at the base of the lungs, and no pain. At the same time, there was far too much action—running about and putting a foot through a window—to fit any of several possible subtypes in the general category of heart disease.

The extra-systoles were a subject for some reflection, but on the whole could be regarded as so common as to be normal. Very likely Tom had had them all his life from time to time, particularly when excited, and had failed to notice because his attention had not been focused on the possibility of his heart being in difficulty.

In order to have time for observation and study, and in order to

What Is the Matter with Him?

make sure that he made no mistake, Dr. Coindreau kept Tom in bed a few days and prescribed sedatives. After that, as nothing more transpired or could be discovered on physical examination, he took his patient to the hospital in the Harbor Town and had X-rays and electrocardiograms made. Neither of these showed any indication of tissue damage or disturbed function—no pathology.

If not a heart condition, then what? Is there any category of symptoms in which the pattern displayed by Tom might be placed? Dr. Coindreau was aware that there is one, an emotional crisis sometimes called "anxiety attack." He had seen a number of these in the course of his practice and he knew that the main features included palpitation, pallor, trembling, gasping for air, strangling sensations, and the expectation of immediate death. To an observer, the patient looked like someone in a state of extreme fear, and were he about to make his first parachute jump or walk to his execution, the behavior would seem appropriate enough. The peculiar feature was that such patients were not in circumstances that would ordinarily be considered terrifying. Sometimes a person would say in so many words, "I'm scared, Doctor, but I don't know what I'm scared of." More often he would say, as did Tom, that he thought he was dying from a heart attack; yet his own account of the sequence of events made it clear that the sensations came first, with the notion of heart failure occurring afterward as an explanation. Thus the condition began with fear, followed later by an object for the fear, a reversal of the logic of everyday experience.

When Dr. Coindreau asked Tom if he had been worrying about anything at the time the crisis started, he was met with earnest denial.

"I had nothing to worry about," said Tom. "My chores was done and everything round the place was where it ought to be. I felt fine. I was thinking about going hunting next month."

The doctor asked Tom to recall everything that was in his mind just before the crisis occurred. What about the hunting? Anything else besides hunting?

Tom was willing enough, but despite his best effort could not produce items that suggested a source of worry. In fact, he could not remember much of anything. As he struggled to recall, however, Dr. Coindreau noticed that he was becoming a little pale and that an artery on his left temple was beginning to pulsate visibly. A moment later, Tom interrupted their conversation to sit up straight and exclaim:

"Doc! I think I'm going to have another spell!"

Dr. Coindreau promptly changed the subject and tried to divert his patient's attention. After staring apprehensively for a few moments and holding one hand to his heart, Tom subsided.

The following day when Dr. Coindreau came again, he tried once more to get the patient to revive his memory, but, as before, the signs of an impending crisis appeared. On this occasion, the doctor desisted before Tom mentioned any discomfort. Dr. Coindreau had seen enough to be convinced in his own mind that the relationship between effort at recall and the indications of a disturbance was not accidental. Referral to the psychiatric clinic seemed appropriate.

While turning over in his mind how best to explain his recommendation to the patient, Dr. Coindreau continued sitting in the Young kitchen, talking with Tom and Marguerite. The conversation wandered away from the patient's immediate condition to the weather, employment, hard times and good times, sickness in Woodside, the chances of a long winter, the way everything seemed to be changing nowadays, and how things used to be in "the old days." In the course of this casual chat, several items emerged which flagged the doctor's attention. First, it seemed that Tom had had spells somewhat like his recent crisis before, perhaps two or three over the last four years. These had been exceedingly mild, however, and Tom had attributed them to:

". . . a little touch of nerves. I've always been one of the nervous type, Doctor. Like my mom and Uncle Jim. He was her brother. You know, I'm kind of a driver, drive myself too hard. Got to see things get done. But the spells never amounted to nothing, not like this one. But maybe they was the start, the first warning that this old ticker was giving way. Don't you think? I guess I ought to have paid more attention. Only got myself to blame."

Another point was the fact that Tom was not so free of worries as he had first appeared. On the financial side, although he had no debts, he had also little capital. In recent years he had been developing beef cattle and would soon have some ready for market. A few days ago, however, a rumor of hoof-and-mouth disease in the area had come to his ears and now he did not know what to think or do. If this story should prove true there was danger not only from the disease but also from an embargo on the shipment of cattle which, if established, would in consequence make local prices of meat drop to nothing. Should he anticipate and get out of cattle at once and so minimize a

What Is the Matter with Him?

loss? If he waited until the information was definite he might lose everything. On the other hand, to act too soon and to find afterward that the rumor was false would be almost as bad.

Tom was particularly sensitive to the risks of shifting markets because some years previously he had been painfully hooked in raising potatoes.

"Hard work and learnin' from your dad ain't enough to make a good farmer any more, Doctor. You've got to have a college education and be a fortune-teller besides. And you need a lot of money so you can afford to lose some of it in bad years and last through till the good years come again."

These matters worried him not only because of strong sentiments of duty toward his own family but also because his parents were getting old and, in the last year, he had had to take on more and more responsibility for running his father's farm as well as his own. That made for long hours of work and things to think about constantly.

"You know, I sometimes wish I was like my wife's people. She is French, like you are, Doctor. You folks don't seem to worry so much. Her folks, now, they work away and nothing seems to bother them."

"Does that raise any problems for you," Dr. Coindreau asked, "your wife being a Catholic and you a Baptist?"

"No, not hardly any. She and the children go to her church and I go to mine. I know Father Toulons well, a fine man, and we get on great. Only trouble I have is with some of my own family, who don't like it so good. They think I should have done different, but I don't pay attention to them."

Dr. Coindreau found it difficult to believe that these problems involving wife, children, parents, future security, and standing in the community had had nothing to do with the patient's emotional crisis. Yet when he put the question to Tom, the latter insisted that, although they were worries, he had not been thinking of these matters when the episode occurred. Moreover, Dr. Coindreau noticed that Tom was able to talk about these difficulties without showing any outward signs of anxiety. He did not get pale, no exaggerated pulsation of an artery occurred, and he did not mention an impending attack.

"Well," said the doctor, "you may be right. Maybe you were not thinking about your worries when the spell came on. But, Tom, your condition is due to your nerves. I've been over your heart, bow and stern, and it is sound in every timber. The X-rays, the lab tests, that cardiogram machine, they all tell the same story. Your heart is set to run another fifty years. Of course, it's a bit jumpy, but you know a skittish horse will live just as long as the steady kind.

"The trouble is in the nerves and I want you to see a doctor who knows about them, Dr. Hopkins at the Clinic."

"Not my heart?"

"No."

"You mean you think I imagine it? Honest, Doctor, I've not been lying to you!"

"Are nerves imagination? You said you were a nervous type. Did you mean you imagined it?"

"Well—no. But is it serious then, Doctor? Is it serious?"

"Yes, it's serious. You will never die from it but you may have more attacks and it can make things rough. Now is the time to put a stop to it before it goes any further. I'll send a referral slip to the Clinic this afternoon and you phone them tomorrow for an appointment.

"Between now and the time they tell you to come, take these pills— one after each meal and one at bedtime. That's four a day. They are not heart medicine. You don't need that. They are nerve medicine, to help the nerves ease up a bit, but they won't cure you. They are just a patch to last till you get started in the Clinic."

After counting out the pills into an envelope and handing it to Tom, Dr. Coindreau took his hat and bag and started for the door. At the threshold he paused once more and said:

"If you have another spell, Tom, remember what I've told you. No matter how God-awful you feel, you are not going to die. Call me if you like, and I'll be glad to come and help you through with it. But you're not going to die."

"Too much of a sinner, I guess."

Thus, on the day Tom Young paid his first visit to the Psychiatric Clinic, the question, "What is the matter with him?" had become somewhat narrowed and clarified. A first answer had been "emotional crisis," and this led to reformulating the question into, "What caused the emotional crisis?"

Putting the matter in this way brings into focus the concept of cause as applied to illness, and this requires some discussion. If we take a person with tuberculosis as a model, it can, from one viewpoint, be said that tubercle bacilli are "the cause" of the disease. Such an explanation, however, becomes inadequate as a frame of reference if one is concerned with treatment, prevention, or the theory of disease process. In the first place, many people harbor tubercle bacilli without ever developing clinical tuberculosis. That is to say, the bacilli are incorporated without producing malfunctioning of the system. This means that, although the bacilli are a necessary condition for the appearance of the disease, they are not a sufficient condition. Other factors must be considered as active in the process, such as the number of tubercle bacilli coming into contact with the patient in a given unit of time, their virulence, and the degree of the patient's resistance to them. The latter item is, in turn, probably under the influence of hereditary factors, events in his past life which have had a permanent effect on his resistance, and events in his immediate environment which are currently affecting his resistance. Each of these main sets of causal or determining factors has many others embedded within, all making a difference as to whether a person does or does not develop tuberculosis.

If one turns to disease entities in which no bacterial or other invading organism plays a central role—such as hyperthyroidism, coronary occlusion, peptic ulcer, or diabetes—it is even more evident that cause must be regarded in terms of multiple interlinked factors which together produce the pattern of disability to which the name applies. In such conditions it is sometimes helpful to conceive cause as divided into predisposing factors and precipitating factors, although it must be recognized that, in practice, it is difficult to distinguish between them. The view does, however, have the merit of keeping in the foreground of consideration the life-arc of the individual. Starting with hereditary factors at conception, causes or dispositions toward disease may also enter during the process of growth and other earlier points along the arc, as well as in the current situation in which the symptoms appear.

Tom Young's condition, the anxiety attack, has obviously more in common with the hyperthyroid type of disturbance than with tuberculosis. Like the former, it is an illness in that it comprises malfunction, unpleasant affect, and is beyond the reach of voluntary control, and also like the former, "the cause" must be sought in multiple factors which may be conceived as predisposing and precipitating, and which stretch over the whole life-arc, including anticipations of the future. The question, therefore, should read, "What are the main causes of the emotional crisis, and at what points in the arc of Tom's life did they enter?"

Chapter III

Derivations of a Psychoneurosis

TOM YOUNG'S ILLNESS belongs in the general category of psychoneurosis, and in the present chapter I shall be concerned with describing main factors that could enter into its production. Although discussion will necessarily focus on this illustrative individual who exhibits a particular pattern of psychoneurosis, interest is not in uniqueness but in those characteristics which this disturbance shares with many other mental disorders. The single case and disorder type are employed only as an aid in laying out central ideas. In the next chapter, consideration will be given to the relationship of these ideas to other kinds of psychiatric disorder.

The ideas themselves are also selective and illustrative. I am not attempting a systematic review of the chief schools of thought in the field of psychiatry, much less summarizing important authors. The aim is rather to present some indications of the range and types of phenomena and process that have to be considered when the question of cause is raised.

I CURRENT CIRCUMSTANCES

As Tom became accustomed to talking with Dr. Hopkins at the Psychiatric Clinic and began to feel at ease, he found his mind expanding about his worries. There was more to talk about than he had at first supposed. He must, he thought, have had all this in him before, but perhaps he had been trying not to see it because it was worrisome and painful. Anyhow, there was some relief in talking to the doctor, even if the things he said seemed to be painting an ever blacker picture of the fix he was in.

Although continuing to insist that there were no worries actually on his mind *at the time the crisis occurred,* he gradually made it plain that he was, in general, deeply concerned about his livelihood and about the future welfare of those dependent on him—wife, children, and parents. It appeared that, no matter how he schemed and planned, he could not get on top of the situation and make life secure. Sometimes he would have nightmares, such as seeing himself on trial before a military court for murder, and many a morning he woke an hour or two before his rising time and was unable to get back to sleep again.

There were periods, however, when he felt in better spirits. Weeks and even months would go by in which he worked without being too much troubled. In fact, work seemed a good antidote for "nerves" and "blues" and he had been increasing it. Because of this, he had cut down on visiting and, indeed, hardly went to church any more. Of course, he did not work in the fields or woods on Sunday, but he would stroll about his own and his father's farm and make plans.

In former years he had been accustomed to talk with his father at such times and got much help, but recently this had been more a source of worry than of comfort. Their views were growing more and more apart, and, worse than this, the old man appeared to be slowing up and growing confused, probably due to advancing years.

"He wants to do everything just the way he used to do it," Tom said to Dr. Hopkins. "He don't realize times has changed. Or if he does realize it, he says it is too bad for the times, they was better the old way, and he's going to stick to the old way and let the times come around back to him. But you can't feed oats to a tractor. So why do you have to grow a field of oats every year?"

As a result of these sentiments, he avoided his father and mother on Sundays and spent most of the time by himself. Occasionally, in the evening, he went with Marguerite and the children to visit her brother John and his family. John, he thought, was more than a brother-in-law; he was one of the best friends a man could have, more like his own brother than a wife's brother. He had had a good education and had traveled a lot, and was real interesting to talk to. Now he had a permanent job in the civil service, in the Bureau of Fisheries, but he was also able to farm a bit and sell timber from his woodlot in his spare time.

"He's lucky, that Johnnie Chatard. He's got a steady job for life with a pension at the end of it, and he's got farm life too, where he is his own boss, no rent, cheap food, and a little cash from timber."

To a question from Dr. Hopkins, Tom replied:

"No, Doctor, I don't talk to John about my worries. I don't talk to anybody. But you know, it's funny, but if I was to talk, he would be the last one. Isn't that funny, and him my best friend?"

Common sense suggests that Tom Young's insecure economic position and all this implies for the welfare of his loved ones, for his position in the community, and for his own self-respect, had been a source of worry and fear, and that the emotional crisis was an expression of that fear. *His behavior might be considered a normal reaction to the situation, much like jumping when a door slams.*

An explanation of this sort has the merit of simplicity as well as apparent plausibility and it suggests remedy in the form of rest, mild sedation, mental distraction, and, if possible, an easing of the burden by taking a fresh look, getting practical help in some way, or developing a philosophy of resignation and trust in Providence.

Derivations of a Psychoneurosis

This analysis of Tom's condition has much in its favor so long as one regards it as only a partial explanation or an account of certain precipitating factors. If, however, one attempts to make it carry the entire load of explanation—regards it as the whole story—certain weaknesses are soon apparent, and a number of salient questions are left without satisfactory answer.

Why does Tom himself feel that the crisis did not arise out of turbulent emotions in regard to his worries? If it is a reaction that resembles the slamming of a door, why can Tom recall the jump, but not the door? Or, at least, not the door at the time he jumped? The doors he recalls are the doors that slammed when he did not jump. Why is there this disconnection in his account, as compared to the common-sense inference another person is apt to make on hearing the story of his circumstances?

Why does Tom have this crisis, whereas others in the same community, enmeshed in very similar economic (and consequently personal) difficulties, do not have similar crises? Does Tom have different sentiments and so perceive things differently, more intensely, more realistically or more unrealistically? If he does, what is the source of this difference? Can it arise also only out of the current situation or must we look elsewhere for major factors?

If the immediate circumstances are the only factors of importance in the emergence of Tom's crisis, why has he never had a crisis like this before? At present, economic loss is only a possibility. In the case of the potatoes, Tom actually experienced the loss, together with a whole web of attendant difficulties and failures. Why was there no crisis at that time?

There are additional questions one could pose before accepting Tom's crisis (and other psychiatric disorders) as primarily reactions to immediate environmental conditions. These three questions, however —why does he feel that the crisis did not arise from his worries? why does not everybody in similar circumstances have such crises? and why has he never had a crisis like this in the past—represent types of issues common in the study of psychoneurosis and lead one to look beyond the immediate situation to other parts of the life-arc of an individual in trying to understand the chain of connected events. Such a review will be attempted in the succeeding pages, but first some additional discussion is necessary in order to amplify the idea of current circumstances.

It should, perhaps, be said first that I am making allowance for the cumulative effects of environmental conditions over a duration of time as indicated by the space between the bars in Figure 1. The words "current circumstances," or the like, imply two characteristics: (1) the effects of experience build up until some kind of threshold is crossed, at which point the personality responds with a marked change, one part of which consists in symptoms; and (2) as a rule, the adverse environmental circumstances not only initiate a disorder but also maintain it or promote its repetition by their continued existence.

With this expansion of "current environmental circumstances" in mind, it can be pointed out that the three main sets of questions offered as challenging this view of cause are based on assumptions which are themselves open to doubt. It may be, for instance, that Tom's inability to recall what he was thinking about at the time of the crisis is not a feature peculiar to this or other psychoneuroses, but rather a characteristic of brain function. As such, its explanation would have to be sought in the much larger context of general psychology and neurophysiology and not be limited to the psychology of this particular emotional disturbance. It could be, in short, that severe upheavals of the nervous system tend to destroy memory for events and thoughts at the time of the disturbance.

There is certainly an analogue for this in the case of a jolt to the system by means of a blow on the head. In such cases, if the blow is severe, it is common to discover that not only is memory of the blow lacking but also memory of events and thoughts for hours, days, weeks, or even months prior to and after the blow. The forgetting that has been observed with severe fright and other intense upsets may be a variant of this general property of the nervous system, a property which is possibly an adaptive mechanism that spares the system from overactivity and fosters recovery. Whether adaptive or not, the main points in this explanation are two: (1) the forgetting has no specific relationship to the nature of a particular blow or fright as such; and (2) the whole reaction, fear, and erasure from memory are responses to the current situation.

In this context it could be asked how was it that Tom showed signs of an incipient crisis when Dr. Coindreau asked him to recall just what he was thinking about at the time his first major upheaval took place. One possible answer is that the reaction came from being pressed by the doctor, not from the content of the questions. Having little re-

Derivations of a Psychoneurosis

49

serve with which to handle emotional situations, and needing a sense of support and help, the strain of being urged to do something he could not do by the one to whom he was looking for that help might have been the primary factor in the appearance of the signs and symptoms of anxiety.

Another problem is Tom's recall of the fear itself, when its cause was forgotten. Why is everything not forgotten? A possible explanation is that the cause of the fear has the power to reawaken the whole cycle, whereas the recollection of the fear itself, without the cause, is much less provocative of a renewed attack.

The second question—why does Tom have this crisis while others under similar stress do not?—may also be criticized for making an unwarranted assumption. How do we know that others in the same circumstances do not have similar reactions? For one thing, the "circumstances"—the kind of stresses involved—have never been described and clarified to the point where it would be possible to make a comparative study and see whether or not others undergoing the same psychological experience have similar reactions. On the surface, it seems obvious that many individuals in Woodside could have a similar crisis and yet not, for a variety of reasons, call Dr. Coindreau—or any doctor. The same may be said for the whole Northeast, and hence we must admit to lack of adequate data when we assume that other people in the same situation as Tom Young do not react as he does.

The matter is further complicated by the possibility that, while every personality might react to a situation such as Tom's with a profound disturbance, all may not do it the same way. To take the analogy of the slammed door again, although virtually everybody reacts to such an unexpected event, the nature of the response varies: some jump, some yelp, some turn pale, some get palpitations, some get a momentary rise in blood pressure or a surge of nerve impulses without external signs, and some get one or another combination of these various responses. It may be that, whereas some personalities react as Tom does, with sensations of fear accompanied by cardiovascular and respiratory disturbance, others react with disgust, depression, or anger accompanied by vomiting, diarrhea, headaches, trembling, weakness, apathy, or fatigue. On such a basis, it might be that Bernie Chiason's alcoholism, his wife Rose's endless fatigue and indifference, Mrs. Gordon Chauncey's intractable bitter gloom, and a sort of complaining weakness of character displayed by her daughter Helen are all different expressions of response to essentially the same psychological stress as that in which Tom Young found himself.

This is more than conjecture. Clinical experience presents many persuasive instances to suggest that such does, in fact, occur. One not only sees different people with different symptom patterns generated in apparently similar situations, but one also sees the same individual display alternatively different symptom patterns, such as a shift from an anxiety neurosis like Tom Young's to peptic ulcer, and then back to anxiety again. This sort of thing may be referred to as "the substitutability of symptoms." [1]

It may be said, therefore, that the substitutability of symptoms casts considerable doubt on any general assertion that "others in the same fix as Tom Young would not respond with illness." We do not know enough about either "fix" or "illness" to make this assertion and must leave open the possibility that the others do respond with something like illness, even though it may not always be so recognized.

While this line of thought casts doubt on the assumption that personalities in equally difficult positions differ radically in their tendency to become ill, it must also be noted that it does not negate this position. What it does is to suggest that the question, "Why do not others in the same fix as Tom Young also become ill?" might read, "Do others in the same fix as Tom Young become ill, and, if so, how do they express that illness?" This, in turn, raises the question as to why some personalities express disturbance one way while others express it another.

Such a question leads us back over the life-arc and indicates that immediate or precipitating factors and earlier, dispositional factors must both be considered if we are to understand the appearance and patterning of psychiatric disorder. Questions of this sort are radically different, however, from one that asks simply why some get ill and others do not under the same circumstances.

The substitutability of symptoms is a matter of profound importance in the entire study of mental health and social environment. It will be touched upon several times in the course of this book as a consideration in the design of the research which will be presented later.

Turning to the third major question raised as a challenge to the "reaction to current environment" concept, namely, why Tom got ill now rather than when undergoing previous disturbances, one can say we do not know enough about the circumstances to assume that the

Derivations of a Psychoneurosis

earlier episode was, in fact, as severe as the present. After all, at that time Tom had only one farm to look after and no children, and his father was still self-sufficient. These and many other differences might be critical.

Having raised these various questions and counterquestions, the opinion may now be offered that any explanation of Tom Young's condition which insists that the main causal factors are all in the current situation is unconvincing. The current situation may be of more significance than many psychiatrists and psychologists suppose, but it seems unlikely that it can carry the whole or even greater part of the burden of explanation. The problem of the individual's sensitivity and susceptibility to current circumstances points strongly to the importance of the kind of personality (sentiments) he brings to the current situation. This underscores again the general orientation given in Chapter I, where it was said that cross-section of the moment and life-story are both aspects of one phenomenon. It is not likely that any major experience and action of the personality can be considered in terms of cross-section alone; elements must be embodied which are the precipitates from previous events on the life-arc.

II HEREDITY

If the conditions attending and immediately preceding Tom Young's emotional crisis are not sufficient to explain his reaction, then it remains to consider additional or other possibilities. The most obvious addition to the idea of pressure from immediate circumstances (the door-slamming hypothesis) is heredity. In its most extreme form, this theory would displace the former and would say that *Tom Young's behavior is due to the composition of his genes, like the color of a black or white mouse.* The role of immediate circumstances would be relegated to that of a mere trigger and would not be considered as necessarily different from the conditions which the average person has to endure. Tom would be viewed as having a genetically determined low threshold to the experiences of life and a genetically determined mode (the anxiety crisis) of reaction. "He is just made that way."

This explanation has its deficiencies, but it does possess consistency and it does meet the three main questions that were raised when the effect of immediate circumstances was considered as the cause (pages

48-52). Thus, the difficulty Tom has in seeing a connection between his worries and his emotional crisis can be disposed of by saying that it is part of the pattern of the reaction, and his forgetting or nonperception, like the rest, is controlled by genes and not by the content of the thought itself. The emotional crisis is, in short, an end-product that surged up in him from physiological processes of which he was unaware, something like a hiccough.

Attributing Tom's reaction to his particular pattern of genes also makes it understandable why he should have attacks in circumstances where others do not. This is, perhaps, the main point and nature of the heredity explanation; since the combination of genes is largely a matter of chance and ancestry, it is also largely a matter of chance and ancestry that some people have such crises and others do not.

The heredity concept, finally, accounts for the appearance of the reaction at one time in Tom's life rather than another. This is because hereditary factors influence the sequence of events in the life-arc, as well as their appearance and nonappearance. Sequence, in short, is part of the pattern. A familiar example of a physical nature is baldness. To a large extent baldness is hereditary, yet most individuals with this potential do not show it until middle life. Hence the period of its appearance in the life-arc is as much a part of the genetic pattern as is the absence of hair and the portion and extent of the head involved. In the field of behavior disorder, Huntington's chorea provides an example of the same thing. Another illustration, one that is a little closer to our subject, is the fact that studies of psychoses in identical twins not only show that if one twin has such an illness, the other is very likely to have one also, but, in addition, show that the illnesses tend to occur at about the same age.[2]

Turning now to difficulties with the heredity explanation in its extreme form, one may note that there are several.[3] A main point is that it assumes too much and relies too heavily on analogy. Thus, although we know a good deal about genetics in plants and animals (including humans), we do not have any evidence in regard to the genetics of anxiety or other kinds of psychoneurosis. The application of genetic principles to these patterns is extrapolation from other phenomena and largely a matter of one's orientation in regard to physiological processes. It is, in short, a question of philosophy or faith.

Accepting this, however, and approaching the subject from a general sense as to how life goes on in organisms, one may point to many

Derivations of a Psychoneurosis

phenomena which suggest a modification of the extreme outlook. Such modification does not eliminate heredity from the complex of events that occur in the total transaction that leads to psychoneurotic symptoms. Although there may be a few clinicians and social scientists who attribute all mental illness to interpersonal relationships, most systems of psychiatric thought give a place to heredity. They vary from one to another as to weight and as to how such factors are conceived to operate, but nearly all include it. In fact, much of dynamic psychiatry may be said to be an explanation of how hereditary defect progressively evolves into a pathological pattern of adult personality.

At the same time, it should be noted that most clinicians do not hold to a fatalistic outlook. Although they recognize the significance of hereditary predisposition or defect, there is also confidence in the potential efficacy of life experience; hence they are able to believe that therapy is a means of modifying the defect and reversing the pathological trend.[4]

With these points in mind, it may be said that a broad view of natural process can lead one to feel that, although genetic determinism may be very marked in certain instances (e.g., eye-color of the fruit fly), it is also common to find that its effects are subject to modification by experiences or manipulation of the organism. Secondary sexual characteristics, for example, which are under the control of genes, can nevertheless be reversed by hormonal manipulation in certain animals at certain ages.

In human beings there is also a range. Mental deficiency, even when apparently very much under the influence of heredity, is susceptible to considerable modification as a result of life experiences. Training, for example, and an emotionally stabilizing environment can in many cases greatly reduce the symptoms and increase the individual's ability to get along in the world. Parental and educational neglect, on the other hand, combined with psychologically stressful conditions may greatly augment the manifestations of deficiency. In the less severe forms of this defect, life experience can make the difference between self-support and institutionalization.

General and analogical considerations also suggest that a genetically determined predisposition is a factor in anxiety crises and other psychoneuroses, but that life experience enters the picture too and is part of the complex of events which, all together, produce the symptom pattern, including both form and degree of severity.

This view opens up the possibility that the main causes are two: the effects of immediate circumstances as discussed in the previous section, and heredity. It can be seen at once that they fit together in a reasonable way and offer a picture that seems a little closer to reality than either one alone. In these terms one could say: Tom Young has a genetically determined predisposition to react with anxiety crises when exposed to difficult circumstances. This includes both the possibility of lower threshold of response than other people and the patterning of the reaction itself, but it also includes a major place for current circumstances as being capable of making the difference between whether or not the symptoms appear.

The two sets of major factors, taken together, offer an explanation of the three questions that were posed on pages 48-52. Thus, Tom's failure to recognize the causal relations between his worries and his symptoms can be regarded as part of the genetically determined pattern, like the rapid heart beats. The fact that he becomes ill in this way whereas others do not is explained partly by the severity of the circumstances and partly by his predisposition. His becoming ill at this particular time in his life is similarly attributable to both the pressure of circumstances and to the possibility that, as a result of the genetic elements, he is more susceptible now than he was at an earlier age.

All this is but a particular variant of a commonplace biological concept: that influences from both heredity and environment flow together in the production of behavior. As a result, in Tom's case, such confidence as one may have due to the logic of the explanation is further strengthened by a feeling that it fits very well within the broad pattern which life processes seem to have. It does not, in short, require premises which are at variance with the general orientation of biology.[5]

The problem of the relative weight of heredity is of course fraught with great difficulty as a research question concerning human beings. For obvious reasons of time and systems of sentiment, breeding experiments are impossible and hence the approach has to be indirect. Furthermore, there is little chance that any facts discovered along the way can be put to practical use in the treatment or prevention of illness.

The study of environment, on the other hand, while also exceedingly difficult, does not have the same severe limitations with regard to time span and permits some experimentation within the frame of ethical sentiments and responsibility for human welfare. Moreover, there are

Derivations of a Psychoneurosis

innumerable "experiments of nature" which offer opportunities for study and comparison. Finally, there is considerable possibility that some of the findings regarding the individual in his environment can be turned to immediate use in treatment and prevention.

It is perhaps for these several reasons that vastly more has been done to study the individual and his environmental relationships—particularly interpersonal relationships—than has been accomplished in the study of heredity, so far as mental health is concerned. In what follows in this book, I, too, shall be concerned with various aspects of the environment rather than with the hereditary factors. They must, however, always be carried in mind as an element of major importance in the total complex of forces leading to the appearance of psychiatric disorder and will be mentioned from time to time.

Before leaving the subject, it should be noted that hereditary factors are themselves open to the influence of the sociocultural environment. Tom Young's ancestors had settled in Woodside in 1785 and all of his predecessors after that date (six generations) had been born in the same general area. The Northeast has many other rural districts in which there has been a similar history of breeding within a small group, some of them for longer periods of time. It therefore seems not unlikely that, at present, the people of such areas might have certain genetic features which have been maintained by the relative absence of breeding outside the local group and which, in some instances, constitute differences from the patterning in the general population.

III LIFE EXPERIENCE

In the course of the two preceding sections the discussion has swung from a consideration of current circumstances (door-slamming hypothesis) to heredity (black and white mice hypothesis), and then to a combination of the two. It is patent, however, that environmental factors can embody more than the circumstances surrounding and immediately preceding the onset of symptoms. Early experiences of the person may be considered capable of leaving imprints and traces which are influential in the development of, or in the prevention of, disorders. The former is the concern of the present section. Looking at the matter from the viewpoint of the life-arc, one may say that, whereas we have considered the cross-section of the moment—in Tom's case, the age of thirty-five—and factors entering into the origin of personality, it remains now to deal with the part of the arc that lies between these two points.

It is convenient to think of life experiences in two major categories, physiological and psychological. It should be recalled, however, that these are aspects, not separate phenomena, and that a single event may affect a person in terms of both categories.

Furthermore the use here of the word "physiological" is somewhat special. In medicine it is commonly employed in two senses: one refers to the functions and processes of the organism as contrasted to the more structural concepts of anatomy and to the lower levels of integration such as the purely chemical; the other refers to normal as contrasted to pathological functioning. My use in the present instance is the former, in which it is permissible to think in terms of physiological pathology. Such items are included as bodily injury, organic disease, and the damaging effects of poor diet, extremes of heat and cold, fatigue, and poisons. These events are characterized by effecting a change in the equilibrium of the organism by means of a direct impact on one or many of its systems, with or without structural change.[6] Psychological life experiences, on the other hand, enter the system solely by one of the functions of the central nervous system, namely, perception.

Physiological Factors. As a starting point for a discussion of physiological factors, it may be observed that accidents can happen to a foetus between the time of conception and birth. German measles in the mother is a well-known example of a condition that is apt to have disastrous consequences, but it is possible that there are other disorders which, although their influence is less immediate and obvious, have, nevertheless, significant effects. Some of these may be of such a nature as to leave the individual with a life-long intellectual or emotional disability.

The birth process itself is a particularly critical period, in which extreme physiological stress may be endured by the child and in which a disability may have its origin. For example, it has long been known that the central nervous system is exceedingly sensitive to the deprivation of oxygen—more so than most tissues. Hence it is plausible to suppose that pressures on the umbilical cord which limit the flow of oxygenated blood even for only a few minutes may have more than a

Derivations of a Psychoneurosis

57

temporary effect. There has been some experimental work with animals which lends support to this view. When guinea pigs are temporarily deprived of oxygen close to the time of birth, many appear as normal as their litter mates in outward behavior, but later, when tests are applied, it is found that their learning capacities are impaired.

The above is merely an illustration of how the process might work. There is no desire to give special weight to oxygen deprivation in itself. The organism is such an intricate, equilibrating system, undergoing such enormous changes at the time of birth, that it is easier to accept the general proposition of permanent effects than it is to accept any particular formula as an accurate picture. The essential point is that, during both the foetal period and the birth process, physiological events may take place which result in emotional and intellectual dispositions that affect the individual in the course of his life very much as has been described for hereditary dispositions. This includes the possibility of a defect's lying dormant for many years before making its appearance in symptoms. Hence, one can suppose that a tendency to react to life's difficulties with an anxiety neurosis could have had its beginning in an early physiological accident.[7]

It is evident that the possibility of such an accident is not limited to birth or the time which precedes it. In childhood and later life, injury, disease, drugs, and other traumata can also leave their mark. The folk belief that an apparently minor blow on the head can work a radical change in personality has some foundation in fact.

Clinical studies with regard to physiological traumata in the years after birth, particularly after infancy, have much more in the way of evidence to offer than studies directed at very early injuries. We know that there are some kinds of diseases and accidents (e.g., syphilis, encephalitis, tumor, dietary deficiency, and subdural hematoma) which do occasionally give rise to symptoms that may be characteristic not only of psychoneuroses but also of personality trait disorders, psychoses, and other mental disturbances. Clinical work has also led to the development of instruments and knowledge for identifying these products of injury (blood tests, X-rays, and neurological examinations).

The fact remains, however, that it is sometimes difficult to make such identifications. For purposes of illustration one can point to those virus diseases which disturb the brain, such as encephalitis. In this illness, the effect on personality appears, as a rule, some months or years after the acute infection. There are occasions, moreover, when the acute phase occurs without too much notice or is mistaken for an attack of " 'flu." One may, therefore, raise the question as to whether or not many of the people with psychoneurotic symptoms have had such infections without knowing it, and without there being any medical records to give evidence.

At the present time there is no useful answer. In Tom's case, one can say only that most clinicians would feel it extremely unlikely that his symptoms had origin in this kind of previous physiological disturbance. Such an opinion would be based on lack of evidence for the virus infection and the presence of considerable evidence for psychological factors, as will be sketched a little later.

It is, however, an intuitive judgment. If we assume that physiological accidents can and do play at least some part in the emergence of psychiatric disorders, then it is appropriate to ask, in view of our central theme, whether or not sociocultural factors could influence their distribution in the population. Even a cursory view suggests that such factors may make considerable difference to the kind of treatment accorded pregnant women and the kind of care taken at the time a child is born. Midwives and home births, as opposed to doctors and hospitals, for instance, are more common among some groups than others. These differences often exist on an ethnic basis, an urban–rural basis, and in terms of socioeconomic status. Similarly, the care of children varies according to group characteristics. Some children are given considerable protection against malnutrition, disease, and injury, whereas others are exposed to these conditions as a by-product of the ways in which their families live. Finally, in later life, differences in occupation—which often go with ethnic and socioeconomic factors—may bring some members of the population in more frequent contact with physiological traumata than others. All of these characteristics distinguish very markedly the group to which the Bernie Chaisons belong from the group to which the Gordon Chaunceys belong.

Psychological Factors. Examples of the category of psychological factors, although not pointed up as such, have already been described in discussing the effect of current circumstances. In what follows, the topic will be treated more specifically and examined in relation to earlier periods on the life-arc of Tom Young.

This brings us to the core of dynamic psychiatry and clinical psychology. Many theoretical schemes have been developed to explain

Derivations of a Psychoneurosis

59

how symptoms come about as a result of underlying psychological processes and how the processes, in turn, have their origin in the life story of the individual. In some respects, these theories are overlapping and supplemental, whereas in other respects they are incompatible and constitute alternative explanations. Very often they are so complex and the words used in describing them so full of alternative meanings that one is left in doubt as to whether elements of theory are, or are not, mutually contradictory. In the pages that follow main points are made which had bearing on the development of this frame of reference.

Some clinicians believe that damage to instinctual satisfactions can occur during the prenatal period and bring about permanent defects of personality. Others, however, are unimpressed by the evidence offered and are skeptical that the nervous system of the organism is sufficiently developed at this time to permit the kind of intrapsychic life that is postulated. Psychological disturbance during the birth process has also received attention, but is open to the same objection.[8]

Turning now to the period of infancy and childhood, problems are encountered of unfolding urges—particularly sex and aggression—and their control. In the "normal" or healthy course of personality growth, basic urges regularly pass through a succession of stages from primitive to mature desires and inclinations. Casting this in terms of the concept of personality given in the first chapter, one can say that there is progression starting with instincts and passing through basic urges to differentiation in a system of sentiments. All branches of dynamic psychiatry subscribe to this view, regardless of the words employed and regardless of whether one accepts the more specialized concepts of oral, anal, and genital stages of sexuality.

During this psychological growth a defect of personality may become established or "fixed" through too great interference with one or more of the basic urges, particularly in connection with training. Sexuality may be suppressed and hence warped by the sentiments and actions of parents; an urge for security may be blocked by harsh and unpredictable treatment; an urge for love by rejection; and an urge toward spontaneity, a reaching out for growth through new experience, by overprotection.

Other items could be added to this list, but enough has been said to indicate the type of misadventure which it is supposed can lead to a distorted or arrested tendency persisting into later life as a component of personality. The origin of the difficulty lies in a blocked urge or in a conflict of urges such as between sexual expression and self-preservation aroused through punishment for the sexual behavior by those upon whom the child is dependent.

In many of the instances in which there is persistence in later life of an early type of urge, the latter does not appear overtly in behavior or in the conscious awareness of the individual. It works, rather, below the surface in the unconscious psychic life where it is kept by means of various psychological defense mechanisms, and is only detectable in the symbols of dreams and in other disguised manifestations that occur in the person's behavior. The relegation of the urge to the unconscious is due to its being in some sort of contradiction or conflict with the sentiments of the person such that its expression would constitute a trend toward disintegration of the personality system. It is a counter-current to the rest of the processes and as such has to be somehow walled off.

The ideas about personality and sentiment outlined in Chapter I may be further developed in relation to this theory. Taking the adult as a point of reference, sentiments have been mentioned as functional and hence by definition playing a part in the integration of personality. This can be made more explicit by saying that one aspect of this functioning is to bind and hold together deeper intrapsychic processes so that the integrity and identity of the whole is not ruptured, so that the unit may survive through the sequences of the life-arc. The schematic representation of personality as a sphere with sentiments on the surface aids in setting forth this idea. The surface web of interdependent sentiments operates to contain the forces arising within, to prevent drastic rupture of the fabric and so preserve the functioning of the whole system.

In thus depicting a surviving but unconscious urge as pitted against the system of sentiments, I am not considering the latter as entities apart from urges. Sentiments are cognitive–affective constructs and the affective quality has its roots in the evolution of the basic urges through the person's life-story. The basic urges in turn have instincts as one of their constituents. The sentiments, therefore, are tied to the past and present complement of basic urges of the personality, including those out of the reach of consciousness, and hence constitute a kind of compromise in regard to these factors. The opposition presented by the system of sentiments is to those urges that are disruptive to this

Derivations of a Psychoneurosis

compromise and balance, to the total system as it exists, and to the general trends in its unfolding.

The theory of retained infantile urges (or *fixation*) holds that when in certain circumstances such urges approach the surface of consciousness—are close to awareness but have not yet broken through as contradictory sentiments—then anxiety appears in the person, like the roughening and darkening of the ocean's surface by a school of fish swimming below. The feeling reaches consciousness ahead of recognition as to its source. The disruptive danger which the unconscious urge holds for the integration of personality is the reason for the anxiety, and the unconscious character of the processes is manifest in the patient's inability to give an adequate account of the cause. According to this view, the effect of current, environmental circumstances is limited to that of a trigger. The fundamental disorder is in the components of the personality and has been there from infancy onward, a precarious balance of conscious sentiments and unconscious factors. Thus, in some circumstances, a person may be able to cover over his defect to the point where no symptoms are evident, whereas in others, his basic pathology is brought close enough to consciousness to produce symptoms.

In these terms, Tom Young's talk of worry about markets would be either unrelated to his anxiety reaction, or related only indirectly as a kind of general influence, reducing his emotional poise and reserve. Indeed, the worry might be a consequence of his condition rather than a cause. His mention of the gun, on the other hand, could be of maximum relevance as a symbolic reference to a penis and hence a clue to his having unconscious homosexual urges. This would suggest that Tom's psychosexual development had never reached full heterosexual maturity, but had retained elements which now took the form of homosexual inclinations. Since an urge of this sort is unacceptable to Tom's system of sentiments, to the conscious surface of his personality where reason and feeling are combined, it has persisted at an unconscious level. The unacceptability is an expression of the sentiments he has learned (or "internalized") from his parents and his age-mates as he grew up, and it has later been reinforced by a realization of widespread and strong social disapproval.

Even though the homosexual tendency has been kept out of consciousness, it is conceived to be actively pressing for expression and to be open to stimulation by events and people. At such times it is close to breaking into consciousness, so that nightmares, depressed moods, and anxiety crises occur. One result of this could be that Tom would, without knowing why, tend to avoid people and throw himself into socially isolated work about the farm, as he was, in fact, doing.

On the basis of an hypothesis of this sort, a therapist, such as Dr. Hopkins, would have his attention attracted by the patient's report that just before the crisis he had been thinking not only of the gun but also of his wife's brother. The doctor would wonder if, in the marriage itself, the wife might not have been a substitute (unconsciously selected) for her brother, and by means of psychoanalytic or projective techniques, he would attempt to explore Tom's psychic life for other indications from which he could, by inference, piece together an interpretation of the processes at work. The long-range objective would, of course, not be to hand to Tom the psychiatrist's diagram, but rather to use it as a therapeutic guide in helping the patient work out a more mature way of dealing with his urges and thus relieving him of the symptoms. The therapeutic attack would be on the underlying psychic processes and not on the symptoms as such, nor on the stresses and strains of the immediate situation.

Before proceeding further with the discussion, it is worth while drawing attention to certain features in this line of thought. As already noted, it points to experience amounting to psychological damage in childhood and the retention of the results in the personality. It involves conflict of urges, mechanisms of control, maturation—particularly moving through stages of instinct and basic urge development— and the possibility that one or another aspect of immature urge and immature methods of control may be retained in adult life. Finally, it gives heavy emphasis to unconscious psychic functions and attributes much of human sentiment and action to events that are not currently available in the individual's awareness.

This last point means that, unlike any other explanation that has thus far been offered regarding Tom Young's illness, his inability to name the source of his anxiety is considered due to the nature of that source. His vagueness as to his thoughts at the time of the crisis and the signs of an incipient crisis he showed when closely questioned by Dr. Coindreau are both explained by the (unconscious) urge itself and its disturbing effect on the personality system as it approached consciousness, or achieved consciousness briefly and was then repressed. It is particularly important to emphasize that inability to recognize or remember one's own motivations and experiences is apparently a feature of many categories of psychiatric disorder and hence this explanation has wider relevance than the particular type of anxiety neurosis displayed by Tom.

It may be helpful to note that the evolution and resolution of conflict in basic urges in the course of the organism's maturation is visualized in classical psychoanalytic theory as taking place in a personality structure composed of three main segments: the *id,* containing the primitive instincts; the *superego,* containing the ideals and values with regard to proper conduct and feeling, and hence at variance with the id: and the *ego,* which contains an appreciation of reality and the function of balancing and pulling together the other two so that a relatively integrated personality is achieved and maintained. In these terms, Tom's anxiety reaction can be seen as a surface manifestation of a basic and unresolved disharmony between id, ego, and superego.

This view may be compared with the concept outlined in Chapter I in which personality is conceived as having a system of interdependent sentiments developed and maintained by a variety of factors, some due to basic urges, some conscious, and some unconscious. In such a light, Tom's troubles could be visualized as arising in an urge that was not directly represented among his sentiments, but which threatened to emerge as a new set and be extraordinarily out of keeping with the rest. Such an event would, of course, endanger the integration and functional capabilities of the whole system. Correspondence may be seen between certain aspects of ego and superego and certain constellations of sentiments having to do with reality, desire, and conscience.

In addition to instincts and derived urges, consideration needs to be given to the web of interpersonal relationships in which the child participates and through which these inner psychic processes are transacted and transmuted. One can assume that ordinarily in the family the growing personality experiences love, hate, achievement, and frustration, with the eventual development of a measure of both inner ease and outer poise in dealing with other people. But something goes wrong, at times, in some individuals and an immature pattern persists, often in a disguised form.

An illustration may be found in the well-known "Oedipus complex," in which the male child is considered to have sexual desire for the mother and a jealous wish to destroy the father as a rival. In normal growth this conflict is thought to be resolved and the basic urges matured toward other goals and into systems of sentiment appropriate to the society and culture. Sometimes, however, this course is interrupted by circumstances. These might lie in the father's treatment of the child so that the latter is unable to work out of his hatred. As a result, the hostility could be continued into adult life and affect his dealings with many people besides his father, particularly those with attributes of a father, such as older age, prestige, and position of authority. This state of affairs could include the existence of unconscious, hostile, and destructive basic urges, and the approach of such impulses to consciousness could evoke anxiety.

In Tom's case, a therapist thinking along these lines might ponder the gun as a symbol arising from a murderous, though unconscious, wish rather than from sexual urges. He would be interested, therefore, to discover that the wife's brother was fifteen years older than the patient, as well as better educated and hence of superior status. He might think it possible that the relationship of the three, patient, wife, and brother, offered a framework that represented and reactivated a never adequately resolved Oedipus complex in the patient. The anxiety seizure could be explained by the approach to consciousness of an abiding desire to destroy the brother. Perhaps there would be significance in the fact that Marguerite had been out visiting her brother when the attack occurred.

In presenting these illustrations, it is important to make clear that they are exceedingly fragmentary. My desire is to give an inkling of a theoretical orientation and to draw out those features which are relevant to the environmental theme of this book. It is hoped that those who are acquainted with dynamic psychiatry will thus see the points in the wider context of their own knowledge, and those who are not so acquainted will find the sketch sufficiently intelligible to permit its use as a stepping stone toward the content of later pages and also, when appropriate, as a starting point for developing more familiarity with the relevant literature.

To resummarize, Tom Young's symptoms are conceived to be the result of a defect in personality. This defect had its origin partly in susceptibility based on heredity and partly in experience during infancy and childhood. Infancy and childhood are a time of vulnerability due to: the unfolding of basic urges, the process of training, and the child's developing and changing relationships of love and hate with

Derivations of a Psychoneurosis

the members of his family. It is a period when patterns of personality are formed and set, including unconscious motivations, and hence it is a period when malformation in the system may occur which then tends to persist the rest of the person's life. In adults, clues to existing unconscious tendencies and to the nature of the earlier process appear in their symptoms, in their sentiments, in the things they cannot remember, in the mention of objects that have symbolic significance, in dreams, in slips of the tongue, and in other, similar acts and expressions.

Within such a framework, it is of course possible to have divergent ideas in regard to what constitutes main features and as to the significance of things the patient does and says. This has been illustrated, in Tom Young's case, by means of two different interpretations of the gun as a symbol. A number of other interpretations are also possible. These multiple inferences are not, however, necessarily incompatible and self-contradictory. It is possible, for instance, that the gun has more than one meaning and that both the interpretations given earlier plus others that could be introduced are correct.

The main criticism to be launched against the above type of psychological explanation is that it puts heavy emphasis on both instincts and a very early part of the life-arc without as yet sufficient evidence. One must hasten to add that certain kinds of evidence are abundantly available. Testimonials exist in great number from both psychiatrists and patients as to their individually persuasive experiences and their inner convictions. Nor can one reject this evidence in any wholesale manner as unscientific since much of it is provocative and cogent with regard to the formation of concepts and theories. The trouble is that it does not as yet go beyond this to the next step in scientific procedure, namely, validation by means of operations which are independent of the subjective evaluations of the patients and psychiatrists involved. It may be that for the present this is largely impossible and hence there is reason to make use of this best that we have, but there is also reason for avoiding a dogmatic position.

It is worth noting in passing that the problem of evidence is often treated with considerable heat by both those clinicians who rely on these concepts of early life and those who do not depend on them so exclusively. This may be because the former are apprehensive of attack on a system of sentiment that is central to their self-confidence in treating patients, and perhaps to an experience in securing help themselves, while the latter have other, but no less personal, bases for their sentiments, possibly related to professional rivalry, or to having rejected a form of treatment which they suspect they need. These factors make it very difficult for anyone to keep a clear head in discussing the topic. They do suggest, however, that a distinction should be made between evidence for evaluating hypotheses regarding the nature of process, and questions having to do with the value of treatment. Just as those engaged in therapy need confidence in a theory that governs what they are doing, so those in research need the freedom of considering alternative hypotheses.

In addition to difficulties of validation, psychological explanations of the type sketched earlier are also open to the complaint that they, like other concepts, beg the question of the relationship of hereditary factors to environmental factors. We are provided with no adequate or consistent statement as to which is which in the process of symptom formation. The time considered significant is pushed backward from the cross-section of the person's life at the time the symptoms appear, but the distinction between "nature and nurture" is no better specified. The element of faith, or general orientation, remains as a component in the conclusions. If you are inclined to heredity, you can say that the psychodynamics tell how the process takes place, while the genes explain why. On the other hand, if you have a preference for environmental concepts, you can say that the question of why lies in the treatment accorded the child in the family.

It is easy to see how personal experience can influence such views. The man who comes from a family that gave him a difficult time emotionally might be inclined to favor an outlook that traced the difficulties of later life to mistreatment in childhood, whereas the parents of a neurotic child might prefer to blame heredity rather than their own practices.

It is perhaps not very comfortable to consider these sources of one's sentiments. After all, it is common knowledge that such factors do exert an influence on most of our human opinions, but it is possible nevertheless to conduct discussion according to fact and reason without bringing them in. Reference to a rival's personal motivations, however probable, would not be considered good taste in a debate. On the other hand, these are the very considerations we take into account in trying to understand and help a patient and it seems worth while to apply them to ourselves in understanding the reasons for such differ-

Derivations of a Psychoneurosis

ences of viewpoint and for difficulties we may have in perceiving the nature of phenomena. These are sentiments, in short, and they have their roots in all the dynamic processes, inter- and intrapersonal, that characterize sentiments. It is appropriate, therefore, to warn the student approaching this subject matter that he should keep these factors in mind when evaluating the opinions of authorities and his own reactions to these opinions.

Turning back to a more central theme, supposing the psychodynamics of child development and symptom formation do follow the pattern that has been sketched, what implications does this have for the effects of the sociocultural environment? It suggests that customs of child rearing, particularly toilet training, feeding, weaning, loving, punishing, and the inculcation of sentiments may make a considerable difference in the organization of personality and hence also in the development of psychiatric disorder. Groups of people with different practices might well have different frequencies as well as different patterns of psychoneurosis. In the Northeast, one may say that it is quite possible that such divisions as French–English, urban–rural, present generation–former generation, and, in socioeconomic terms, upper–lower, do involve significant differences in this regard. If one looks outside the Northeast, there is opportunity for finding much greater contrast between groups in different parts of the world.[9]

It is necessary, now, to consider another, though a related, psychological concept. This also emphasizes childhood and is not necessarily incompatible with the preceding view, but it leans toward a later part of the life-arc and a somewhat different level of abstraction. Detailed schemes of basic-urge development and resultant struggles in the unconscious between semi-anthropomorphic entities are replaced by more general ideas regarding urges and conflict. A need for love is given a prominent place and also a need for freedom from excessive pain and fear. Deprivation of love is considered one of the greatest hazards to personality development. It produces distorted emotional development, distorted sentiments regarding people, and other characteristics crippling to the personality which can, in later life, lead to inappropriate outbursts of hate, fear, and anxiety or distortions of character such as excessive passivity or an excessive tendency to be domineering.[10]

A second major threat to personality is thought to arise from experiencing inconsistent treatment. This is to say that, in addition to the matter of deprivation of love, there is also the question of its inconsistent availability. Where this is extreme, the emerging personality may respond by developing a set of sentiments about the world as a place both dangerous and unpredictable, where one exists in a state of fear without hope of being able to cope with the blows and rejection to which he is subjected. As a result he may be indiscriminant and oversensitive in his apprehensions.

To the ideas of deprivation of affection, and inconsistency of treatment, may be added a third major source of disturbance to the growing personality, namely, overprotection. This presupposes that a child needs sufficient latitude to express his spontaneity, to reach out and to learn by his own experiences, including some painful (but not too painful) encounters. Excessive protection interferes with maturation and fosters revolt or dependent, passive relationships, so that, when the protection is withdrawn, as usually happens sooner or later, the person is left a prey to the uncertainties and functional inadequacies of his own underdeveloped personality.

In all of these circumstances, fear plays an important part. Adverse conditions are adverse largely because they inspire such uncomfortable sensations. Permanent damage to personality takes place when the child can find no escape, or finds an escape at the cost of establishing a pattern in his personality that is in the long run malfunctional.

In this connection the possibility must be considered that the child can acquire anxiety because those with whom he is most intimately associated display such a condition. In the early family situation it could well be that it is more rewarding to be anxious than otherwise where the mother's love and approval are such important factors. Patterns learned at this period of life might be very difficult to extinguish later even though no longer appropriate. Thus a person could carry through life a timid sensitivity, a complement of apprehensive sentiments, and a tendency to worry and overconcern for the threats and difficulties that come his way.

Sullivan has advanced the view that anxiety in the mother can inspire anxiety in the child by a process which seems to function something like electrical induction. He applies the word *empathy* to this concept and considers that the anxiety so derived has a paralytic effect on certain aspects of the development of personality, leaving it with a permanent defect.[11]

In considering Tom's case, Dr. Hopkins was impressed by the fact

Derivations of a Psychoneurosis

that Tom's early recollections of his mother were of a person forever warning him about dangers, who was excitable and prone to nausea, fainting, and a day in bed with blinds drawn after relatively mild events such as a grass fire which might have, but did not actually, burn their barn. On this basis it was possible to suppose a number of inter-related factors that could have been at work in Tom. He could have acquired a tendency to anxiety by learning or empathy. There is also the possibility that his mother's anxiety and fearfulness rendered her treatment of him inconsistent and impulsive, thus generating inse-curities in him.

Still another possibility is that the mother's anxiety was a disguised form of rejection. That is to say, for reasons that had their roots in her own personality, she might have felt considerable hostility toward Tom. Since such feelings toward a child are not admissible as such due to other sentiments, they are apt to be largely unconscious, but their approach to the surface could produce anxiety. Such hostile ele-ments might be perceived by a child and lead to fears of rejection. One response could be a superhuman effort to be good, to avoid rejection by exemplary behavior. In later life this might be translated into a driv-ing effort to conform to authority and to live up to ideals. Tom's senti-ments about being a good farmer, good citizen, and good husband are open to this interpretation. His wife, Marguerite, would thus be a central figure in the current situation and he would have in relation to her many patterns derived from his relations with his mother. The possibility of failure as a farmer might therefore have meaning for him that went far beyond the obvious. It could comprise the fear of rejec-tion by his wife and below this the evocation of a life-long fear from which he had never been able wholly to free himself. There might be at bottom a suicidal impulse as one form of escape, and it could be that this was the psychological element stirred up by the gun. His anxiety crisis, in short, could have been due to the welling up of an unrecognized yet frightening thought of escape through death.

A still different interpretation tied to the same underlying problem of early relations to his mother would view the gun as a symbol of sentiments having to do with manliness. Seeing this and thinking of his wife out alone in the storm could give him a sudden, acute feeling that he was inadequate and that he would lose her.

These views, it can be seen, embrace the idea of Tom as largely unaware of what was going on within him, including the early origin of his sentiments and dispositions. Lack of awareness is also conceived to be, in a large measure, due to the painfulness of recognition—hence his inability to connect his worries with his crisis. This kind of "unawareness," however, although dynamic and motivated, is less specific, so far as detail of theory goes, than the classical analytic idea of the unconscious previously mentioned.

The four items that have been touched upon—deprivation, inconsistency, overprotection, and exposure to fearful sentiments—merely illustrate a level of conception. Numbers of other items could be added and the discussion vastly extended. The aim here, however, is to demonstrate a way of looking at the influences of childhood which, though it may shade into and overlap with the previous type of concept, is, on the whole, different in emphasis.

It can be criticized for its lack of specificity, for being a little too close to the obvious, and for failing to offer a satisfying theoretical explanation as to precisely how the kinds of influences postulated bring about personality characteristics that result in psychiatric disorder. There is no diagram of personality comparable to the id–ego–superego, nor any such intellectually neat ideas as the Oedipus complex, or the concept of certain surface symptoms being necessarily the result of an unconscious homosexual urge.

On the other hand, one can also say that the absence of heavy commitment to such specific theory is an advantage so far as research is concerned. The general propositions open avenues for empirical study and consequently for the gradual construction of theory based on objectively demonstrable phenomena. These points can be summed up by saying that, while the more general theories have the disadvantage of lacking specificity, they also avoid the danger of what Whitehead called "misplaced concreteness": they acknowledge doubt at every turn and thus, while they may be intellectually unsatisfying, they are not misleading.[12]

In passing, it may be noted that a matter of considerable interest along these lines is emerging from work with animals. This tends to show that the developing individual does pass through stages of susceptibility to certain kinds of social influence. Events occurring at such times, involving fear and other emotions, may have lasting effects, while the same events occurring at other times, either before or after the critical period, do not seem to have these long-range results. Such work lends support to the general notion of critical stages in human development.[13]

When one looks at this more general level of psychological orientation in terms of possible sociocultural influences, it is evident that what has been said about the previous more specific formulation also applies here. Even though there are emphases on different mechanisms whereby personality damage and the emergence of symptoms take place, both tend to see the same type of environmental situations as significant in the initiation of the chain of events. Both stress conditions which arouse fearful or hostile emotions in such a manner as to interfere with psychological growth. Family patterns of child treatment and sentiment are implicated and these obviously vary in different parts of the sociocultural environment.

One can go further than this, however, in conceptualizing and emphasizing the bearing that patterns of interpersonal relationships, and hence sociocultural environment, have on the development of an anxiety neurosis. The personality system of a given individual may be conceived as an emergent derived from his experience with other persons. Of most significance is the mother or "mothering one," but father, sisters, and brothers also count and so too do persons coming later in life, as for instance teachers and age-mates. The individual perceives the performance of these significant other persons and of self in relation to them as recurrent patterns of action and experience. His own personality emerges largely as a composite of these patterns or roles built in the course of growth and maturation and through avoiding anxiety and seeking approval into a more or less harmonious system. When the system is more rather than less harmonious, the personality is regarded as healthy, but when there is conflict and incompatibility between the expectations of the different roles, the personality system functions in a disintegrated manner with the result that anxiety and other symptoms of disorder become evident. Since roles together with their expectations are recurrent phenomena and a part of the social system, this viewpoint gives great weight to the influence of sociocultural factors in the genesis of malfunctioning personalities.[14]

Role may also be considered in terms more external to the personality and as having effects not only at early periods of the life-arc but also at later periods, including that which, with relation to the appearance of psychoneurosis, has been called at the beginning of this chapter "current circumstances." A society and its culture is from this point of view again regarded as encompassing a network of roles, but the emphasis is on patterns of behavior associated with particular positions such as fathers, mothers, ministers, policemen, farmers, teachers, foremen, and so on. The problem for personality is the stress arising from attempting to fulfill simultaneously two or more incompatible roles, or attempting to fulfill a role that is regarded with different and contradictory expectations by persons and groups occupying different positions in the social system. Being a career woman and a mother can under some circumstances be an example of the first. An instance of the second would be a situation in which parental expectations of a child are at variance with those held by teachers, and both of these considerably different from the expectations of peers. There are, in short, problems of conflict between roles, of poorly defined roles, and of contradictory expectations for a given role.[15]

Environmental views of personality formation can be carried to extremes, whether couched in terms of role, culture, or both. When this happens the problems of psychic motivation appear to be by-passed and each individual is seen as a living mold cast by his society, unique only because no two people ever have exactly the same experiences. All human beings are assumed to be essentially similar in their biological and psychological composition and no allowance is made for variations in affect, cognition, and basic urges as a result of either heredity or physiological factors. If some people are neurotic and others not, this is entirely a matter of situations, past and present.

Such an extreme view is probably not held by many behavorial scientists, but one does occasionally encounter something approaching this. It is open to the same objections that were raised in connection with exclusive emphasis on heredity. Although it cannot be either supported or refuted with direct evidence so far as anxiety reaction is concerned, what indirect evidence there is (such as genetic factors in other types of psychiatric disorders) suggests the likelihood of some hereditary influence. And the same points apply with regard to physiological factors.[16]

In moderate form, concepts such as role and culture do not ignore heredity, physiological factors, or the problems of motivation and intrapsychic process. At such a level, role analysis performs considerable service in drawing attention to the patterning of interpersonal

Derivations of a Psychoneurosis

73

relationships as one among a number of crucial factors. It corrects some tendency to think of the child and adult as having this or that conflict of urges and sentiments without reference to situation, and to the social and cultural characteristics of the human beings with whom he is interacting.

A hint of the role concept in Tom's case has already been given in discussing his relationships with his wife, Marguerite. These might be analyzed in terms of a conflict between the role of husband and a dependent role of child. Such a current conflict would be traced back to early experiences with father and mother and to faulty maturation with regard to such roles. It could be said that as a result of the way his parents had conducted themselves toward him he had never fully assimilated the father role nor altogether freed himself from the role of a child dependent on his mother.

A personality system composed of these defective role relationships would be particularly susceptible to a number of additional conflicts evident in Tom's current situation. Being the Protestant father of a Roman Catholic family that was really led by his wife's brother would be one of these. Another would be the reversal of father and son roles inherent in his taking over the management of his father's farm.

Looking at the relationship of psychological experience to the different segments of the life-arc, it is possible to discern two distinct conceptions. One maintains that the essential characteristics of personality necessary for the appearance of psychiatric disorder are laid down once and for all at an early age and that, as a result, later events make little difference. If an individual with such a defect in personality develops a set of adaptations and compensations so that no symptoms are apparent, then later environmental stresses may evoke symptoms by disturbing the compensations and unmasking the underlying condition. In no sense, however, do they cause or create the disorder.

The other view attaches more importance to successive factors, and hence to the whole curve of the arc intervening after childhood. While granting that infancy and childhood are particularly significant for the crystallizing of personality pattern and hence for psychiatric disorder, each successive segment of the arc is also thought to have some influence, making it possible for later circumstances and later experience to alter a personality either toward or away from disorder. Thus, Tom Young's personality, at any given moment or cross-section of the arc, may be regarded as a kind of platform composed of hereditary disposition and the physiological and psychological effects of previous years. On this platform, the experiences of the present unite and fuse to compose the personality of the next moment.

Personality is, in short, a continuous emergent. Although events in early years have, as a rule, greater influence than those of later years, all have some relevance, and it is entirely possible for an event in adult life that profoundly stirs the emotions to have a major impact.

It has already been observed that a worrying mother was a prominent feature of Tom Young's infancy and childhood. This was continued, of course, in his adolescent years, and her objections, fears, and prohibitions posed a number of obstacles to Tom's development of relations with boys and girls of his own age. The situation was not helped by the absence of brothers and sisters, or by the fact that the father, whose temperament was calm and steady, was away from home a good deal, especially in the winter, working in the woods or in shipyards.

Tom had a desire to be liked, which gave him an agreeable approach to others, but it was more effective with adults than it was with his age-mates. Although he had, in school, two or three close friends with whom he snared rabbits and fished, he was never a member of any of the young people's cliques in Woodside and he never got over feeling uneasy at parties or other occasions when he had to mingle in large groups. He also had to fight a tendency to become the pet of his various teachers.

In talking to Dr. Hopkins about himself, he said he realized now that he had carried many of these tendencies with him when he entered the army during the Second World War. Despite his years of service, two of them overseas, and despite the fact that, on the surface, he got on well with people, he always felt outside, or at least on the edge of, every intimate, informal group. Accompanying this inner sense of isolation was a feeling of inferiority and apprehension, from which he sought escape by keeping busy.

"In some ways," he told Dr. Hopkins, "I was like my mother. I remember I used to think the way she kept busy in the house, cleaning, cooking, sewing, working all the time, she acted like she was trying to get away from something. You know how you can work to take your mind off things, Doctor, and you can work with your head kind of down so somebody that is coming along will go by and not talk to you? Hide behind it like a bush? Well, I used to think my mother was doing both them things. I don't know why, it was just my idea.

"And I guess I done the same in the army, kept busy so I wouldn't have time to think or talk, and no one would find out how worried and lonesome I was—nobody would find out, including me."

Since Tom's intelligence was good and he exercised judgment in selecting his tasks, he had qualified as a radio technician and risen to the rank of technical sergeant. Thus each step in his life led to the next in building his personality and in confirming his tendency to an active inner life of apprehension, covered over with numerous intervening preoccupations that were at least in part escapes rather than solutions.

When he left the army at the end of the war, he soon missed being a member of a vast organization, with the particular kinds of security it provided. Adjustment to civilian life constituted a new set of problems. In the midst of them, and with hope of solution, he had married Marguerite and invested his savings and veteran's loan privileges in a farm and modern equipment. It is not irrelevant that she was a member of a large, extended family and of a vast, highly organized church.

Although it is likely that the sequences of life experience and events have more cumulative force in the molding of personality and the evolution of disorder than do major dramatic events, it still remains possible for emotional upheaval to play a decisive part. Such an episode came to light as Tom told Dr. Hopkins about his war years.[17]

He had been in a forward area for over six months, repeatedly exposed to fire. One morning, in Italy, his unit was ordered to take a wood in which German snipers were carrying out a rearguard action. Before he knew it, he was crossing an open field under fire.

Tom was found later in the wood in a dazed state, the only survivor of his company, the others having gone down in the long crossing of that field. It had seemed like a dream afterward, and he did not even have a particularly keen memory of having been frightened. He was, however, hospitalized for a short period and he recalled being bothered by nightmares for a while. It was at this time that the dream of being on trial for murder had first occurred. By the time he was given his discharge, it all seemed vague past history, and he was conscious of very little thought about it.

He did notice, however, after he came back to Woodside, that he had lost his taste for hunting. Before the war he had been very fond of taking his gun and stalking slowly through the woods and across clearings in quest of partridge. Now he never felt the inclination, and in fact had not been deer hunting since his return from the army. At first he gave this scant attention, being usually too busy to go hunting even if he had wanted to, but by degrees he became aware of some kind of block in him. He felt a bit ashamed and inferior when he heard his neighbors talking about hunting each year and saw deer hanging in their yards. Recently his brother-in-law, John, had been needling a little, urging him to go along this fall. Tom had made up his mind that he would, spurred mainly by a sense of shame and determination to overcome something he regarded as foolish.

It was evident that he had been thinking of hunting just before his crisis of anxiety and, after considering this together with his experience in crossing the field, gun in hand, toward the German-infested wood, he told Dr. Hopkins that there might have been some connection. In the week after this matter had been touched upon in an interview, he was bothered by a succession of nightmares, felt extremely nervous, and was tempted to break off treatment at the clinic.

This bit of information about his past, together with the patient's reaction after having reviewed it, suggested that his war experience might have had some bearing on his episode of acute anxiety. With this as a hint, one could turn to the general clinical experience with war neuroses and draw out some ideas as to what might have happened. It could be that Tom's feelings in crossing the field and entering the wood, while all his companions were shot down on either side of him, were frightful in the extreme. So horrible were the recollections that they had been pushed from consciousness, but remained active outside of awareness in the network of his motives and inhibitions, being manifest in nightmares, unpleasant feelings, and pounding heart when taking a gun in his hand or in crossing open fields. In short, hunting amounted to a situation which threatened to allow the painful recollections of his psychological trauma to break through into consciousness. In thinking about hunting, while looking at the rifle on the wall —which was in fact a carbine—he had partially evoked the war experience. The full memory had not come back, he was not aware of what had frightened him, but he did experience manifestations of terror.

There are points of particular vulnerability on the life-arc beyond the age Tom had reached (thirty-five) at the time of his anxiety reac-

Derivations of a Psychoneurosis

tion. One of these is the involutional period, generally in the late 40's and early 50's, while another is the time of onset of old age. These are, of course, not relevant to Tom's illness, but had he been older they might have been, and hence deserve mention here.[18]

In concluding this chapter, it is appropriate to attempt summing up the ground covered in outlining sets of alternate or combinable factors that may be involved in illuminating the question, "What is the matter with Tom Young?" or, in its more refined form, "What are the main causes of his emotional crises and at what points in the arc of his life do they enter?"

It will be recalled that, after Tom's condition was identified as belonging to the anxiety reaction category, and other conditions such as heart failure were eliminated as exceedingly unlikely, attention was given to sets of causal agents which may be grouped under three principal headings: hereditary, physiological, and psychological. It is at once noteworthy that, although these three are conceptually separate, they are exceedingly difficult to distinguish in nature. Most significant items of human behavior are apt to be, so far as one can tell, composed of all three, though to varying degrees.

This kind of sliding together of causal factors is even more characteristic of the etiological subdivisions that one can make under the three headings, and is particularly true in the case of psychological items. As a result, one encounters a range of different types of theory, some tending to consider the phenomenon with which they deal as isolated from all other influences (e.g., Oedipus complex or emotional shock from war experience), others tending to deal with the relationship of several different factors (e.g., current events are disturbing partly in their own right, but also because they evoke internal conflicts that were established during childhood in a personality rendered susceptible by genetic defect).

Despite their overlapping, intermingling, and fusing in process, hereditary, physiological, and psychological influences may be apt to enter the human organism at different parts of the life-arc. Although the effects of genes are present throughout life, there is after all only one moment at which these can enter the system—namely, at conception.

Physiological influences can enter the personality system at any time between conception and death, but for conditions such as Tom's anxiety reaction, it seems likely that prenatal and infancy periods are particularly important. This statement is, of course, based on guess-work, and yet from both known fact and general theory there is some justification for accepting it. Regardless of time of entry, physiological influences may, like hereditary factors, have consequences that pervade the rest of the individual's life, and hence have bearing on the appearance of symptoms during adult years.

With regard to psychological factors, theory places greatest weight on infancy and early childhood as the segments on the life-arc when their entrance has the greatest potential for permanent effect. After this stage, one can postulate a gradual lowering of susceptibility to disturbance by new psychological events, but with the reservation that it is always possible. As noted earlier, it is sometimes argued that trauma in later life is effective in evoking disorder only in persons with personalities already damaged by experiences in childhood and infancy. One can but observe that this kind of argument is also applied to the period of childhood and infancy. In such a case it is said that only those children with a constitutional defect sustain permanent damage from traumatic experience. It would follow that each type of psychological experience and each period on the life-arc is to some degree determined by preceding events.

To generalize and so oversimplify, it can be said that the time of entry for heredity is at the start of life (though the influence obviously continues throughout); the peak time of entry for physiological factors is during the prenatal and early infancy periods, with a tapering that extends through the rest of life; and the peak time for entry of psychological factors is the infancy and childhood period, with again a tapering for the remainder of the arc. "Tapering" has to be understood, of course, as allowing for fluctuation. Certain segments of the arc, such as adolescence, the involutional period, and old age, probably have higher susceptibility to disturbance than others.

This chapter has presented a sampling and sketching of ideas about psychological types of traumata along the life-arc from infancy to the moment when symptoms appear. At the same time, it has been suggested that various items in Tom Young's current illness, behavior, and life-story offered circumstantial evidence in favor of most of these types of theory.

In making this point, it is obvious that both exposition of theory and data in regard to Tom have not been given in sufficient detail to constitute a clinical formulation. Certainly, no responsible clinician

Derivations of a Psychoneurosis

79

would be willing to offer a diagnostic evaluation on the basis of such illustrative fragments. It is assumed, however, that were the inquiry pressed to the full extent possible in therapeutic sessions, and were the doctor to give equal and systematic attention to data relevant to all the main areas of theory, he would continue to gather more and more circumstantial evidence in favor of most of the theories. Nor is Tom's case unique in this. Although it is true that some cases seem to fit one theoretical construct much better than another, the view in this book is that a great many of them provide evidence for most theoretical views, and, taken in the aggregate, provide some evidence for all.

In this situation, it is inadvisable at present to accept any theory without reservation. It is equally inadvisable to reject them all. One is led to consider the possibility that there may be an underlying set of common denominators in terms of which they are each, to some extent, correct. Specifying such a set of common denominators, in terms of a frame of reference that is all at one level of abstraction, would seem to be a necessary step in trying to understand the possible effects of sociocultural environment. Or, if the frame of reference cannot be constructed at one level of abstraction, at least all the levels employed should be articulated with each other so that the whole has sufficient logical consistency to permit the laying out of research operations. Hence, in Chapter V and what follows, an effort will be made to achieve such a goal.

In the present chapter there have been indications in favor of many of the theoretical explanations offered in connection with different points along the life-arc; there has also been repeated suggestion that sociocultural factors may exert an influence on the hereditary, physiological, and psychological conditions which predispose to the formation of illness. More than this, there has been some indication under the psychological heading that, even where dynamic theories have different content, they may agree in recognizing most of the same environmental factors as important. Although the bases for this are, so far, diffuse and lacking in precision, one is led to expect that there may be connections between psychiatric symptoms, the march of human affairs, and the variations in patterns of human living which fill the hollows, hills, towns, fields, woods, and shores of the Northeast. One can, perhaps, begin to see the alarmed Tom, the widow Chauncey, the crew of the wrecked *Westway*, the indifferent Rose, the drunken

Bernie, and the new red Chiason baby as all somehow related, as borne on the same flood, affected differently, yet interdependently, in the flow of human events.

CHAPTER NOTES

Three different purposes were in mind in the formulation of the notes which follow each chapter. One purpose is to offer commentary and to acknowledge indebtedness to those who have influenced the development of ideas upon which this frame of reference rests. Another is to point out the works of other authors who have used similar ideas, although they may not have had a direct influence. A third is to give the interested reader a start on further reading regarding topics which are mentioned briefly in the text. There is, however, no attempt to provide exhaustive coverage.

1. Although the idea of the substitutability of symptoms is widespread in clinical psychiatry, the terminology for its designation has not yet been standardized. I am grateful to Dr. Josephine Hilgard for pointing out a number of references which deal with some aspects of the matter. While there has been research into the possible inverse relationship between psychosomatic symptoms and psychoses, most authors seem to agree that the "changing," "alteration," "replacement," and "equivalence" of symptoms involves more than a simple one-to-one relationship. Browning and Houseworth refer to instances of the process which I have in mind when they say:

"It has long been known that hypnotic removal of conversion symptoms is often followed by reappearance of the same symptom within a short time, or by the development of new substitute or replacement symptoms. In a recent report Seitz demonstrated in a patient with conversion hysteria that replacement of symptoms not only occurred invariably when the original symptom was removed hypnotically, but also that the substitute symptoms were psychodynamically and symbolically equivalent to the original symptom.

"Whether the symptoms of psychosomatic disorders may

Derivations of a Psychoneurosis

be removed by medical and surgical treatment without replacement by new symptoms is not yet established. The present investigation was designed to test the hypothesis that removal of the symptoms of psychosomatic disorders, without removal of the conflicts giving rise to them, may be followed by the development of new symptoms" (p. 328).

See: JAMES S. BROWNING and JOHN H. HOUSEWORTH, "Development of New Symptoms Following Medical and Surgical Treatment for Duodenal Ulcer," *Psychosomatic Medicine*, Vol. XV, no. 4, 1953, pp. 328-336; EMANUEL M. HONIG "Psychosis and Peptic Ulcer," *Bulletin of the Menninger Clinic,* Vol. 19, no. 2, 1955, pp. 61-67; ALEXANDER THOMAS, MARVIN STERN, and ALFRED LILIENFELD, "Relationship of Psychosis and Psychosomatic Disease," *The Journal of Nervous and Mental Disease,* Vol. 123, no. 3, 1956, pp. 249-256; W. DONALD ROSS, "Psychosomatic Disorders and Psychoses," in ERIC D. WITTKOWER and R. A. CLEGHORN (Eds.), *Recent Developments in Psychosomatic Medicine* (Philadelphia: Lippincott, 1954), pp. 397-418.

2. *See,* for instance, FRANZ J. KALLMANN, "Genetic Aspects of Psychoses," in *The Biology of Mental Health and Disease, The Twenty-seventh Annual Conference of the Milbank Memorial Fund* (New York: Hoeber, 1952), pp. 283-302. A more extended account of Kallman's views may be found in FRANZ J. KALLMAN, *Heredity in Health and Mental Disorder* (New York: Norton, 1953).

3. In this emphasis on an extreme view of genetic cause, I realize that I am to some extent conjuring up an imaginary adversary. The same is also true with regard to the template offered earlier of "current circumstances." It is probable that few students of human behavior will be found who really hold exclusively to such extremes.

My approach, however, seems warranted on two counts. In the first place, it is a way of leading by simple steps into the vastly complicated tangle of factors that are presently to be considered. In the second, it is not entirely beside the point to discuss some of the reasons an extreme view is questionable. Although few people may hew to the absolute extreme, there are some who are close to it. This may be more a question of popular view than of scientific attitude, but it is nonetheless powerful and widespread. There is something subjectively concluding and satisfying about the idea "He is made that way," and it is impressive that numbers of people who consciously reject the exclusive hereditary outlook nevertheless habitually think in almost those terms. Practical men, including physicians, are often of this stamp and they are apt to make decisions of some importance to human life under the influence of such ideas.

4. The view that it is important not to equate heredity with unmodifiability is also found among biologists. For instance Dobzhansky says:

"Health and disease are desirable or undesirable states of one's body, of one's appearance, of one's phenotype. Curability and incurability refer to phenotypes, not to genes. Therefore, there is no difference in principle between hereditary and environmental diseases with respect to their susceptibility to curative treatments. There exist plenty of curable and of incurable environmental and hereditary diseases. . . .

"What we inherit are genes, not characters or traits. However, the genes interact with the environment in which they are placed. By so doing they determine the direction, the path, the trajectory which the development of a given person takes from conception, to birth, to maturity, to senescence, to death. We, geneticists, often speak or write as though the genes determined merely final states of various characters, especially those of the adult body. This is unrealistic; the development is never completed and the processes of senescence are just as much a part of the normal development pattern as are growth and organ formation. The genes, accordingly, do not determine any particular stage or goal of the development, they bring about the development as a whole, both the ascending portion in youth, and the descending part of the trajectory known as ageing and senility. In short, the genes determine processes, not states." See THEODOSIUS DOBZHANSKY, "The Biological Concept of Heredity as Applied to Man," in *The Nature and Transmission of the Genetic and Cultural Characteristics of Human Populations* (New York: Milbank Memorial Fund, 1957), pp. 12, 14; also, BENSON E. GINSBURG, "Genetics as a Tool in the Study of Behavior," *Perspectives in Biology and Medicine*, Vol. 1, no. 4, 1958, pp. 397-424.

Derivations of a Psychoneurosis

5. The viewpoint with regard to genetics that has influenced the frame of reference has its roots in a course (mainly laboratory) taken many years ago under George Harrison Shull. To mention this impact is to acknowledge a debt to a remarkable teacher, one who managed somehow to bring student and nature in contact with each other in such a way that the former could learn more or less directly from the latter.

The Dobzhansky article (published after our research was underway) may be noted again because of the vivid manner in which this kind of orientation is summarized:

"Are, then, the genes or the environment more important as determinants of the process of living? Clearly, this is the wrong way to ask a question. There is no organism without genes or without environment; both are absolutely necessary to life, for life is interaction of genes and environment.

"The nature-nurture [*sic*] must be stated differently to make it susceptible of meaningful study and solution. It is a matter of observation that human individuals and groups differ in all sorts of ways—physically, physiologically, psychically, and culturally. What is the origin of these interpersonal and intergroup differences? They are brought about by the existing variety of human genotypes, and by the variety of the environments in which people live. It is, then, legitimate to inquire what part of the observed variance in a given trait is due to the diversity of human genotypes, and what to the environments in which men develop. Experience has shown that both genotypic and environmental diversities are to some extent responsible for the observed variability of almost all human traits.

"The question at issue is what are the relative weights of the genotypic and environmental variables in the causation of the observed differences among men. No single or simple answer to this question is possible, because these weights are not the same for different traits. For example, the observed variance in the blood groups is, as far as known, wholly genetic. The diversity of languages which people speak is very largely or entirely environmental. Other traits form a spectrum, mostly between these extremes. Unfortunately, the location in this spectrum of numerous human characteristics and qualities which we regard as important in our fellow men is known only sketchily or not at all." DOBZHANSKY, "The Biological Concept of Heredity as Applied to Man," in *The Nature and Transmission of the Genetic and Cultural Characteristics of Human Populations,* p. 15.

6. The following definition of "physiology" is given in *The American Illustrated Medical Dictionary,* by W. A. NEWMAN DORLAND (22nd ed.; Philadelphia: Saunders, 1951): "The science which treats of the *functions of the living organism* and its parts."

The Oxford Universal Dictionary, 3rd ed., 1955, says: "The science of the *normal functions* and phenomena of living things."

The italics are mine. The first definition is the broad view and includes both normal and pathological functioning. The second is restricted to "normal." Such usage may be seen in the following sentence: "Consequently, whereas experience in treatment of the sick enables rules to be laid down which roughly divide the degrees of disturbance in an organism into normal (physiological) and abnormal (pathological) ranges, the mechanisms which maintain an equilibrium in the body are equally concerned in health and disease." *See* F. R. WINTON and L. E. BAYLISS, *Human Physiology* (4th ed.; Boston: Little, Brown, 1955), p. 2.

7. A report on some work of this character may be found in:

WILLIAM F. WINDLE, "Anoxia: Its Effects on Structure of the Brain," in *The Biology of Mental Health and Disease, The Twenty-seventh Annual Conference of the Milbank Memorial Fund* (New York: Hoeber, 1952), pp. 327-334.

For a discussion of the importance of nonhereditary factors in the production of "congenital" defects *see* ROBERT M. STECHER, "Identical Twins Discordant for Interventricular Septal Defect and Absent Radius and Thumb," *The American Journal of Human Genetics,* Vol. 9, no. 3, Sept. 1957, p. 218.

"During the last century it was customary to consider that deformities of new born children were hereditarily determined. This principle was first questioned by Jonathan Hutchinson who showed that children born with syphilis did not inherit the disease but received it as a transplacental infection in prenatal life. Within recent years many infections, rubella, toxoplasmosis, varicella, influenza, variola, vaccinia and herpes zoster, have been known to cross placental barriers to damage the fetus (Bass, 1952). Besides infections other forms of stress, injury, nutritional deficiencies and anoxemia during critical periods of pregnancy have been responsible, in experimental animals, at least, for congenital defects such as cataract, cleft palate, heart disease and other abnormalities (Ingalls, 1956). Some congenital defects appear to depend entirely upon prenatal environmental influence, others upon purely hereditary factors and still others upon a combination of such factors. In the case of hereditary diseases becoming manifest only in middle or later life the environmental factors are of increasing importance."

For a recent statement of a medical viewpoint along these lines, see THEODORE H. INGALLS, "Causes and Prevention of Developmental Defects," *The Journal of the American Medical Association,* Vol. 161, no. 11, 1956.

This article deals only with gross defects, but it points out the known factors and some principles of their operation. It is plausible to assume that the same factors and principles can also produce milder and less clear-cut defects. This has been found true of virtually every well-studied constellation of pathogenic agents and circumstances.

8. For theories of prenatal psychological process and of birth trauma *see:* PHYLLIS GREENACRE, *Trauma, Growth, and Personality* (New York: Norton, 1952); NANDOR FODOR, *The Search for the Beloved* (New York: Hermitage, 1949); SIGMUND FREUD, *The Problem of Anxiety* (New York: Norton, 1936); OTTO RANK, *The Trauma of Birth* (New York: Basic, 1952).

For a general review, *see:* GERALD S. BLUM, *Psychoanalytic Theories of Personality* (New York: McGraw-Hill, 1953); RUTH L. MUNROE, *Schools of Psychoanalytic Thought* (New York: Dryden, 1955).

9. There is a large literature dealing with culture and personality and with national character. Among the prominent authors are Ruth Benedict, Lawrence K. Frank, Erich Fromm, Geoffrey Gorer, A. I. Hallowell, John J. Honigmann, Abram Kardiner, Clyde Kluckhohn, Weston La Barre, Ralph Linton, Margaret Mead, and Edward Sapir.

Some critical overviews which also contain extensive bibliographies may be found in: ALEX INKELES and DANIEL LEVINSON, "National Character: The Study of Model Personality and Sociocultural Systems" in GARDNER LINDZEY (Ed.), *Handbook of Social Psychology* (Cambridge: Addison-Wesley, 1954); A. IRVING HALLOWELL, *Culture and Experience* (Philadelphia: Univ. Pennsylvania Press, 1955); JOHN J. HONIGMANN, *Culture and Personality* (New York: Harper, 1954); DOUGLAS G. HARING, *Personal Character and Cultural Milieu* (3rd ed.; Syracuse: Syracuse Univ. Press, 1956); S. STANFIELD SARGENT and MARIAN W. SMITH (Eds.), *Culture and Personality* (New York: Wenner Gren Foundation for Anthropological Research, 1949).

For indications of work more focused on the relationship of culture to psychiatric disorder, the following books and their bibliographies may be consulted: JOSEPH EATON and ROBERT J. WEIL, *Culture and Mental Disorders* (Glencoe, Ill.: Free Press, 1954); RALPH LINTON, *Culture and Mental Disorders* (Springfield, Ill.: Thomas, 1956); MARVIN K. OPLER, *Culture, Psychiatry and Human Values* (Springfield, Ill.: Thomas, 1956).

One review article is particularly worthy of attention because of its selected references and evaluative comment: PAUL K. BENEDICT and IRVING JACKS, "Mental Illness in Primitive Societies" in *Psychiatry: Journal for the Study of Interpersonal Processes*, Vol. 17, no. 4, 1954, pp. 377-389.

For periodicals, *see: Newsletter of Transcultural Research in Mental Health Problems,* Transcultural Psychiatric Studies, Allan Memorial Institute, 1025 Pine Avenue West, Montreal, P. Q., Canada; *International Research Newsletter in Mental Health,* Postgraduate Center for Psychotherapy, 218 East 70th Street, New York 21, New York; *The International Journal of Social Psychiatry,* Avenue Publishing Co., 9 Fellows Road, London, N.W.3, England.

A bibliography comprising 512 items may be found in: MORTON I. TEICHER, "Comparative Psychiatry, Some References in Ethnopsychiatry," *Revue internationale d'Ethnopsychologie normale et pathologique,* Vol. 1, nos. 1 and 2, 1956 and 1957.

In addition there have been a number of studies focused on various sociological characteristics such as class position or occupation as they relate to psychiatric disorder. *See,* for example: AUGUST B. HOLLINGSHEAD and FREDERICK C. REDLICH, *Social Class and Mental Illness, A Community Study* (New York: Wiley, 1958); ARNOLD M. ROSE (Ed.), *Mental Health and Mental Disorder* (New York: Norton, 1955); S. KIRSON WEINBERG, *Society and Personality Disorders* (New York: Prentice-Hall, 1952).

A bibliography of psychiatric literature which includes more extensive lists of reading in a number of the categories suggested here is KARL A. MENNINGER, *A Guide to Psychiatric Books with a Suggested Basic Reading List,* The Menninger Clinic Monograph Series, No. 7 (New York: Grune and Stratton, 1950).

10. The effects of maternal deprivation have received particularly significant development at the hands of John Bowlby and this may be found in his *Maternal Care and Mental Health* (Geneva: World Health Organization, 1952).

More recently he has been carrying forward analysis of the nature of the child's attachment to the mother and placing emphasis on a number of linked instincts rather than on either the classical concept of libido or on learning through satisfaction of primary physiological drives. *See* JOHN BOWLBY, "Symposium on the Contribution of Current Theories to An Understanding of Child Development (I) An Ethological Approach to Research in Child Development," *The British Journal of Medical Psychology,* Vol. 30, Part 4, 1957, pp. 230-240.

11. *See* HARRY STACK SULLIVAN, *The Interpersonal Theory of Psychiatry* (New York: Norton, 1953), p. 41.

For a more detailed theoretical scheme with regard to how anxiety or irrational fear may be learned, *see* J. DOLLARD and N. E. MILLER, especially Chap. 11, "How Symptoms are Learned," *Personality and Psychotherapy: An Analysis in Terms of Learning, Thinking and Culture* (New York: McGraw-Hill, 1950).

12. Alfred North Whitehead's ideas with regard to "misplaced concreteness" may be found in Chap. 3 of his *Science and the Modern World* (New York: Macmillan, 1925). For instance, on page 72 he says, "There is an error; but it is merely the accidental error of mistaking the abstract for the concrete. It is an example of what I will call the 'Fallacy of Misplaced Concreteness.' This fallacy is the occasion of great confusion in philosophy."

This point of view was brought to my attention by Adolf Meyer who felt the warning had important application to psychiatry and frequently used it in his teaching of psychodynamics. Much of his criticism of classical psychoanalysis was embodied in this point.

13. Well-known authors in this area are Konrad Lorenz and J. Paul Scott. A review may be found in JOHN PAUL SCOTT, *Animal Behavior* (Chicago: Univ. Chicago Press, 1958), *see* particularly Chap. 8, "Social Behavior and Social Organization."

14. These ideas of role and personality development come mainly from Leonard S. Cottrell, Jr., Harry Stack Sullivan, and Norman Cameron, who in turn were much influenced by George Herbert Mead and Charles H. Cooley. Communication from Cottrell and Sullivan was primarily through personal discussion. *See,* however: L. S. COTTRELL, JR., "The Analysis of Situational Fields in Social Psychology," *American Sociological Review,* Vol. 7, no. 3, 1942, pp. 370-382; L. S. COTTRELL, JR., "The Adjustment of the Individual to His Age and Sex Roles," in THEODORE M. NEWCOMB and EUGENE L. HARTLEY (Eds.), *Readings in Social Psychology* (New York: Holt, 1947); H. S. SULLIVAN, *Conceptions of Modern Psychiatry* (New York: William Alanson White Foundation, 1947).

Acquaintance with Cameron's views came from his book, *The Psychology of Behavior Disorders, A Biosocial Interpretation* (Boston: Houghton Mifflin, 1947).

With regard to Mead and Cooley, *see:* CHARLES H. COOLEY, *Human Nature and the Social Order* (New York: Scribner, 1922); GEORGE H. MEAD, *Mind, Self and Society* (Chicago: Univ. Chicago Press, 1934); ANSELM STRAUS (Ed.), *The Social Psychology of George Herbert Mead* (Chicago: Univ. Chicago Press, 1956).

15. This view of role is derived mainly from Ralph Linton as set forth in his *The Study of Man* (New York: Appleton-

Century, 1936) and *The Cultural Background of Personality* (New York: Appleton-Century, 1945).

Role theory is complex and as yet not well codified. Terms and concepts are used in a variety of ways by workers in sociology, anthropology, social psychology, and psychiatry. In these pages we are concerned not with a review of the field, but only to indicate how the frame of reference has been affected by it. For an overview, *see:* NEAL GROSS, WARD S. MASON, and ALEXANDER W. MC EACHERN, *Explorations in Role Analysis* (New York: Wiley, 1958); LIONEL J. NEIMAN and JAMES W. HUGHES, "The Problem of the Concept of Role—A Re-Survey of the Literature," *Social Forces,* Vol. 30, no. 2, 1951, pp. 141-149; THEODORE R. SARBIN, "Role Theory," in GARDNER LINDZEY (Ed.), *Handbook of Social Psychology* (Cambridge: Addison-Wesley, 1954), Vol. I.

16. *See* Notes 3 and 5 of this chapter.

Some examples of those who seem to give more weight to cultural determinism than is embodied in this frame of reference are Weston La Barre, Ruth Benedict, Margaret Mead, and Geoffrey Gorer. It is fair to say that even those who put the greatest weight on sociocultural factors do not deny the possibility of genetic factors. What they do is to ignore these as a significant influence on personality variation between ethnic groups. *See,* for instance, the following:

"Newborn children differ from one another in inherent constitutions and almost certainly in temperament. It is possible that they also differ in intellectual and emotional potentialities; but despite a very great deal of work which has been done on this subject, this assumption is still unproved. So although each child (with the exception of identical twins) is born with its unique genetic constitutions, it seems reasonable to assume that in any large group the different potentialities cancel one another out, as it were, and that newborn infants represent a random sample of constitutions and temperaments. When human genetics have developed further, it may be necessary to modify or abandon this hypothesis; but in the meantime it seems more scientific to ignore genetic determinants when considering the development of a group of infants." *See* GEOFFREY GORER, "The Concept of National Character," in C. K. KLUCKHOHN, H. A. MURRAY and DAVID M. SCHNEIDER (Eds.), *Personality in*

Nature, Society, and Culture (New York: Knopf, 1953), p. 253.

More congenial to the view of this book are the following observations by Ralph Linton: "Under such circumstances the problem of what constitutes normality becomes quite complicated. It seems that one must distinguish between absolute and relative abnormality. All societies provide examples of psychotics, neurotics, and hysterics, who are recognized as such by the members of that society. The symptomatologies associated with these abnormal states differ from society to society in ways which strongly suggest that they are shaped by cultural influences. The methods employed by different societies in dealing with individuals of these different types, including the social utilization of certain forms of psychic abnormality, also differ. However, it seems certain that abnormality of this sort is absolute and probably has physiological basis. Individuals having the constitutional defects responsible for such abnormality would be abnormal in any society. At most, particular cultural factors may lead to the manifestation or suppression of symptoms at various levels of defect intensity.

"Relative normality, on the other hand, is a matter of the individual's adjustment to the cultural milieu and the degree to which his personality configuration approaches the basic personality of his society." *(Culture and Mental Disorders,* p. 62.)

In touching on ideas as to how sociocultural factors may influence personality formation and malformation, I have used roles as an illustrative example. This viewpoint is perhaps characteristic of sociologists. Anthropologists have tended to place emphasis on child rearing practices as such.

These approaches are not, of course, mutually exclusive, but may, indeed, reinforce each other. My point here is to recognize that I have somewhat slighted in my illustration a major area of thought and inquiry—the differential effects of various cultures on personality formation as mediated through their respective patterns of socialization.

17. A great deal has been written concerning the relationship of wartime experiences and psychiatric disorder. For example, *see:* ROY R. GRINKER and JOHN P. SPIEGEL, *Men Under Stress* (Philadelphia: Blakiston, 1945); WILLIAM

SARGANT, "Eight Years Psychiatric Work in England," *Journal of Nervous and Mental Disease,* Vol. 107, June 1948, pp. 501-516.

A collection of abstracts on this topic is to be found in NOLAN D. C. LEWIS and BERNICE ENGLE (Eds.), *Wartime Psychiatry, a Compendium of the International Literature* (New York: Oxford Univ. Press, 1954).

18. For a review concerning the processes of aging as they relate to personality change, *see* OSCAR L. KAPLAN, *Mental Disorders in Later Life* (Stanford: Stanford Univ. Press, 1945).

Chapter IV

Patterns of
Psychiatric Disorder

THE CONDITION from which Tom Young suffered is one
instance of an illness sometimes called *anxiety attack*. Anxiety attacks
are themselves a subdivision of a larger category, *anxiety reaction*,
which in turn belongs in a still more general group of disorders, *psy-choneurosis*. The psychoneuroses are one of eight or ten gross divisions

of subject matter that can be made for the sake of convenience in the the total field comprised by clinical psychiatry.[1]

In discussing the derivations of Tom's anxiety reaction it was indicated that many of the points were not limited to this particular kind of disturbance. It would seem wise, therefore, in the interest of clarification to suggest how widely they may apply. As a step in this direction I shall move from the single case to a brief outline of the range of psychiatric disorders, and then to their derivations. This will include anxiety, phobic, obsessive-compulsive, depressive, dissociative, conversion, and neurasthenic reactions which, together with hypochondriasis, all fall in the general category of psychoneurosis. There will also be mention of personality disorder, sociopathic disturbance, psychophysiological disorder, psychoses, mental deficiency and brain syndromes.

It might be argued that it would be better to rely on references to one or more of the many texts that have been written describing the field of psychiatry. This could not only save space in these pages but also avoid inadequate coverage. There are, however, at least two points in favor of the effort. In the first place, the texts are comprehensive rather than selective and their array of descriptive and conceptual information tends to obscure those features which are most relevant to the theme of this book.

Secondly, it is particularly important to be clear about what one is going to mean by "a psychiatric case." Because there are not one but many categories of psychiatric cases and because the different categories probably have different assortments of derivations, it is also probable that they are differentially affected by sociocultural factors. It is possible to be exceedingly obscure, therefore, if one talks about psychiatric disorder in general; it is necessary to indicate the categories he is going to use in projecting such disorder against the sociocultural background.

That this is no easy matter is evinced by the amount of discussion that has occurred in recent years in regard to what constitutes a psychiatric case. The core of the matter is actually not too difficult. It is possible to find numerous instances in which virtually everyone will agree. The margins are what raise the problem, the boundaries between different categories of cases, and the lines between ill and well.

It is perhaps for this reason that most authors in dynamic psychiatry are vague as to the limits of the entity to which they refer. In reading many of the most insightful writers it is often impossible to tell how broadly a postulated pattern or mechanism is conceived to apply. Does it embrace all or only some psychoneuroses? Does it include some or all psychoses? Does it include conditions manifested primarily in physiological disturbances such as ulcers and high blood pressures? Does it happen in well people, or is that a contradiction in terms?

It is not necessary to insist that the authors who have put forward such theories based on their clinical experience ought to have concerned themselves with the limits. They seem justified in leaving this for later research to explore. For the purposes of this book, however, it is obligatory that we delineate, even if only very tentatively, our points of reference in psychiatric disorder. Some specification as to what a case is and is not has to be given before relations with social environment can be examined. For it is certain, as a general principle, that the actions, interactions, and relationships of a phenomenon in nature cannot be observed unless that phenomenon is designated with sufficient clarity to make identification possible.[2]

We must start, however, with the realization that there is not sufficient knowledge or theory to provide a satisfactory definition of psychiatric disorder in general. Nor, indeed, can a definition be found that is applied consistently or with unanimity of opinion to most of the subdivisions of psychiatric disorder, such as psychoneurosis and psychosis.

The ideal would, of course, be to have a definition in terms of features which are the exclusive property of psychiatric disorder, and much thought has been given by many people to this end. Such a definition would point out that which is central to all psychiatric cases and absent from nonpsychiatric cases. Thus, no matter how much instances of psychiatric disorder might differ from each other in many aspects, they would all have this one pattern in common. An example of such a definition is to say that acid is a compound that dissociates in aqueous solution with the production of hydrogen ions. A substance which possesses this characteristic is an acid regardless of color, quantity, temperature, shape, and other elements present in the compound such as sulphur or chlorine. Nothing approaching this has been achieved with psychiatric disorder.

Some attempts have been made to write out definitions according to theories of cause. This leads to the delineation of dynamic models of the process according to which the clinician interprets the signs, symptoms, dreams, and other expressions of his patient. These models, as for instance the Oedipus complex, fall within one or another of the psychological types of explanation outlined in the previous chapter. A difficulty arises in that the models seem to foster a monistic type of explanation, whereas the phenomena of psychiatry give every indication of being expressions of multiple factors. As partial explanations the models are exceedingly important and helpful, but they may become overspecific, too neatly rounded out, closing off ends that really are, because of lack of knowledge, open.

Another problem is that definitions based on etiological concepts rarely offer easily detectable outward signs by means of which a case can be distinguished from a noncase, or one type of case from another. Prolonged, intensive study is usually mandatory and even then judgments are apt to vary considerably from one clinician to another, including instances in which they subscribe to the same theories and are concerned with the same patient.

A different solution is to rely on easily detectable outward characteristics as a basis for identification and grouping in categories much as the taxonomists have done with species. In psychiatry, this means groupings based on signs and symptoms; yet, even so, such efforts are apt to become contaminated with some admixture of etiological considerations (e.g., mental disturbance due to arteriosclerosis or physiological disturbance due to emotional difficulties).[3]

The great drawback to a purely descriptive approach is that the categories, because largely based on surface manifestation, may include cases under one heading which are very different in their underlying nature. Counterwise, the categories may divide, artificially, cases which are essentially similar in process. In considering this matter it is well to remember that the natural sciences have in the main progressed from first, approximate definitions and classifications based on surface phenomena, through successive stages of refinement until reorganized in terms of fundamental processes. Thus, whales were once regarded as fish, but as their anatomy and physiology became known (and that of other creatures as well) it was possible to identify them as mammals despite their external appearance and habitat. Turning the matter around, the Tasmanian wolf and the kangaroo seemed on first sight to be radically different, yet closer study showed their common marsupial nature.

Many disease categories have undergone a similar progression from being seen as patterns of symptoms to being recognized as patterns of process. This is dramatized in Pasteur's establishment of the part played by microörganisms in cases of infection, thus opening up the possibility of categorization according to agent and mode of infection. The same point is also illustrated by discoveries regarding malfunction of endocrine glands and the effects of vitamin deficiency.

Psychiatry is moving in the same direction, but remains as yet in a fairly early stage. The desirability of getting away from classification based only on surface phenomena is evident to almost everyone. At the same time, aspiration is not the same as means or achievement; we are as yet lacking in a knowledge of process that might serve as a system of classification. Theories there are, of course, in abundance, but, as suggested on pages 66-68 in the last chapter, these are not as yet sufficiently established. One can be fairly sure, however, that when hereditary, physiological, and psychological factors are better differentiated and established through replicated research, then many of the categories of psychiatric disorder we are currently using will have to be changed. It is likely, for instance, that numbers of cases now lumped together as schizophrenia or anxiety will turn out to be products of markedly different processes.

From all of this the conclusion may be drawn that at the present state of knowledge in psychiatry one has reason to mistrust both surface appearance of things and theoretical inferences as to process. One has to work with the patterns he can see, yet he must work warily.

This position of balance and the employment of tentative categories is not easy to maintain. It is a sort of juggling act of suspended judgments and it has to be held against the fact that classification in terms of symptoms is largely out of fashion among many psychiatrists, and subject to ridicule. One has to be prepared to encounter a somewhat undiscriminating rejection of such categories on the grounds of sterility and lack of dynamics, an attitude which bears the marks of battles in the progress of psychiatry.[4]

Despite their limitations, symptoms do provide the basis for a working definition, a handle whereby cases can be identified as they occur in nature and some rough estimates made in regard to the impairment of the person's family relationships, work, recreation, and social inter-

Patterns of Psychiatric Disorder

course. They provide a basis for explaining environmental factors as part of the investigation of the connections between surface phenomena and deeper-lying processes and causes.

An additional point is the problem of distinguishing between categories, whatever the system of classification employed. There are bound to be marginal cases; that is, those which do not fit well into any category. Emergence from these difficulties depends on further advance of knowledge in the total field of psychiatry. Such advance may in part be achieved by analysis and concept building on existing clinical insight, but it is also dependent on systematic concept checking in multiple research operations. As part of this we need to know more than we presently do about prevalence and incident of the case types we are already using.

Problems of discrimination are common whenever man tries to group and analyze phenomena. It is only from a distance that demarcations look sharp. Take this line:

At reading distance on the printed page its edges appear definite. Put it under successive magnifications of increasing power and the edges lose their clarity. Precision of margin is relative, and adequacy of category distinction is a matter of degree of precision in relation to a purpose.

Such questions of differentiation apply to many diseases and disorders outside the field of psychiatry. They also apply between illness and wellness generally, and to some of the commonest practical distinctions of everyday living, such as between plants and animals, or between the organic and the inorganic. Most people can tell a tree from a horse, and a man from a rock, but there are no definitions in terms of essential nature which hold well for all organisms and which tell, for instance, whether some of the flagellates are to be classed as plant or animal and whether the tobacco mosaic virus is alive or is an organic chemical compound.

I TYPES OF DISORDER

As already noted, Tom's pattern of symptoms occurs with such frequency among people as to have drawn medical attention and to have been given a name, *anxiety attack*. In any general clinic of the Northeast and in the practice of most physicians, people with such a condition appear from time to time seeking help.

Most anxiety does not, however, come in attacks. If anxiety is defined as the subjective feelings and physiological signs characteristic of fear arising in a situation in which there is no plausible, commonsense, and conscious source of that fear, then we may say there occur cases of chronic anxiety.[5] It may be added that these make up the great bulk of the conditions that can be tagged as *anxiety reaction*. If this were Tom's condition he would be suffering most of the time, not just in crises, from inner feelings of apprehension, accompanied by a rapid heart, sweating, broken sleep, nightmares, pallor, general nervousness, or other related symptoms, but lacking the extreme intensity and short duration of the "attack" described in Chapter I.

Anxiety as evinced by subjective state and the physiological signs of fear is not limited to the anxiety reactions. It pervades most of the rest of the psychoneuroses and many other psychiatric conditions as well. In the anxiety neuroses, however, it appears in more or less pure form—that is, uncomplicated by additional symptoms and outward signs, whereas in the remaining psychiatric disorders other types of behavior dominate the picture. Some of these may be considered as devious expressions of anxiety. In such cases assumptions regarding the presence of the anxiety are more a matter of somewhat extended inference than impression from direct observation.

With Tom the anxiety was manifest and his symptoms were its expression. There was little question, after the medical work-up, that an inner psychological state like fear accompanied the outward symptoms and signs, and explanation became then a matter of finding causes of the anxiety. In other types of psychiatric conditions, we must be prepared for the causal relationship of anxiety to symptoms being much more obscure.

To take some examples, Tom had an aunt on his mother's side who had an unreasoning and uncontrollable fear of fire. One of Gordon Chauncey's brothers had a terror of syphilis. Numbers of other people live in the Northeast who have a similar fear of cats, snakes, high places, or crowds. Neuroses in which this type of behavior predominates are called *phobic reactions*.

There is considerable clinical evidence to suggest that many phobic reactions are a kind of logical alternative to the anxiety neurosis.

Patterns of Psychiatric Disorder

99

Where Tom and others of his kind have *no object* for their feeling of being afraid, phobic people have the *wrong object.*

It may be argued that Tom's concern about his heart was an instance of belief in a wrong object. To some extent this did have a phobic flavor. He was, however, open to demonstration and persuasion by his doctors on this count, whereas if he had been genuinely phobic his view could not so easily have been changed.

Studies made in the course of therapy suggest strongly that the objects to which phobic fears are attached bear some symbolic relationship to the underlying psychological factors involved in the anxiety. If Tom, for instance, had had a phobic fear of guns, we could see from what has been said how this might be related to his inner problems. This kind of linking, when it occurs, and, indeed, the underlying anxiety itself, are largely unconscious. The fearlike symptoms are generally evident only when the individual is confronted with the object of his phobia. By avoiding this he can often secure a fair measure of peace—at the conscious level anyhow.

The phobia, therefore, seems to function as a defense against anxiety and is a way of rendering tolerable most of the other dimensions of living. The condition becomes socially crippling only when it is a matter of an object that is encountered frequently, such as automobiles and trains.

Closely akin to phobias, and showing the same tendency to serve as a means of avoiding feelings of anxiety, are *obsessive-compulsive reactions.* Patients are said to have this difficulty when they have repetitive ideas, carry out elaborate rituals, and are rendered actually miserable, even panicky, if prevented from doing so—for example, bathroom procedures of some persons (procedures which suggest the sterile techniques of the operating room and make getting up and retiring a matter of several hours each) or the need for washing hands thirty or forty times a day.

The Chauncey brother who feared syphilis was compulsive as well as phobic, since he had an unvarying, complicated system for using toilets without touching them, and for carrying slips of clean paper so he would not have to catch door knobs in his bare hand. A sister of Dr. Coindreau's wife had similar behavior, but with a pattern based on religion rather than hygiene. She was overconcerned with details that were inconsequential from the viewpoint of her church. The priest, no less than the doctor, recognized her condition as illness, but referred to it as "scrupulosity" rather than as an obsessive-compulsive psychoneurosis.[6]

A notable feature of both obsessive-compulsive and phobic behavior is that the patient himself often realizes the abnormality of what he does, but like an addict is unable to give it up. He finds that the discomfort he experiences when he attempts to stop is worse than the social discomfiture produced by his symptoms.

The psychoneuroses touched upon thus far—anxiety, phobic, and obsessive-compulsive—may be described as malfunctioning types of fear. But fear is not the only affect that may appear in such an exaggerated form as to indicate and partially constitute distortion of the personality system. Sadness and discouragement may be so severe, or so inappropriate, as to amount to illness. Mrs. Chauncey had had such difficulties since Helen's childhood. By degrees she had come to take a hopeless view of everything. She did her work, took care of Helen and her two sons, looked after the house, and fulfilled her social obligations with poise, but never seemed to derive any pleasure from what she was doing. She appeared rather to be dryly and bitterly marking time, waiting for some inevitable catastrophe and seeing its advance signs in all sorts of daily events around her.

The word "bitterly" suggests another emotion, anger, which may get out of hand. In Mrs. Chauncey's case, it did not require a very astute observer to perceive that her prevailing unhappiness was composed of fruitless, gnawing anger as well as sadness. Like the blue mood, its source was unknown to her, and also like the blue mood, it colored without reason all sorts of persons and events. She was, in short, a sad and hostile woman, displaying a *psychoneurotic depressive reaction*.

In some patients, the most obvious feature of their illness is extreme and continuous concern with the functioning of one or more parts of their bodies. There may be, for instance, persistent harping on the bowels, stomach, kidneys, or "female trouble"; or the site of the complaints may shift around all over their persons, disappearing in one area only to appear in another. In nearly all such cases there is a fairly clear emotional state consisting in some combination of anxiety, gloom, and hostility.

Dr. Coindreau had seen many people of this sort in the course of his practice. The patients were sure that their emotional state derived from organic difficulties, and in the beginning of his examination and study, the doctor was always ready to entertain this as the major probability. When the best medical techniques he could apply, however, revealed either no organic basis for the difficulties or else an exceedingly minor disturbance, he was led to feel that the emotional state was the primary aspect of the illness and the bodily complaints were both a result and some kind of explanation or excuse that was acceptable to the sentiment system of the patient.

If impressions along these lines were made known to the patient, he was pretty sure to feel that the doctor had failed to find the "true" (i.e., organic) cause, something that could be cured with surgery or pills. Although Dr. Coindreau was inclined to wonder about this himself and to believe that such might be the fact in particular cases, his experience and familiarity with his patients extending over many years convinced him that with some, the emotion was the primary disturbance and that the bodily preoccupation was a way of expressing it. Indeed, so out of proportion was the worrying of certain of these patients that not only did the doctor feel that there was something psychologically amiss but so also did friends and relatives. They often made remarks such as "He's half mental," "He ain't sick, it's only his imagination," "He is just trying to get attention," or "If he would get his mind off his guts he would be O.K." *Hypochondriasis* is a term sometimes applied to symptoms of the above type.[7]

Related to hypochondriacal symptoms, at least in appearance, are states of fatigue which the patient (and very often the doctor also) attributes to thyroid disorder or low blood pressure. In numbers of cases such physiological malfunction may be primary, but in others, there is little evidence of organic difficulty, while a study of the patient suggests strongly that the outer symptoms of fatigue are the product of an emotional state, comprising anxiety or sadness or anger, or some mixture of these. Symptoms of this sort may be called *neurasthenic reaction*.[8]

A type of neurotic reaction which is very different in appearance from those mentioned thus far may be seen in a cognitive difficulty, namely, in spells of extensive forgetting. This is called amnesia and often involves the temporary loss of whole segments of one's past life. Study of these cases almost invariably suggests that the forgetting is protecting the patient from awareness of some event or situation that is charged with unpleasant emotions such as fear or resentment.

There are also people who "forget" how to use a unit of their body, as for instance an arm, a leg, or the sense of vision or hearing. These conditions are fairly easy to detect, as a rule, through neurological examination because they do not conform to the patterns found when paralysis is based on damage to nerves or to the brain itself. Frequently these paralyses are precipitated by a dramatic event. Rose Chiason had a cousin who went blind when lightning struck a pine near their house one afternoon. She remained completely unable to see for three weeks and then vision came back almost as abruptly. She said it was "just like a curtain going up at a show."

The relationship of these types of paralysis or loss of sensory function to underlying emotional problems is apt to be fairly evident on study of the patient. As in amnesia, the central process is an escape from intolerable feelings. The amnesias and related types of disturbances are called *dissociative reaction* while the paralyses and sensory disturbances are called *conversion reaction*. Another name for the latter is "hysteria." [9]

It is hoped that the examples which have now been given are sufficient to suggest something of the range of complaints and symptoms that are found in the category *psychoneurotic disorder,* and that Tom Young's condition may be seen as one type in this larger grouping.

Leaving the psychoneuroses, let us next look at a category which has many resemblances, *personality disorder.*[10] As the name suggests, the symptoms of this condition pervade virtually all aspects of the personality, and seem to be life-long in duration. For example, some cases appear to have chronic difficulty in making realistic appraisal of the world around them. They live in their own imaginations to such an extent that they are constantly making mistakes in everyday activities, in their expectations of and responses to other people.

Some types of personality disorder take the form of affective swings from gloom to gladness and back again in such a way as to render the person's behavior unpredictable to himself and others. He may be able to perceive social relations realistically enough as an intellectual act, yet be incapable of responding with an adequate degree of appropriateness and consistency.

Another type of case has the characteristic of being intrinsically suspicious. He is prone to appraise the actions of other people in terms of hidden motives and mendacious schemes that will be injurious to him.

Still other persons have violent tempers that are easily set off by

Patterns of Psychiatric Disorder

103

trivial events, so that life is pervaded and damaged by this uncontrollable tendency. In contrast to this there are some personality disorders in which the individual is meek and self-effacing almost to the point of self-extinction.

Again, one may see cases that have no characteristic pattern except general instability. They fly apart emotionally and intellectually under slight pressure and get so excited as to be ineffective. This, incidently, is the type of behavior covered by the everyday rather than psychiatric use of the word "hysteria." When the reaction is triggered easily, these people have great difficulty in meeting the ordinary demands of life.

As can be judged from what has been said, the category of personality disorder is more diffuse than that of the psychoneuroses. Furthermore, although a descriptive definition can be given which sets it apart from the psychoneuroses, in actual practice a differential diagnosis is often exceedingly difficult to make. For example, if the patient is one who suffers from a chronic depressed mood, as did Mrs. Chauncey, it may be hard to say whether her condition should be called psychoneurotic depression or a depressed type of personality disorder. In her case, it would seem that the psychoneurotic label was more appropriate because the condition did not develop until she was in her middle thirties, and hence could not be considered as life-long, at least in its manifestations. Because personality disorders are, by virtue of their pervasive characteristics, difficult to treat, the category often becomes a name for cases that do not respond to therapeutic effort.

An example of a personality disorder may be seen in Tom Young's mother who all her life had been an excessive worrier and a person so easily frightened by trivial events that she could not carry out adequately all the duties of a farm-wife and mother.

The psychiatric categories that have been sketched so far may all be grouped together as constituting difficulties primarily for the patient. In every instance, the focal point is behavior or emotions, or both, which bother him. In contrast to this, we may now consider other conditions in which the main symptoms bother other people, namely, *sociopathic disturbance*.[11]

Alcoholism, such as that displayed by Bernie Chiason, is an example. He was a spree drinker, and half a dozen times a year—depending largely on how much money he could get—he was drunk for a week or even a month without interruption. As a result he had a bad reputation among employers, and earning a living, never easy for most people in the Northeast, was harder still for Bernie. His wife and children suffered from lack of adequate food and shelter. They suffered even more from the unpredictability of his behavior and from lack of an adequate father and husband. He had little respect or standing among his fellow men. Most of the woodsmen and mill hands were not squeamish about drinking, but Bernie went too far. They considered him "a dead beat and a bum." Bernie knew it and used to say to his dog Rover, lying by his bunk, "Even the bums think I'm a bum."

Not all alcoholics, of course, are found at Bernie's low economic and social level, nor does the dependency always involve alcohol. A variety of drugs can serve the same function, from barbiturates to morphine. The nature of the socially disturbing effects varies with the context of the individual.

Besides excessive use of, and dependency on, alcohol and drugs, deviant sexual behavior, especially that which victimizes others, may be classed as sociopathic; and so also a type of insensate hostility, in which attacks are made and cruelty perpetrated apparently for its own sake rather than for gain, as in stealing, or because of delusions of persecution.

Psychoneurosis and personality disorder, including sociopathic disturbance, cover a wide area of human conduct fronting a number of additional patterns of disorder. These must now be taken up.

Bordering, at least in terms of symptoms, on the hypochondriacal patterns is a large array of conditions which can be called *psychophysiological autonomic and visceral,* or, more briefly, *psychophysiological disorders.*[12] In such cases the organic defect is objectively clear enough and it may have severely crippling repercussions for the individual. Some examples are high blood pressure, paroxysmal tachycardia, migraine, asthma, peptic ulcers, colitis, indigestion, and dermatitis. The reason for their inclusion among psychiatric conditions is the clinical observation that sometimes emotional disturbances appear to play a major role in the onset and course of these diseases. It is important to realize the "sometimes," since there may be cases in which the psychological component is either nonexistent or unimportant.

Dr. Coindreau himself had a tendency to high blood pressure which he knew varied according to his emotional state. As he noted the frequency of coronary deaths among physicians, he often wondered if he had chosen the right profession. There had been times when, prior to

Patterns of Psychiatric Disorder

Tom Young's attack, he had envied the latter. Coming down through Woodside in his car from a sick call in the backwoods, he had admired the clean fields, browsing cattle, and fine stand of white spruce in the hollows. *"Là quelqu'un peut vivre à l'aise et paisiblement, regarder la vie croître et s'éteindre avec le retour des saisons, remplir ses devoirs en élevant sa famille sans se presser, sans trop d'embarras ou de contretemps, ajustant son train de vie au rythme des marées et à la révolution de la Grande Ourse autour du Pôle."* ("There, one could have a decent even existence, letting life grow and decline with the turn of the seasons, fulfilling his task in raising a family without hurry, scramble, or interruption—living at the pace of the tides, and the turn of the Great Bear around the Pole.")

Dr. Ralph Hopkins, the psychiatrist, on the other hand, was subject to asthma. This condition had been severe when he had been a medical student, had improved with psychotherapy, but it would re-emerge on occasion. His asthma, together with the experience in psychotherapy, had been largely responsible for awakening his interest in psychiatry and steering him toward this branch of medicine as his specialty.

Turning now in a different direction it may be noted that in the psychoneurotic category of disorders, affective difficulties—that is, moods and emotions that are distressing, persistent, and hard to control—are prominent features. Associated with them are also found some disturbances in cognition such as perception and logical thinking. These malfunctionings are not, however, entirely out of control. They are crippling rather than disabling, and the people concerned can as a rule work, raise families, maintain a place in society, and enjoy some recreation, even though they do so inadequately compared to what might be the case without the handicaps of their symptoms.

More severe conditions do, however, occur. Although there is no certain and reliable line of demarcation between them, *affective psychoses* may be contrasted to the *psychoneuroses* as often exhibiting such extreme and pervading disturbances of mood, emotions, perception, and thinking as to render the person unable to live as a member of society unless the society makes special concessions on his behalf. He has to be in a hospital or given comparable care by somebody in order to have food, shelter, and protection from the consequences of his own acts.

Psychotic depressions, in contrast to the less intense though chronic and rankling psychoneurotic depressions such as Mrs. Chauncey exhibited, comprise extremes of gloom and black mood in which the patient cannot eat, sleep, or work. He may have delusional ideas, particularly of having committed some unforgivable crime, or his delusions may be of a bodily sort, such as having no stomach, no brains, or no blood.

The mother of a large family on a farm down the road a bit from the Young place had become like this about the time of her "change of life." Gradually she had got so that all she would do was sit in a rocker, muttering and staring. The family kept her at home, despite the way she terrified children and the fact that the adults of the neighborhood were apt to find excuses for not crossing the threshold. Eventually, however, it became evident she was starving to death because of her refusal to eat, and the family finally agreed to her commitment in a public institution.

In addition to various types of depressed mood, there are also psychotic elations in which shifting, fantastic imagination and ceaseless energy render the individual a major problem to himself and to all with whom he comes in contact. Gordon Chauncey had had a manager once who had developed this condition. In the beginning, Chauncey's hopes were high for the man because of his unusual energy and sharp, active wits. It had seemed to Chauncey that responsibility and experience would cure him of a tendency to be a bit scattered and to go off half-cocked. When, however, the manager, inspired with a plan for reviving in modern terms an historic trading of the Atlantic seaboard, bought an aeroplane to fly lumber to Trinidad, Chauncey was forced to recognize that there was more wrong with him than too much brilliance and initiative.

As is well known, there is sometimes a sequential linkage between depression and elation in the same personality and hence the label *manic-depressive* for this subgroup of psychoses.

Parallel to these types of illness in which, at a superficial level anyhow, the disturbance seems primarily a matter of too much affect, there are also conditions in which the difficulty seems to be mainly (though not exclusively) a twist or defect in the processes of perception and thinking, that is, cognition. These are the cases of *schizophrenia* and constitute most of the spectacular types of insanity—the inventors whose creations nobody can understand, the victims of elaborate plots, involving the presidents and dictators of the world, the people who think of themselves as saints, gifted with supernatural powers, or as the descendants of the lost Dauphin, people who hear voices and are influenced directly by radio waves, people who withdraw entirely from the world and lie in bed as if in a coma.

Sometimes, when driving to a fishing village at a cove some miles from Bristol, Dr. Coindreau would glance at a rocky headland jutting out into the ocean in anticipation of seeing the white figure of Willie Smallie sitting alone at the edge of the promontory. For years and years Willie had kept vigil on the rocks, dressed in flowing white, like a Biblical shepherd, with hair and beard blowing in the wind. Only the bitterest winter days could drive him from his rock. For the rest of the time he remained there day and night, rain, fog, or sunshine. Very often he could be seen holding his arms outstretched, as if impaled in a crucifixion, and maintaining the posture, motionless, for hours on end. Dr. Coindreau, on the several occasions when at the family's request he had given Willie a physical examination, found that the muscles of his arms and shoulders had become enormously developed, evidently because of this practice. Although the family kept food and water available at the rock, Willie would go for days at a time without touching either.

Once in a while he would descend from the rock of his own accord, take a small boat, and row out on the ocean. He would row toward the skyline and eventually disappear; then, after a day or two, reappear, rowing back again. The first time this had happened there had been alarm and consternation on the part of the family and neighborhood, and Willie had been followed by a motor boat, but this had so enraged and upset him that he was let alone thereafter. People were still uneasy when they saw him rowing straight out on the limitless sea, but more than one believed that some special protection of Providence watched over Willie Smallie.

Dr. Coindreau had first become aware of Willie some twenty years before when he had signed commitment papers and sent him to a mental institution. At that time the doctor had learned something of the man's story. Willie had always been of a shy and silent disposition, but there had been no real sign of abnormality until he was over thirty. By that time he had become an extremely capable master craftsman in building sailing ships, among them the *Westway*. He had worked hard to learn his trade, but the years of effort and expectation led to nothing when this type of shipbuilding vanished. He was left with a distinction that had lost its prestige and abilities no one wanted. In this setting he had become mute; then, after a time, he had begun to grimace and strike postures. He had been committed to the mental hospital but after five years in which his condition neither improved nor got worse, his family took him out against medical advice and the vigil on the rocks began.

Before leaving the subject of the affective and schizophrenic psychoses it is necessary to modify what was said earlier to the effect that such conditions are more severe and sweeping in their disturbance of personality than is the case with the psychoneuroses. This is in general, but not always, true. It is important to emphasize that there are pattern differences as well as differences of impairment and that it is possible to encounter psychoses which are less disabling than some psychoneuroses. For example, one can find persons with schizophrenia who are not so handicapped as are certain cases of obsessive-compulsive psychoneurosis.[13]

All types of psychiatric disorder thus far considered have involved affect, physiological difficulties, and cognition—the latter as reflected in peculiarities of thinking such as delusions and hallucinations. The processes termed intelligence, however, have not been called in question. Even the psychoses, despite the fact that they contain severely distorted thinking, do not imply dull or retarded mentality. A rough parallel could be made here regarding the difference between physical incapacities that result from a crippled limb, and incapacities that result from a generalized weakness which involves all the limbs.

Mental deficiency,[14] in consequence, is to be regarded as a separate psychiatric category. This is a distinction which is taken as a matter of course by most clinicians, but is sometimes a point of confusion in the minds of those who are not professionally concerned with mental health.

Unlike any other type of psychiatric disorder, mental deficiency is primarily a statistical concept. Normal in this instance is really intended to mean the norm in terms of numbers. The mentally deficient person is thought of as one who lacks the ability in perception, learning, and reasoning which most others possess. In practice this usually means with reference to some tested population.

Another peculiarity of the category is that it has no upper limit. Like other forms of illness it is bounded on one side by the ultimate in malfunction, namely, death. The other illnesses, however, have an upper boundary too, at least in terms of everyday thinking. Although it may be that no one ever achieves it, "perfect health" is not hard to conceive and you cannot be more healthy than that; you cannot be more balanced than balanced.

With intelligence, however, one is apt to think in terms of an endless extension. It is like money: no matter how much you have, you can always have more.

Mental deficiency in a person is usually brought to the attention of others while he is a child, through comparison with age-mates. He does not learn so well as they, nor so quickly. One has to be on guard, of course, to avoid confusion with childhood schizophrenia and with effects arising from deafness, poor eyes, malnutrition, and difficult emotional situations. On the whole, however, although clinical errors can always be made, and no kind of diagnosis is ever free from the need for caution, it seems fair to say that the patterning of mental deficiency is distinctive, persistent, and testable.

When the *Westway* grounded at Cap aux Anges, this event had been due only partially to the storm. Ordinarily her auxiliary engine would have kept her off the coast, but the day before the wreck the machinery had been damaged by lack of oil. This had occurred because a youth, George ("Goofy") Field had failed to carry out his job. Goofy had left school at fourteen after spending six years in three grades. Intelligence tests indicated that his I.Q. was about 60. His limitations were well known and ordinarily he would not have been given a job like keeping track of the oil, but because there was no longer any future in working on sailing ships, it had become difficult to get an adequate crew for the *Westway*. As a peculiar survivor of a way of life that had gone, she offered little attraction to those who were interested in either opportunity or security. Hence the crew was apt to contain at least a few members who were taken on because no others were available.

The final major category of psychiatric disorder to be considered here is one in which disturbance of affect, cognition, and behavior spring from evident damage to the brain—*acute and chronic brain disorders.*

The commonest of these is probably that which occurs in later life due to sclerotic and senile changes. The symptoms range from slight difficulty with memory for recent events to extensive disturbances which may include the whole pageant of excitement, depression, hallucination, and loss of contact with the world. Tom Young's father, as pointed out in Chapter III (p. 46), had begun to show a mild form of this disability in his rigidity and resistance to change, regardless of circumstances. He also showed marked loss of memory for recent events, though he could recall the old days vividly.

Almost every kind of infection can produce psychological disturbance during the peak of its severity. This is the common condition of *delirium* which occurs in some illnesses; it generally disappears without a trace on the subsidence of the toxicity. In certain instances, however, infections may have an apparent aftermath. This is particularly notable with epidemic encephalitis, following which there may gradually appear major and permanent distortions of personality. Tom Young knew a backwoods farmer and lumberman who had an habitual pokerface and glassy stare and who was given to uncontrollable rages in which he would maim his animals. He had been known to kill a horse with an ax because it could not move a log. Tom had always considered him a "born bastard" to be avoided, but, in actual fact, the man was the victim of encephalitis contracted in childhood.[15]

Endocrine disturbances, cancerous growths, brain injuries, and familiar but little understood conditions such as epilepsy and multiple sclerosis, may all have psychological concomitants of the disturbance of the brain. The list is extremely long and varied.

The purpose of this section—to sketch the range of different patterns of personality that may be subsumed under "psychiatric disorder"—is preliminary to discussing different kinds of cases in relation to different kinds of derivations, and hence toward considering the influences of sociocultural environment.

A number of cautions and relevant problems have been pointed out in the course of presenting the range of patterns. The sketch itself is obviously illustrative rather than exhaustive. The system of categories employed is operational and based mainly on appearance (symptoms) rather than on the fundamental nature of the disorder processes. Even this manner of organizing the data is not consistent, since in some categories, such as brain disorder, the groupings stem from a combination of appearance and underlying process. Inconsistencies of this sort may be explained by the goal stated earlier—whenever possible, to utilize knowledge regarding process to define categories, and doing so also in situations where such knowledge is incomplete.

Patterns of Psychiatric Disorder

The use of appearance as the primary mode for demarcating categories runs a risk that has also been mentioned earlier: Cases may be placed in separate categories, because superficially different, when actually they are the same so far as origins and essential process are concerned. Similarly, there is danger of grouping together cases which on the surface seem alike, but which differ in these fundamental respects.

The seriousness of this problem is enhanced by a number of other considerations. One of these has been mentioned previously, namely, the substitutability of symptoms.[16] Anxiety may be an underlying and primary affective disturbance, but its surface appearance may range from a frank anxiety attack to peptic ulcers. The same is true of other types of emotional disorders. At the present stage of knowledge, however, we can only say on the basis of clinical experience that this type of thing happens. Its extent and frequency are unknown, and hence also its magnitude as a problem in arriving at a definition of the phenomena we wish to examine in relation to sociocultural factors.

In addition to the substitutability of symptoms, there is the fact that, as psychiatric cases pass through different stages in the course of development, they often look like each other. For instance, an early phase of a psychotic depression may seem exactly the same as a psychoneurotic disorder. Worse still, however, is the fact that large numbers of cases never show symptoms which place them clearly in any one category. No matter what system of classification one employs, there are always some instances of disorder which fall between the boundaries he sets up. To call these psychoneurosis, personality disorder, psychosis, etc., is an act more of baptism than of accurate designation.

The picture is still further complicated by two concepts which in one form or another pervade most thinking in dynamic psychiatry. These are *latency* and *compensation*.

The paradigm for *latency* may be found in heredity, and has already been illustrated in Chapter III (p. 53) with reference to an organic pattern, baldness. The tendency to lose hair in middle life is in many cases an inborn, hereditary predisposition that is undetectable for many years. In psychiatry, latency refers to psychological characteristics which are present in the personality system but unexpressed in behavior or consciousness until a particular point on the life-arc is reached, or until precipitated by some particular constellation of environmental factors. Some kinds of schizophrenia, for instance, may have this characteristic.

Latency is not, of course, limited to hereditary factors. A latent defect may have its origin in an organic disease. This was the case with the violent-tempered backwoods farmer who killed a horse. His disorder had its roots in encephalitis, but it remained latent for a long time between the acute infection and the eventual appearance in disturbed behavior.

Psychological experiences in infancy and childhood are also thought to be the sources of defect which may be present but hidden for years. Latency means, therefore, that at any given point on the life-arc a personality may harbor a faulty psychological process without its being as yet manifest or even detectable. Hence, in psychiatric disorders, as in other fields of medicine, such as tuberculosis, absence of symptoms does not necessarily mean absence of a defect. Unfortunately, in psychiatry, despite clinical skills and special tests such as the Rorschach and TAT, there are not, so far, such methodological resources as exist for detecting asymptomatic tuberculosis. As a result, the conception of underlying defective process in personality is necessarily more inferential, more abstract, and less defined in terms of objective indices than is the case with many asymptomatic disorders among the organic diseases. To put it starkly, the autopsy does not often reveal occult cases of psychiatric disorder.

The idea of *compensation* is akin to the idea of latency, and both must be understood in the context of the concept of function outlined in Chapter I (p. 25). A paradigm for psychological compensation may be seen in the functioning of the heart. The organism as a whole is conceived to be a system in equilibrium with tendencies to counterbalance any disturbance which threatens its continuity. If, through disease or malformation, one of the valves in the heart has a defect which lets a little blood slip backward at each stroke, the heart muscles will develop and the heart size increase until the extra strength and capacity compensate for the leak. As long as this compensation is maintained, the person is free of symptoms. Neither he nor any other person may ever be aware of his condition unless it is found by accident in the course of a medical check-up for something else, or at autopsy.

In psychiatry, although the equilibrium model has to be qualified, the idea of psychological mechanisms which are compensatory in character is exceedingly prevalent, and one often finds in the study and treatment of individual cases much persuasive evidence. For example, a severe anxiety sometimes appears to be controlled by means of relatively mild and even socially acceptable obsessive-compulsive behavior. It is therefore plausible to suppose that many people who show no symptoms at all may nevertheless have underlying compensated defects and thus be, from one point of view, ill. Indeed, one may carry the matter one step further and say it is plausible to suppose that, in some instances, people with no symptoms at the moment may actually harbor defects of personality which are more serious than do others who show frank, though mild, indications of illness.

All this adds up to a formidable state of affairs from the standpoint of research regarding the causal influences of sociocultural factors. One could well be discouraged by a field in which the various types of cases go about disguised as each other and in which on occasion the seemingly well may be actually more ill than the seemingly sick. The picture is not improved by the realization that we have not even touched on the additional and extraordinarily difficult problems raised by cultural relativity.

Some encouragement may be taken, however, from the fact that problems of this nature are characteristic of biology and that the earlier the stage of development of a science, the worse they appear. It is obvious that we need better definitions of the phenomena with which we deal if we are to make advances through research. But one has to start some place, and the principle of successive approximations that has been mentioned several times would suggest the advisability of taking hold by means of the approximations that are available. The hope then would be that, through trial and use in research, progressive refinement might take place.

Such an orientation has a number of implications, most of which will become manifest in the subsequent course of this book. One is that the level of approximation in which one is working should always be borne in mind so that overrefinement of method and conceptualization can be avoided. That is to say, while recognizing that one needs a certain level of accuracy and detail in thought if progress is to be made, there is a danger of going too far so that time and energy are spent on elaborating concepts and the application of exquisite methods, only to have them swept away as irrelevant at the next level of approximation. Overrefinement is not only wasteful but a hindrance to progress because the broad characteristics which it is essential to keep in view tend to become lost from sight in the detail. One result of this can be to work slowly, carefully, and painfully up blind alleys. Blind alleys cannot be avoided in research, of course, but the broad view can reduce the time one spends in them. It is a question of preference in strategy.

A second point inherent in this orientation is the need to make certain tentative assumptions in the course of stating hypotheses so they can be examined by observation, correlation, and experiment. In the ideal experiment, there are no unknowns except the question that is being asked in examining the hypothesis. In practice, however, some of the elements upon which the hypothesis under scrutiny rests are themselves assumptions rather than established facts. If the experiment turns out as expected, then the result is considered evidence in support of those underlying assumptions as well as of the critical point being investigated. If the experiment fails to confirm the hypothesis, then the underlying assumptions—among other matters—may be due for reassessment.

In general, the broader the view one takes, and the closer to a first approximation, the more such tentative assumptions have to be made. Unless one is willing to do this, he is apt to become overwhelmed by interdependent experiments. It remains important, however, to specify as clearly as one can what he considers these assumptions or "scientific fictions" to be, their relationship to established fact, and their relationship to the problem at hand. It is out of such considerations as these that the need for a frame of reference arises.

II DERIVATIONS OF PSYCHIATRIC DISORDERS

Chapter III, following the presentation of a case of psychoneurosis, gave a review of some etiological possibilities. Section I of the present chapter was concerned with an outline of the various kinds of disorders that are encompassed by psychiatry. Following the same logic of development it remains now to discuss the chief types of etiology in relation to this wide field. It should be understood, however, that what follows is far from being an authoritative summary of professional views; it is rather a personal selection made tentatively as a necessary part in the development of the frame of reference.

Patterns of Psychiatric Disorder

The etiological factors will be considered in terms of the main divisions already discussed in the previous chapter: heredity and life experience, with the latter further divided into physiological experience and psychological experience. It must be kept in mind that such broad approximations do less than justice to the subtle blendings and complexes of nature. The problems are not really problems of "which" or of "either or," but rather problems of relative weight.[17]

Psychoneurosis. In discussing Tom Young the greatest emphasis was put on psychological factors, and this may be considered the general inference with regard to psychoneurosis. Hereditary factors are not, of course, excluded as contributors. It is believed that they may be the source of defects, (e.g., excessive timidity) in the person which predispose to the development of psychoneurotic symptoms. They are considered, however, as additional or predisposing, rather than indispensable. It is presumed that life experience alone can produce psychoneurotic symptoms. This amounts to saying that everyone is capable of developing a psychoneurosis, but, due to heredity, some individuals are more prone to this kind of behavior pattern than others.

As to physiological factors, it may be supposed that, under some circumstances, they produce defects which act very like those derived from heredity. Oxygen deprivation at birth and early infections have already been mentioned as possible examples. Their resultants may, in some instances, amount to constitutional defects and operate so as to predispose an individual to the appearance of one or another psychoneurotic reaction. There is also, however, the possibility that physiological injury (e.g., vitamin B deficiency), occurring later in the course of life, may act directly on the nervous system and produce one or more of the symptom patterns of psychoneurosis.

This raises the question of how often these different etiological sets occur. It is assumed in this book that the great bulk of psychoneurotic patterns are primarily derived from life experience with varying degrees of hereditary and physiological predisposition. Only a few are thought to occur on a purely physiological basis. On the other hand, the fact remains that nobody knows for certain, and one of the potentialities of sociocultural studies in relation to psychiatric disorder is the gathering of evidence that will help clarify such problems.

These tentative assumptions may be restated in summary form:

1. Most cases of psychoneurosis are derived primarily from psycho-

logical experience, with heredity and physiological factors contributing in varying degrees.

2. A few cases that show psychoneurotic symptom patterns are derived primarily from physiological traumata, with psychological experience and heredity contributing in varying degrees.

3. Few cases occur in which heredity is the primary factor.

The heavy emphasis on psychological experience in connection with psychoneurotic patterns prompts the question of where on the life-arc these factors are conceived to be at work. The range of views in this regard has already been sketched in Chapter III. The assumption is that factors are at work all along the arc and the effects tend to be cumulative, although infancy and childhood are the periods of greatest potential for permanent results from psychological influences. After this age, it is supposed that traumatic experiences have progressively less likelihood of durable effect, but at no time is the individual thought to be immune from their consequences.

Personality Disorder. This disturbance is conceived to be basically "constitutional," that is, whatever the cause, the condition arises early, pervades the personality, and remains relatively fixed throughout life. For the most part, constitution implies heredity, but it may also be due to physiological trauma, before or at birth. In addition, it can be argued that life experiences at a very early age can act in the same way. According to this view, it is the early stage of development at which the disturbing events occur which produces the rigidity of pattern. The fact that the patterns appear at times to run in families is explained not by heredity, but by repetition from one generation to the next of patterns of infantile relationship, a kind of cultural transmission within families.

Although a choice is difficult in the face of deficient evidence, the view here leans away from psychological factors and toward heredity:

1. A great many cases of personality disorder are primarily due to heredity, with physiological and psychological factors contributing in varying degrees.

2. Some cases of personality disorder are primarily due to physiological trauma, with heredity and psychological factors contributing in varying degrees.

3. Relatively few cases occur in which psychological experience is the primary factor.

Patterns of Psychiatric Disorder

In thus giving psychological experience a minimal part, there is one consideration which it is important to bear in mind, namely, that the differential diagnosis between psychoneurosis and personality disorder is exceedingly difficult to make. It requires lengthy study and the assembly of considerable data bearing on the individual's life-story before adequate discrimination is possible. Hence one should be prepared to find that, in any compilation of cases, there will be a good deal of mixing of these two categories.

Sociopathic Disorder. Although this grouping is actually a subdivision of personality disorder, case studies suggest that a great many of the persons showing sociopathic symptoms are in fact psychoneurotic, psychotic, retarded, suffering from some other kind of personality disorder, or suffering from an organic brain disease. Thus the category is something of a repository for cases which, arising in a variety of different conditions, have symptoms that happen to take a socially disrupting form. Although the behavior, due to its nature, is relatively easy to identify, its components are mixed and hard to disentangle. In such a situation, a conservative orientation would be to assume that the three major categories of cause are about equally influential:

1. Some cases of sociopathic personality are primarily due to psychological experience, with heredity and physiological factors contributing in varying degrees.

2. Some cases of sociopathic personality are primarily due to heredity, with psychological experience and physiological factors contributing in varying degrees.

3. Some cases of sociopathic personality are primarily due to physiological factors, with psychological experience and heredity contributing in varying degrees.

Psychophysiological Disorders. This category of disorder differs from those which precede and follow in that the symptoms *per se* are organic rather than psychological. Hence, unlike the others, its place as a focus of attention for psychiatry is dependent on the presence of psychological factors as causal agents.

If, however, we take the symptoms as our point of reference, we may postulate that:

1. Some cases are primarily due to heredity, with physiological factors and psychological experience contributing in varying degrees.

2. Some cases are primarily due to physiological factors, with heredity and psychological experience contributing in varying degrees.

3. Some cases are primarily due to psychological experience, with heredity and physiological factors contributing in varying degrees.

Of these three, only the last may be properly considered in the field of psychiatry—that is to say, psychophysiological—although to the extent that psychological factors contribute at all, any case may be said to have some psychiatric aspects. When it comes to the question of how numerous are the cases that are primarily due to psychological experience as compared to others, there is very little basis for opinion. In this frame of reference it is assumed that this varies according to system of the body and type of symptom. Peptic ulcers, for instance, and low blood pressure are thought to have a psychogenic component in some instances. Anemia, on the other hand, is thought to occur rather rarely on such a basis. These questions will be discussed at more length in Volume III, but as an over-all guess it can be said that about one-third of all complaints referable to a system of the body have their roots mainly in psychological factors and that in another third these same factors play a significant though not leading part. In saying this, it is realized that the prevalence of psychological conditions may be vastly over- or understated, but, by making the assumption, a point is fixed in terms of which examination of the problem may be planned.

Psychotic Disorders. The psychotic disorders give the appearance of being midway between the position of psychoneuroses and the position of personality disorders, as far as causes are concerned. This is represented in the following assumptions:

1. Most cases of psychosis are primarily due to heredity, with physiological factors and psychological experience contributing in varying degrees.

2. A few cases of psychosis are primarily due to psychological experience, with physiological factors and heredity contributing in varying degrees.

3. A few cases of psychosis may be primarily due to physiological factors, with heredity and psychological experience contributing in varying degrees.

Patterns of Psychiatric Disorder

These statements require some discussion. My thought is that in both the schizophrenic and the affective psychoses, heredity is a major factor. This is a disputed point, however, with much strong feeling on both sides. Although I am inclined to be impressed by clinical experience with individual cases and their families and also by the work of Kallmann, it must be conceded that psychological experience often plays a notable if secondary part, and may do a great deal either to mitigate or to foster and precipitate overt symptoms. Thus, although item (1) above gives emphasis to heredity in most cases, it should be appreciated that psychological conditions are nevertheless of importance.

With regard to item (3) it is understood, of course, that reference is not being made to any of the conditions now recognized as brain disorders. The thought is that some of the cases which are currently labeled schizophrenia may turn out eventually to have a toxic or infectious origin. A number of organic disturbances such as pellagra and paresis are well known as capable of producing behavior that is indistinguishable from some patterns of this psychosis. Allowance must therefore be made for the possibility of occult toxins, infections, dietary disorders, and hormonal disturbances.

Mental Deficiency. 1. Most cases of mental deficiency are primarily due to heredity, with psychological experience and physiological factors contributing in varying degrees.

2. Some cases of mental deficiency are due to physiological factors, with heredity and psychological experience contributing in varying degrees.

3. Few, if any, cases of mental deficiency are primarily due to psychological experience.

As with all previous statements of assumptions, there are some clinicians and students of behavioral sciences who will disagree.[18] In particular, the proponents of very early psychological experience, and those who give strong emphasis to the power of culture in the molding of personality are apt to feel that item (3) is in error. Some, for instance, point to such examples as the "Wild Boy of Aveyron" and other isolated children as examples of how lack of normal human environment during infancy and childhood can result in behavior like that of a person who is mentally deficient.[19] The trouble with most such cases is that we cannot be sure that the child was normal in the first place.

Brain Disorder. As noted in Section I, the central feature of this disorder is that behavior disturbance is caused by or associated with impairment of brain tissue. As far as the behavior itself is concerned, the category is made up of an exceedingly heterogeneous collection of subcategories. The same is true with regard to the types of agents which may cause or be associated with the behavior. Blows, drugs, poisons, infections, the aging process, and damage from unknown sources may all be involved and affect one or many different parts of the brain in all sorts of ways. Furthermore, these conditions may be of short duration, as in delirium, or chronic, as in arteriosclerosis.

In the face of such an array of different patterns, it is difficult to make summary statements of even the very rough level of approximation that has been employed so far. Although one might think that surely here it is possible to put everything on a basis of physiological factors, such is not the case. Heredity continues to exert its predisposing influence and may be a primary factor in some kinds of illness, as for instance epilepsy. Similarly, psychological experience may be of first-order importance, as for instance in an early onset of senile and arteriosclerotic deterioration.

The last point needs, perhaps, a little expansion. The thought is that emotional wear and tear throughout life can lead to physiological alterations which in turn produce more or less inevitable anatomical changes that interfere with brain function. Thus psychological experience as well as genetic and directly physiological experiences can make a difference in who develops senile brain disorders and who does not. All three must be considered in attempting to explain the difference between the elder Mr. Young and Gordon Chauncey in this regard. The latter up to his death at eighty-seven did not show the difficulties already evident in Tom's father at seventy.

In addition to wear and tear along earlier portions of the life-arc, there is also the matter of current circumstances in which psychological experiences may precipitate affective and cognitive difficulties not otherwise present. Thus:

1. Most cases of brain disorder are primarily due to physiological factors, with heredity and psychological experience contributing in varying degrees.

2. Some cases of brain disorder are due to psychological experience, with physiological factors and heredity contributing in varying degrees.

Patterns of Psychiatric Disorder

3. Some cases of brain disorder are due to heredity, with physiological factors and psychological experience contributing in varying degrees.

CONCLUDING COMMENT

Assumptions regarding relationship of the main categories of psychiatric disorder to the three main derivations have been outlined, taking the categories one at a time. By way of summary, each of the derivations may be considered in relation to its assumed effect in each of the main categories.

HEREDITY—*predominant in:* personality disorder, psychotic disorders, and mental deficiency; *plays some part in:* psychoneuroses, sociopathic disorders, psychophysiological disorders, and brain syndromes.

PHYSIOLOGICAL FACTORS—*predominant in:* brain disorders; *plays some part in:* psychoneuroses, personality disorders, sociopathic disorders, psychophysiological disturbances, psychotic disorders, and mental deficiency.

PSYCHOLOGICAL EXPERIENCE—*predominant in:* psychoneuroses and psychophysiological disorders; *plays some part in:* personality disorder, sociopathic disorder, psychotic disorders, mental deficiency, and brain disorders.

Before ending this chapter, it is worth while giving some thought to how different kinds of explanation and concepts of etiology may be related to each other. This has been attempted in a previous publication with reference to paranoid conditions, and can be paraphrased here in more general terms.[20]

1. A psychiatric disorder may be viewed as the product of a constitutional defect in an otherwise normal personality. The source of the constitutional defect may lie in heredity or in early physiological trauma, but in either case it amounts to an injury, something like a patent foramen ovale (hole in a partition of the heart), which endures through life. By degrees, as the person matures, the defect produces more and more distortion in the personality, until psychiatric disorder becomes overt.

2. A psychiatric disorder may be viewed as the product of a psycho-

logical experience which, occurring during a particularly vulnerable phase of development, becomes part of the personality. In the course of later growth this acquired defect produces distortion of the personality, much as in the previous instance. The point of difference between the two is primarily the way in which the defect originates.

3. It may be assumed that neither constitutional defect nor psychological experience alone is sufficient for the appearance of psychiatric disorder, but that both are necessary. That is to say, there has to be an inborn or physiologically acquired disposition followed by an injurious life experience.

4. Given any of the previous, one may hold that the pathological process, once started, progresses automatically to the development of psychiatric disorder. Later events such as therapy can mitigate or stop the process, but if left to itself it necessarily persists.

5. An alternative view is that the disorder will not run such a course, but rather that natural functions to restore and maintain personality will come into operation unless neutralized by a persistently adverse psychological climate. This means that constitutional defect and psychological experience are necessary but not sufficient conditions, even when combined.

6. A still different view suggests that, given a disposition as from constitutional defect or psychological experience, the development of psychiatric disorder is a sequential phenomenon. Thus, the first step is conceived to take place as an adaptation to an immediate discomfort. This adaptation produces relief (makes life more "livable") but soon requires another step in order to maintain the first, and so on. In this way the personality, through a kind of persistent habit formation and habit elaboration, builds progressively away from healthy types of functioning.

It is perhaps appropriate to observe that psychological experience should not be considered as being equivalent to sociocultural environment. All three main types of causal factors—hereditary, physiological, and psychological—are subject to influence by sociocultural factors, although in different ways. Sets of alternatives along these lines will be discussed later.

This chapter rounds out in brief description the main kinds of psychiatric disorder. There are of course many intermediate patterns and combinations not touched here. What has been given, however,

Patterns of Psychiatric Disorder

123

serves to illustrate both range and characteristics. From here on, in this book, this is what I am talking about when I speak of psychiatric disorder. I mean people like Tom Young, his father, the depressed farm wife, Willie Smallie, Goofy, Bernie Chiason, Mrs. Chauncey, Rose Chiason, Dr. Coindreau, and Dr. Hopkins. I mean all of them, and all the variations they encompass, from the problems of mental deterioration in old age to the problems of a mind that never developed in the first place. I also mean capable minds enmeshed in the surgings of difficult emotions in difficult situations. There are many implications in such diversity and an attempt will be made to deal with these in subsequent chapters.

If you are going to cast an epidemiological net that will catch all the entities in the field of psychiatric disorder, it must be able to hold all these people. If you choose something less than the total field, then you are confronted with the problem of the substitutability of symptoms.

CHAPTER NOTES

1. To say that the nomenclature of psychiatry lacks standardization is to utter an understatement of some distinction. Although a number of different sets of definitions have been published, few of us adhere consistently to any one, but rather use words as we have formed habits based on the authors we have read and the particular colleagues and teachers with whom we have worked.

In order to obtain as much clarity as possible in the present volume, to lay the foundations for terminology in the subsequent volumes, and to give the reader some points of departure should he wish to look further in regard to meaning, the *Diagnostic and Statistical Manual of Mental Disorders* (Washington, D.C.: American Psychiatric Association, 1952) has been selected as the main reference. Due to some difference of opinion and orientation I shall not always follow this system precisely, but where such deviations occur, they will be noted.

As additional sources regarding nomenclature, the following may be mentioned: *A Psychiatric Glossary, The Meaning of Words Most Frequently Used in Psychiatry* (Washington, D.C.: American Psychiatric Association, 1957); JULES H. MASSERMAN, "Glossary," *Principles of Dynamic Psychiatry*

(Philadelphia: Saunders, 1946); L. E. HINSIE and JACOB SHATZKY, *Psychiatric Dictionary, With Encyclopedic Treatment of Modern Terms* (2nd ed. with suppl.: New York: Oxford Univ. Press, 1953); NANDOR FODOR and FRANK GAYNOR, *Freud: Dictionary of Psychoanalysis* (New York: Philosophical Library, 1950).

Regarding the problems of definition and diagnosis, *see* PAUL H. HOCH and JOSEPH ZUBIN (Eds.), *Current Problems in Psychiatric Diagnosis* (New York: Grune and Stratton, 1953).

2. For discussion of this point as it bears on the type of research being considered in this book, *see* PAUL V. LEMKAU, "The Epidemiological Study of Mental Illnesses and Mental Health," *The American Journal of Psychiatry*, Vol. 111, no. 11, 1955, pp. 801-808.

3. A frequent source of confusion in psychiatry arises because people use definitions that are at the same time substantive and explanatory without recognizing the fact. This is most apt to occur where it is a question of psychological processes. A parallel problem with the term "culture" has been noted by Kluckhohn and Kelly:

". . . For some anthropologists 'culture' is primarily a descriptive concept; for others it is primarily an explanatory concept. So-called 'definitions' are always constructed from a point of view—which is all too often left unstated. Not all definitions are substantive (that is, 'descriptive'). Nor is 'explanatory' the only other alternative. Some of the definitions which have been partially stated or implied have been 'functional'; others may be characterized as epistemological—that is, they have been intended to point toward the type of phenomena from which we gain our knowledge of 'culture.' . . . However, the distinction between 'explanatory' and 'descriptive' seems to be most central." (CLYDE KLUCKHOHN and WILLIAM H. KELLY, "The Concept of Culture" in RALPH LINTON (Ed.), *The Science of Man in the World Crisis* [New York: Columbia Univ. Press, 1945].)

4. For instance, consider the mildly pejorative tone of the following taken from the definition of "dynamic psychiatry" given in the *Glossary* of the American Psychiatric Association: "Dynamic psychiatry implies the study of the active, energy-laden, and changing factors in human behavior, as opposed to the older, more static and descriptive study of clinical patterns, symptoms, and classification."

A discussion of a research approach through symptom patterns which is also "dynamic" (although embodying reservations about the concept of psychic energy) may be found in Chap. XII, p. 398 of ALEXANDER H. LEIGHTON, JOHN A. CLAUSEN, and ROBERT N. WILSON (Eds.), *Explorations in Social Psychiatry* (New York: Basic Books, 1957).

5. This definition of anxiety, or something like it, is common but not universal in psychiatry. According to the *Glossary* of the American Psychiatric Association: "Anxiety: apprehension, tension, or uneasiness which stems from the anticipation of danger, the source of which is largely unknown or unrecognized. Anxiety is primarily of intrapsychic origin, in distinction to fear which is the emotional response to a consciously recognized and usually external threat or danger. Anxiety and fear are accompanied by similar physiological changes."

A further description may be found in the Association's *Diagnostic and Statistical Manual*, pp. 31 and 32.

The important point from an analytic and descriptive orientation is the contrast with fear, a distinction introduced into clinical psychiatry by Freud.

For a discussion of anxiety concepts and bibliography *see* PAUL H. HOCH and JOSEPH ZUBIN (Eds.), *Anxiety* (New York: Grune and Stratton, 1950). *See also* MARK D. ALTSCHULE, "Medical Intelligence, Ideas of Eighteenth-Century British Medical Writers About Anxiety," *New England Journal of Medicine,* Vol. 248, April 9, 1953, pp. 646-648.

6. According to *The Catholic Encyclopedia, An International Work of Reference on the Constitution, Doctrine, Discipline, and History of the Catholic Church* (New York: Appleton, 1919), p. 640: "Scruple . . . an unfounded apprehension and consequently unwarranted fear that something is a sin which, as a matter of fact, is not. It is not considered here so much as an isolated act, but rather as an habitual state of mind known to directors of souls as "a scrupulous conscience."

7. This subclass of psychoneurotic disorders is not given in the *Manual.* It is however listed in the *Glossary,* and I include it because it seems to me sufficiently common and distinctive as a symptom pattern to warrant a place alongside the phobic and obsessive compulsive reactions.

8. In the *Manual* this condition is listed as "psychophysiologic nervous system reaction" and not classified under the psychoneurosis (although the reader is given the option of doing so in particular cases). The rationale of this categorization escapes me and seems contrary to clinical experience and impression. The *Glossary* on the other hand lists neurasthenia under "neurosis," which term is in turn given as equivalent to "psychoneurosis."

9. It was the analysis by Freud and Breuer of a woman with hysteria that opened the modern era of dynamic psychiatry. Of interest to note in passing is the fact that this condition, once apparently common, is now relatively rare. Such a change may be an indication of how alterations in sociocultural factors can affect patterns of psychiatric disorder.

10. In my use of this term I am following the *Manual,* but it is important to note that the words "personality disorder" have for many clinicians a much broader meaning, namely, the whole field of psychiatric disorder. This is, in fact, the most obvious interpretation and is in harmony with the definition of personality outlined in Chapter I. Alternative labels for the condition under consideration, such as "character disorder," have, however, their own quota of objections and hence there does not seem to be sufficient reason for deviating in this instance from the *Manual's* proposal.

11. The *sociopathic* category is placed in the *Manual* as a subdivision under *Personality Disorder.* It is recognized, however, that such symptoms can be a manifestation or aspect of other patterns, such as the psychoneuroses, already discussed, and the psychoses, which are to be taken up presently. Sociopathic disturbances, therefore, are to be viewed as having a preponderance of behavior that is disruptive for society. This is the surface definition in its most extreme and vague form.

12. The reference here is to conditions often called "psycho-somatic." The latter is a simpler term, but the *Manual* has an excellent reason for avoiding it: "[Our] term is used in preference to 'psychosomatic disorders' since the latter term refers to a point of view on the discipline of medicine as a whole rather than to certain specified conditions" (p. 29).

13. It seems very likely that "psychosis" as a category is even more heterogeneous than most others in the standard no-menclature. Certainly depressions and schizophrenias appear to be dissimilar patterns of behavior in most instances. Even within the schizophrenic category it seems probable that a number of basically different kinds of psychological processes are being lumped together. Bleuler, the originator of the word, spoke of them as "the schizophrenias." *See* EUGEN BLEULER, *Dementia Praecox, Or The Group of Schizophrenias* (JOSEPH ZINKIN, trans.) (New York: Internat. Univ. Press, 1950).

For comment on the concept of psychosis, *see* OSKAR DIETHELM, "The Fallacy of the Concept: Psychosis," in PAUL H. HOCH and JOSEPH ZUBIN (Eds.), *Current Problems in Psychiatric Diagnosis* (New York: Grune and Stratton, 1953), pp. 24-32.

14. In everyday language "mental deficiency" would only be employed for severe cases. In the technical usage of the *Manual* it covers all degrees, with "mild," "moderate," and "severe" as qualifiers.

15. There is some question as to whether the later symptoms of encephalitis are due to a chronic progressive infection or are the result of damaged tissue and function after the infectious process has subsided. According to Grinker and Bucy the accumulated evidence is in favor of the former view. In either event, the external picture is of a latent period and then the emergence of symptoms which are often progressive. *See* ROY R. GRINKER and PAUL C. BUCY, *Neurology* (4th ed.; Springfield, Ill.: Thomas, 1949), p. 651.

16. *See* Note 1 of Chap. III.

17. For perspective on heredity, the reader might again consult Notes 4 and 5 of Chap. III. The meanings intended

here for the words "physiological" and "psychological" are indicated on page 57.

18. For a brief review and selected bibliography *see* Chapter 22 in ARTHUR P. NOYES, *Modern Clinical Psychiatry* (4th ed.; Philadelphia: Saunders, 1953).

19. *See:* J. M. G. ITARD, *The Wild Boy of Aveyron* (New York: Appleton-Century, 1932); KINGSLEY DAVIS, "Extreme Social Isolation of a Child," *American Journal of Sociology,* Vol. 45, no. 4, 1940, pp. 554-565; KINGSLEY DAVIS, "Final Note on a Case of Extreme Isolation," *American Journal of Sociology,* Vol. 52, no. 5, 1947, pp. 432-437; WAYNE DENNIS, "The Significance of Feral Man," *American Journal of Psychology,* Vol. 54, no. 3, 1941, pp. 425-432.
The cases of socially isolated children where the evidence and observations are adequate appear to do no more than confirm the reader in his original prejudices. If he leans on genetics, they encourage this, if he leans to social conditioning, he finds support for this too.

20. *See* LEIGHTON, CLAUSEN, and WILSON (Eds.), *Explorations in Social Psychiatry,* p. 74.

Psychiatric Disorders and Sociocultural Factors

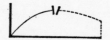

PART TWO

Psychiatric
Disorders and
Sociocultural
Factors

Chapter V

Propositions Relating Psychiatric Disorder and Sociocultural Environment[1]

I T HAS BEEN NOTED several times in the course of these pages that a main objective is the development of a frame of reference. In the preceding chapters, a beginning has been made through an outline of the chief patterns of psychiatric disorder and a brief illustrative discussion of their derivations. In the present chapter, the effort will be to formulate a set of propositions which, building on the basis already set down, constitute the central part of the frame of reference. Before embarking on this, however, I shall in the interests of clarity pause a moment and restate the character and purpose of the frame of reference itself, both with regard to previous chapters and those to come.

A frame of reference is conceived to mean a descriptive account of the salient features of the phenomena under consideration. It is a *frame* in that it imposes limits and consists in an orderly presentation.

Setting limits is necessary since we live in a universe in which every phenomenon ultimately touches every other phenomenon, either directly, or indirectly through interconnections. Because of this reticulation, one cannot completely describe all the ramifications of any single event, much less groups and successions of events. On the other hand, setting limits too narrowly may cut the student off from seeing the very relationships that would constitute new discovery. The frame, therefore, has to be large enough to encourage the perception of complex interconnections and small enough to avoid aimless wandering in limitless network.[2]

The orderly presentation of the phenomena means some kind of answer, however tentative, to the question, "How do the main aspects of this thing fit together and how do they affect each other?" Such a logical arrangement can blend observed fact and inference; and inference can legitimately include the speculative as well as the better established.

Reference connotes the use to which the frame is to be put, namely, as a guide in exploration. It may be likened to early maps of the Known World in having omissions, distortions, and numerous corners where it would be appropriate to state "Monsters Abound Here," and yet in being usable, with caution, as a means of orientation. A frame of reference can serve as a context in which hypotheses may be shaped, research operations carried out, and results interpreted.

Although it is a frame, the structure is malleable rather than rigid. It has to be stiff enough to permit use (one must be able to assume that it is true, at least temporarily), but also plastic enough to change as new data and new inferences emerge. In this it again resembles the maps which grew and were reshaped as a result of use.

A frame of reference is not necessarily the same as a theory, particularly a new theory. It can serve its purpose well enough if it does no more than organize existing theories and fragments of theory into a presentation that is relevant to the problem under consideration. In the present volume we are, actually, more concerned with the well established than with the new. The attempt is to describe as accurately as possible the main aspects of the phenomenon with which we propose to deal—the relationship of sociocultural environment to psychiatric disorder. Nevertheless, inasmuch as this phenomenon is imperfectly known, the description is compounded of fact, accepted theory, tentative assumption, and somewhat personal speculation, as is illustrated in the account that has been given of the derivations.

Of particular note is the following: since the frame of reference is composed of ideas drawn from different theories and from different disciplines, it must therefore utilize restatement and simplification in order to bring them together. Due to many disciplines being concerned with the study of man, we are faced with a situation in which various aspects of a single dynamic phenomenon are expressed in various technical languages. Any attempt to sketch salient features demands not only abridgment and generalization but also translation into one comparable set of terms.

Because of the endeavor here to meet these needs, the reader is apt to encounter many familiar and even commonplace ideas in unfamiliar form. He is likely to find, moreover, that they are unattended by some of the specific qualities which give them greatest meaning in the theoretical system which he believes accords with the true nature of psychiatric disorder. Thus, one of the root assumptions to be introduced presently—that human beings exist in a state of striving—may seem to lack essential content to those who feel that libido is the primary motivational force. The same will be true for those who emphasize escape from anxiety, the need to express aggression, or the desire to hold power and dominate. What is being sought in these pages, however, is precisely the common characteristic in all of these, shorn of the attributes which would limit it to one or another theoretical system. This is a reversal of the customary practice, when discussing several theories, of stressing the distinctive.

I TWO ASSUMPTIONS

Let us focus attention on the types of derivations that have been called psychological in Chapter IV. In doing this we should note once more that, although heredity and physiological experience are being set aside for the time being, their importance is not to be neglected. Although the main interest is in sequences composed of sociocultural factors, psychological experience, and psychiatric disorder, it is to be recognized that sociocultural factors can also exert influence on psychiatric disorder through heredity and physiological events. We may assume, moreover, that the characteristics and relative importance of sociocultural factors acting through psychological experience can only be evaluated when there is a sufficient knowledge of how such factors also influence dispositions based on heredity and physiological experience.

Turning, then, with this proviso in mind to psychological derivations, two fundamental, underlying assumptions may be designated: *A given personality exists more or less continuously throughout life in the act of striving;* and *Interference with that striving has consequences which in turn often lead to psychiatric disorder.*

More or less is employed in order to allow for fluctuations such as between sleeping and waking.

Striving may be illustrated from Tom Young's story in his effort to be a successful farmer, husband, father, and son. These were prominent in his life at the cross-section of the moment in which his anxiety attack occurred. But any cross-section along the arc of his life at earlier times would also include patterns of striving of some sort—to survive under enemy fire, to be accepted by his fellows in the army, to be well regarded by his boyhood friends, to be esteemed by his father, to be loved by his mother.

It should also be noted that "striving" is intended to include the negative as well as the positive aspects; escape is encompassed just as much as the notion of pursuit. Hence, "to be a successful farmer" could be stated as "to avoid economic disaster"; "to survive under fire" as "to escape death"; and "to be loved by his mother" as "to avoid rejection." Finally, although these illustrations are taken from the story of a person suffering from a psychoneurotic illness, it can easily be seen that they depict a characteristic of all personalities. Striving sentiments, in short, constitute a significant part of the total complement of sentiments encompassed in any given personality.

Interference is a more recondite concept and needs to be considered at greater length. The general idea is manifest in the economic difficulties Tom Young faced, together with their consequences. Indeed, the presence of interference is self-evident in all the explications of psychiatric disorder which emphasize current circumstances as discussed in Chapter III, beginning on page 46. When it comes to psychological factors at other points on the life-arc, however, it seems worth while to touch briefly on each of the main concepts outlined in pages 59 to 77.

The theories of intra-uterine influence and birth trauma both include the principle of interference. At such a stage of development, one must, of course, think more in terms of completely instinctual strivings than of those differentiated into sentiments. The womb is pictured as a place of maximum satisfaction; and disorder as coming into being as a result of disturbances to this condition. In the birth process the foetus is torn from a position of secure emotional and instinctual satisfaction and projected through harrowing experiences into a world where deprivations and interferences abound.

In both infancy and childhood, interference with gratification remains a central concept. This applies equally well whether one is talking in terms of instincts, of the more evolved and experience-conditioned basic urges, or of the still more differentiated sentiments. It also applies whether one is thinking in terms of specific psychoanalytic theories or in other systems of abstraction. The whole process of bringing about the child's adaptation to society is one that develops striving sentiments from basic urges and opens avenues for gratification, but it is also fraught with numerous interferences, including intersentiment conflict.

If, as a result at least in part of such blocking in childhood, the adult personality contains an immature, deviant, or otherwise unacceptable urge, interference again enters the picture. In Tom's case this was sketched in terms of homosexual and hostile tendencies. Because such gratification could not be achieved directly, it was pictured as existing at an unconscious level. Circumstances which increase the urge are thought also to step up the intensity of the discomfort from interference. Hence anxiety may arise due to a threatened breakthrough to consciousness of the unacceptable urge, or other symptoms may result as part of the devices employed to disguise it.

The role concepts of personality disorder also embody the essential idea of conflict and hence of interference with expectation and striving. This is, indeed, one of their main points.

What has been said of the early years, infancy and childhood, ap-

Propositions Relating Disorder and Environment

137

plies also along subsequent segments of the life-arc. Striving, and interference with striving, may occur cumulatively, to result in and maintain the patterns of psychiatric disorder. They are also ingredients in acute psychologically traumatic episodes in adult life, such as Tom's experience in combat. Here was an instance of gross interference with sentiments concerned in survival by sentiments concerned with being worthy—reinforced, perhaps, by limited opportunity to do anything else except carry on.

Implicit in the above are two kinds of conflict: one intrapersonal, that is to say, between subsystems within the personality system, and the other between the personality and factors in the environment. These may be thought of as internal and external interference, although we may suppose that the one nearly always involves the other.

Also of note is the matter of perception and expectation. That something should seem, or threaten, to interfere is the significant aspect so far as effect on personality is concerned. The importance of anticipation in personality was pointed out in Chapter I while discussing the life-arc, and a return to the topic will be made presently (page 142).

II THE ESSENTIAL PSYCHICAL CONDITION

The act of striving implies an object,[3] whether the striving be toward (positive) or away from (negative). Common observation makes it clear that the striving sentiments of each personality are concerned with many objects and that they vary in degree of associated feeling and effort. Some objects are the focus of affectively strong sentiments while others involve only weak feelings. It is also evident that personalities often differ from each other very markedly in the kinds of objects they emphasize, and that cultural groups, too, may be in sharp contrast in this respect.

Dynamic psychiatry recognizes the multiplicity of objects and the varying degrees of attachment people have to them, and asserts that these objects are means to an end. There are, however, different theories as to the nature of this *end* and the processes involved in its attainment and maintenance. This is, indeed, very close to the core of the matter so far as differences and dispute in psychiatric theory are concerned.

Important as the areas of dispute are, particularly since they are capable of generating new discoveries, it is also important to keep in sight that there are ideas shared by most, if not every, school of thought. All the concepts outlined in Chapter III dealing with the bearing of life experience on psychiatric disorder have in common the idea that there is an optimal psychological condition and that many kinds of object striving are basically concerned with its achievement or maintenance. This may be phrased as absence of anxiety, the gratification of instincts, the reduction of tension, and many other terms. But whatever the content of a specific theory, all postulate a process that intervenes between life experiences and the development of the kinds of psychiatric disorder that have been noted as related to such experiences. In order to emphasize this pivotal concept and at the same time avoid the particulars of any one theory, the name *essential psychical condition* will be used.[4]

This *condition* is, to repeat, conceived as a process, not as static. It is perpetually being lost and recovered and hence is to be regarded as fluctuations about a point that moves along the life-arc, maintained only through constant activity on the part of the personality system. The factors which influence it arise both in the environment and within the personality. It has, therefore, considerably different character at different points on the life-arc.

From the foregoing it is possible to construe the essential psychical condition as a kind of dynamic equilibrium, but this is not exactly what is meant. The functioning of a person as a whole—personality—*is* considered a dynamic equilibrium, with the qualifications regarding spontaneity noted in Chapter I, page 25. The root pattern here is anabolism and katabolism balancing to constitute metabolism within the rise and fall of a life-arc. Thus there is endogenous change in the system, as well as response to external circumstances. The whole exists, however, during the life-arc by virtue of being built up as it is torn down, and exchange of energy is involved in the process.

The construct, *essential psychical condition,* is conceived as one aspect of the functioning of this totality. Although it is a process that is going on continuously, it is but one of a number of such which make up the whole. Hence the kind of balancing or restoration postulated for the *condition* does not necessarily involve balanced quantities of energy. On the contrary, the *condition* most likely exists in the brain as an interplay of signals and triggered responses. Such processes do, of course, draw on the energy resources of the organism, but the balancing maintained is not according to the laws of the conservation of energy; rather, it is in accordance with the inherent patterning of the system. The pain you feel when a pin is applied to the skin is not directly proportional to the force with which the pin is applied, but to the number and kind of receptor organs it triggers, to the quality of attention and sentiment you bring to the event, and to much else. Even less is the energy you expend in getting away from the pin, and so restoring the absence of pain, related to the force behind the pin.

Similarly, with altogether intrapsychic events, no quantitative relationship of energy need exist between antecedents and consequences, and hence between factors upsetting and factors restoring the essential psychical condition. I do not look on instincts, basic urges, unconscious motives, and affect as analogues of physical energy and it is not necessary to think of them as strong or weak in quantitative terms, as if they were hydraulic forces. There is a temptation to do this, of course, due to the subjective qualities of those that can be felt and the compelling characteristics of those that are unconscious. But this is control and control is not necessarily based on amount of energy.

Let us consider the idea of control. Hereditary factors established in the single cell when sperm and egg unite exert control on the subsequent growth and differentiation, and determine that the organism will be human and not a bird, will be a male rather than a female, and so on. This is influence, but it is not force or energy. In the player piano, it is the pattern of the punches in the music roll that controls the piano's energies, so that music rather than noise is produced. In the giant calculators, it is the program punched on the tape that determines the distribution of the machine's physical energies in problem solving.

In some such terms the constellation of factors which compose the essential psychical condition control the energies of the total human organism. They are assumed here to have existence in the electrochemical processes of the brain, and the question of dominance by one factor in relation to another is not quantitative but a matter of sequence and position. In short, the basic urges and affective controls on behavior are no more forces than are the compelling characteristics of cognitive processes such as logic. Hence, though they can be exceedingly persistent and can dominate, they do not have these characteristics by virtue of a quantity of energy that must go somewhere. They are patterns, and as such, and in contrast to energy, they can in some circumstances be destroyed.

These points have been made because some theories of psychopathology contain implicitly or explicitly the idea of a psychic energy which can be transformed, but never destroyed. This leads to thinking of psychological forces in terms parallel with physical force and to concepts of balance based on a quantitative distribution and transformation of energy. A kind of psychic economy constituting a closed system is postulated. Such theory is not incorporated in the concept of the essential psychical condition set forth here.[5]

Having noted the *condition,* the nature of striving sentiments can be restated with a little more precision. Saying, as was done earlier, that in the functioning of a person an object is "a means to an end," suggests a linear process leading to a final result, like a parachute leading to a safe landing. An object (meaning the representation of something in the mind) is better described as having a function via the sentiment system in the achievement and maintenance of the essential psychical condition. Thus, its place in a continuous, though changing, process is emphasized; and also that it acts in a web of simultaneous relationships and not in any simple, straight line of cause and effect.

III THE FUNDAMENTAL PROPOSITIONS

With this discussion in hand, we are now in a position to consider the two assumptions given earlier on page 136. The first of these is represented by a diagram in Figure 2.[6]

FIGURE 2: *A fundamental characteristic of psychical life*

P represents a person, the arrow indicates striving, and O stands for object. For any given P, the latter includes an enormous number of different particular objects which could be represented as O^1, O^2, O^3, etc.

Personality, that is the functioning of a person (P), would encompass the whole diagram. The relationship of the essential psychical condition to the psychical activity shown in the diagram is one of dependency. This may also be represented schematically as in Figure 2*a.*

Propositions Relating Disorder and Environment

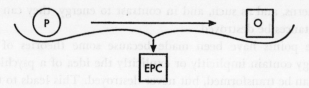

Here P and O have the same meaning as in Figure 2, while EPC stands for essential psychical condition.

The second assumption goes a step beyond these two diagrams and asserts that psychiatric disorder often (but not inevitably) appears as a result of interference with the striving represented in the arrow. Let us set the disorder part of this aside for the time being, and examine this idea of interference in relation to the essential psychical condition.

As indicated earlier, the objects in the sentiment system of any given personality are not all of equal, functional importance to that personality. Some are peripheral to the essential psychical condition, whereas others matter a great deal to its maintenance. Of the latter, some are interchangeable objects, that is can be replaced if removed from an expectation of achievement, but others are more unique and essential in their relationship to the process. Postponing for the time being the question of what kinds of objects fall in these various categories, it may be concluded that interference is significant when it bears on objects that are important with regard to the essential psychical condition and that cannot easily be substituted for. Furthermore, inasmuch as the essential psychical condition is always in a state of being lost and regained, the interference, to be dangerous for the system, must be drastic, must be of such magnitude, quality, or duration as to constitute a displacement far beyond the common fluctuations of most such systems and to tax severely the restorative capabilities.

Pervading all these considerations is a point already made, namely, that the disturbing effect of an interference in relation to a given personality depends on perception and expectation. Interference may not be "real," as strictly objective other persons might define it; the indispensable quality is that the person (P) perceive it as such. Perception and quality of anticipation in turn are determined by the sentiments he brings to an event or series of events. Hence an instance of interference with object striving consists in some kind of coming together within the personality of sentiments that are affectively and/or cognitively incompatible: "I need X, but I fear I cannot have X," "I want X, but I ought not to want X," "I do not want X, but I ought to want X," and so on.

As noted in Chapter I, the functioning of personality in the blending of the life-story and the cross-section of the moment is largely concerned with attempting to predict and be ready for the approaching part of the life-arc represented by the dotted line (Figure 1). In all of this, the sentiments which have been built by the interplay of basic urges and experience with the world have a major part. The sentiment system may be considered as existing in the cross-section of the moment, derived from the past, and looking to the future. In this sense the future exerts a powerful influence on the essential psychical condition of the present. Striving in relation to an approaching need may thus be crucial for the maintenance of the essential psychical condition and hence for the functioning of the person.

The mention of perception raises the question of unconscious process. The word "object" is limited here to entities which a given personality has readily available to awareness. Hence striving sentiments are by definition conscious or available without much difficulty to consciousness. What may be unconscious is a part of the chain of connections relating an object to the essential psychical condition. That is, in consciously striving for an object a person is generally not aware of all the functions which this object (a representation in the mind) and this striving are playing in the integration and equilibrium of his personality. In Tom Young's case, supposing that the inferences about the gun being a sexual symbol are correct, it can be seen that he was by no means aware of all influences at work in his striving to have and maintain Marguerite as a wife, particularly the significance of her brother. Thus, through numbers of devices shielding the essential psychical condition, the basic urges connected with various objects may be hidden from consciousness.

In pointing to unconscious urges as underlying object striving the way is opened for speaking about "unconscious objects." Bernie Chiason, for instance, drank because of an unconscious wish to destroy himself which in turn came from an unconscious desire for revenge on Rose (in origin, on his mother) by means of suicide. It would be possible to refer to alcohol, suicide, and revenge as all three objects. In this frame of reference, however, the word *object* is reserved for the items available to consciousness in such a web of interconnected factors and the others are designated as *motives*. The alcohol, therefore, is a (conscious) object, while suicide and revenge are (unconscious) motives.

This terminology is arbitrary, of course, but employed because it points to an important distinction. It is worth noting that it also submerges the middle ground between the conscious and the above type of unconscious. It suggests that object striving occurs because of conscious factors (events both perceived and answered through sentiments) or because of unconscious motives that operate something like secret plots of power politics, or because of some mixture of both. This view may suffice as an approximation in certain cases of neurosis as exemplified by Tom and the gun and by Bernie and alcohol. In other instances, however, there appears to be a prominence of factors which are not readily classified at either of the two poles. This has been touched upon in Chapter III (page 71), but it is worth expanding a little at this juncture.

The sentiments of Tom's father for growing oats can be used as an illustration. It is evident that the object, growing oats, was not appropriate to the realities of the situation, as Tom himself pointed out with some irritation. Given the changes that had occurred in both markets and farming methods, there was no rational basis for the old gentleman's insistence on this crop. On the other hand, to assume that the oats must therefore be a sexual symbol or any other symbol of that order, the secret of which is locked away in *the* unconscious, is to overlook intermediate factors of some importance.

One of these is the effect of organic changes with age on the mental processes, including difficulty in remembering recent matters and new techniques, while recollections for old days and old ways stand clear as the landscape on a sunny morning in spring. This point, it may be noted in passing, is an instance of the need mentioned in Chapter I for keeping alert to the organic levels of integration when dealing with personality from the orientation of psychiatric problems. Such considerations are sometimes overlooked or thought to cancel each other out by those concerned in theories of personality, particularly if their background is in psychology, sociology, or cultural anthropology.

It would be foolish, of course, to think that the matter of aging was more than one among several factors. Another aspect might well be a common, non-specific tendency among human beings to cling to the familiar when bewildered or in doubt. Mr. Young had some of these feelings, not only because he was growing old but also because of the rapid changes in the world and a general difficulty adjusting to them. He had many of Tom's worries, yet less education and experience to employ in dealing with them.

Another consideration is the set of guideposts to which Mr. Young had always looked in life—the other farmers of his own generation and the respected elders representing previous generations. These people had always said "grow oats" and Mr. Young had more faith in their wisdom than he had in the notions of his son's generation, even if he could not meet their glib (to him) arguments. The culture of the generation to which the elderly farmer belonged was in many ways different from that of his son. And, as the numbers of the younger generation rose and those of the older receded, Mr. Young had become more and more like an immigrant to a land of strange customs and ideas. He had made many adjustments, of course, but like most immigrants, especially those of later life, he had retained some of the sentiment patterns acquired in the culture of his origin.[7]

One may suppose therefore that the oats have symbolic significance, but it is of a different order from that mentioned earlier in connection with the gun. It is rather that the oats symbolized a set of sentiments, a way of life and a link with other days and other ways in which there was confidence and for which there was nostalgic yearning. The oats gave him comfort.

Now, although it is possible to discuss these and other factors which bear on Mr. Young's attachment to oats, this is not to say that he himself could analyze his feelings in such a manner, or easily accept such an analysis if it were offered to him. He knew his sentiments about oats, but he would, if asked, attribute them to their own inherent correctness rather than to a complex of influences. This could in part be due to lack of experience in the analysis of psychological factors, but it is also in a large measure a protective blindness. Were he to achieve such an objective analysis, there would be some doubt as to the cognitive and realistic basis of the sentiments, and a consequent danger of severe upset to his essential psychical condition. This could appear as damaged pride, increased uncertainty, diminished self-confidence, and similar trends. He could anticipate the discomfort of these feelings and struggle to avoid their emergence by clinging to his sentiments about oats without being aware of the underlying processes.[8]

Propositions Relating Disorder and Environment

From the foregoing it is evident that striving sentiments (both for and against) involve three major types of factors: those of which the person is aware; those of which he is unaware including functional as well as accidental features in this unawareness; and those which, as more specific unconscious urges together with defenses against them, are in keeping with prevailing psychoanalytic theories. I shall continue to use the word "unconscious" for both the latter two of the three types.

The main points made thus far may be summed up in three propositions.

SERIES A. THE FUNDAMENTAL PROPOSITIONS

A1. All human beings exist in a state of psychological striving.
A2. Striving plays a part in the maintenance of an essential psychical condition.
A3. Interference with striving leads to a disturbance of the essential psychical condition.

It should be emphasized again that psychiatric disorder is not conceived to be the inevitable outcome when the essential psychical condition is disturbed. Insofar as the effects of the interference-with-striving pattern are concerned, the disturbance of the essential psychical condition is necessary but not sufficient. Later on we shall consider the factors which are concerned with determining whether or not a disturbed essential psychical condition leads to such disorder. For the present, attention is focused on the processes whereby the essential psychical condition becomes disturbed in a major way, and on the part that can be played by sociocultural factors.

IV ESSENTIAL STRIVING SENTIMENTS

It has been noted that the objects for which people strive are enormous in number and diversity, and this makes it necessary to consider some way of organizing them into categories in order to achieve conceptual management. The multiplicity of objects is easily seen even in such fragments of lives as have been presented here from the Northeast. Tom Young wanted security in his home, a roof over his head, and protection for his wife and children. He also wanted the love of his family and the good opinion of his neighbors. His farm was a means to these ends, but it was a means to another end too. It was a chance to create something—to develop his stock, to grow his produce, and bring order out of the tangle of nature.

Gordon Chauncey wanted to be rich and powerful. His wife aspired to being a lady in the tradition of Victorian Britain; the prestige of gentility was her heart's desire. Helen wanted to get married; to have children and a place of her own. Bernie Chiason wanted to be loved and to respect himself, and he wanted to compose songs and sing them to his own accompaniment on the guitar. Rose wanted money and relief from childbearing and physical toil. Dr. Coindreau wanted to be a good Catholic, a good family man, a good representative of the best in French Acadian traditions, and a good general practitioner contributing to the welfare of his community. Dr. Hopkins wanted to rise in his specialty and one day have a substantial private practice. Willie Smallie wanted to be let alone in the world to which he had retreated and from which he drew a sense of fulfillment.

The striving sentiments of all these people were obviously far more numerous and complex than these few illustrations indicate. Moreover, at earlier stages in their lives they had had other objects: mother love, victory over brothers and sisters, sexual objects, objects they would like to eat, objects they would like to attack, and objects from which they would like to escape.

Given this endless series of striving sentiments, many of them collapsible into each other depending on how they are defined, can some kind of order be developed? Can they be grouped in categories so as to facilitate the delineation of relationships? It is the familiar problem of pattern and classification (Chapters I and II, pages 17 and 38).

A criterion for building categories relevant to our purposes here is the saliency of objects with regard to the essential psychical condition. Unfortunately, there is no way of ascertaining this directly, but some indications can be had from clinical psychiatry. One may ask what kinds of objects appear in those interferences with striving that are important in the disorders of patients. Such objects, according to what has been said above about necessary and sufficient conditions, must be among those closely tied to the maintenance of the essential psychical condition. There may, of course, be other objects intimately connected with the essential psychical condition which never come to clinical attention because of no interference, successful compensation, or other reasons. At the least, however, it can be said that the objects which do emerge in clinical work are a partial list of those important to the essential psychical condition.

With this as a guide, a list of essential striving sentiments according to object types has been compiled.[9] Although the number is ten, it is apparent that this total is most arbitrary. Given the complexity and intertwined character of human patterns of behavior, the number could be compressed or expanded according to purpose. The effort here has been to make the list as short as is compatible with the aim of using the frame of reference for a guide in research and hence ultimately mapping operational categories.

Inasmuch as the types of objects have relevance only as they are part of sentiments closely connected to achievement and maintenance of the essential psychical condition, the categories will be called *essential striving sentiments*. It is to be recognized that each is actually a cluster of many topically related sentiments.

1. Physical security.
2. Sexual satisfaction.
3. The expression of hostility.
4. The expression of love.
5. The securing of love.
6. The securing of recognition.
7. The expression of spontaneity (called variously positive force, creativity, volition).
8. Orientation in terms of one's place in society and the places of others.
9. The securing and maintaining of membership in a definite human group.
10. A sense of belonging to a moral order and being right in what one does, being in and of a system of values.

It is not necessary to assume that all these kinds of essential striving sentiments are equally significant in the achievement and maintenance of the essential psychical condition. Indeed, one or more may turn out to be of little influence; in terms of the map analogy, some may prove to be false continents. The list is intended as a collection of probabilities, as a statement of major striving patterns in human behavior. It is likely that their relative importance varies at different points along the life-arc.

These ten sentiments will be central from this point onward in the frame of reference. Directly and indirectly, much of the discussion will revolve around them and their implications for studying the effects of sociocultural environment on psychiatric disorder. Hence it may be appropriate to remind the reader that a sentiment is a construct that is always part of a personality, a subsystem of a system. Although the ten sentiments are listed, they are conceived not as more or less separable elements but rather as interdependent combinations that are integrated and integrating in the functioning of persons. Each personality is a system which incorporates within its totality some patterned assemblage of these ten as it moves through the sequences of the life-arc.

Furthermore, it may be recalled that sentiments are considered to be differentiated through experience out of basic urges, and the basic urges are in turn derived in a similar way from instincts.[10] All three, however, may be regarded as present at any given cross-section of a life-arc. This is to say that in the mature personality with a highly differentiated system of sentiments, the basic urges and instincts persist in a manner which can be represented schematically as "underlying." [11]

V TYPES OF INTERFERENCE WITH STRIVING

Situations arising in the environment may interfere with essential striving sentiments. Figure 3 represents such conditions.

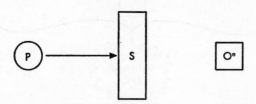

FIGURE 3: *Interferences due to intervening circumstance*

S is a situation arising in the sociocultural environment that cuts through one or more of the striving sentiments and bars the person from achievement or the perception-anticipation of achievement of the relevant object. P stands for person and O^e for objects in those striving sentiments which pertain most intimately to the essential psychical condition. Personality as the functioning of the person would again encompass the whole diagram.

Propositions Relating Disorder and Environment

At the place on the life-arc represented by this scheme, the personality is thought of as having been up to now adequate in its striving capabilities, and the types of specific objects for which it strives (the O^1, O^2, O^3, etc., which make up O^e) are thought to be appropriate in terms of the opportunities ordinarily available in the society and the culture.

Loss of money or the threat of it might act in this way through affecting the essential striving sentiments concerned with physical security, recognition, and orientation in terms of one's place in society and with maintaining membership in a definite human group. This kind of thing has been illustrated in the current circumstances of Tom's trouble (Chapter III). Some of Rose Chiason's difficulty could also be considered in this light.

Another illustration is bereavement, which can operate in a similar manner through affecting sentiments related to giving and securing love, sexual satisfaction, and the expression of hostility. Rejection in love commonly touches on a number of the same kinds of sentiments as bereavement.

Recalling Figure 2a, the effect of such interference on essential psychical condition may also be diagramed, and this is shown in Figure 3a.

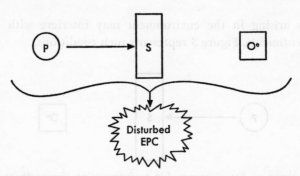

FIGURE 3a: *The relationship of interference to essential psychical condition*

Here the meaning of P, S, and O^e are as in Figure 3. EPC stands for essential psychical condition, and the margins are jagged to indicate disturbance.

This same relationship of interference to essential psychical condition also obtains with regard to Figures 4 and 5, which follow, but it does not seem necessary to repeat the diagram in each instance.

The nature of the object incorporated in one or more of the essential striving sentiments may interfere or seem to interfere with their achievement. This is represented in Figure 4.

FIGURE 4: *Interference due to the nature of the object*

The irregular outline of O^e indicates defect in the object. Otherwise the functioning of the person and his pattern of striving are assumed to be adequate.

A man could, for instance, work over a period of years to qualify himself for a particular occupation from which he expected to gain physical security, recognition, orientation in society, membership in a human group, love, and other items relevant to the ten clusters of essential striving sentiments. If, however, by the time he has become qualified, a technological change has made obsolete the occupation for which he prepared, then one can say the object has become defective so far as its function in the essential striving sentiments is concerned, and as a means toward the integration of his personality. By its very nature it prohibits fulfillment. Such a failure is due to changes in the society which it is conceivable have similarly affected many other persons preparing, or prepared, for the same way of earning a living. Willie Smallie's story presents this kind of sequence, even though here allowance must be made for an inborn defect of personality as well. Had shipbuilding continued, the appearance of his symptoms might have been postponed, or perhaps would not have occurred to such an extent as to disable him. The same kind of situation touches Tom Young's father in his oat-growing and other aspects of farming and also in his woodlot techniques, and of course, it is a threat to Tom Young himself.

With Mrs. Chauncey the case is similar, although here it is not a question of earning a living but of a social technique. Numbers of her essential striving sentiments, particularly those concerned with recognition, spontaneity, membership in a human group, and the sense of being right were tied to objects that might be summed up as the genteel way of life. She was a social leader; but in the midst of her success the way of life that she understood melted away. After the economic depression of the 30's and the following war, she found herself, like Mr. Young and Willie Smallie, in a world where the things she valued most and could do best were out of keeping with the times.

Helen, an only daughter with loyalty as well as dependence for love binding her to her mother, suffered from some of the same difficulty. Her upbringing had been in terms of her mother's standards and hence, even though she had been able to learn much herself, she was imbued with many of the latter's sentiments, expectations, and manner of response. She had difficulty consequently in contacts with people of her own age, particularly men. Not knowing how to get through her reserve, she covered her fear of others with an air of superiority, while all the time filled with unsatisfied strivings.

Failure of objects to provide a component for sentiments such that the latter can be fulfilled is but one of three primary difficulties that can be posited. A second type of defect appears when the person strives for mutually incompatible objects. Thus, he may have an occupation which provides physical security but is low in recognition. The converse can also exist, as is often does with ministers and teachers. More dramatic, and possibly more dynamically significant, is the situation in which the objects of sexual satisfaction and love run counter to adequate fulfillment of most of the other essential patterns. Here the conflict with the need to belong to a moral order and feel right in what one does may be particularly sharp.[12]

The third type of defect which may stem from the nature of objects is the situation in which the objects available for incorporation in the essential striving sentiments are so multiple, so ill-defined, or so few that it is very difficult for the personality to develop a consistent or stable set. Thus, no one road to physical security, love, recognition, membership in a human group, or place in a moral order is clear enough to permit the establishment of sentiments that are functional in the personality system. One finds himself surrounded by vague, shifting objects toward which he is unable to develop strong attachment. Everything appears like everything else and nothing provides a reliable opportunity for fulfilling the patterns upon which the essential psychical condition depends.

This sort of thing happens not infrequently when a society is in transition from one culture to another. A state of affairs is sometimes reached in which the people lose many of their traditional sentiments without replacing them with a functionally adequate new set. Much of the disorganization that characterized the essential sentiments of Bernie and Rose Chiason, and of the sister who went temporarily blind, came into being in this kind of setting. There was here the ignorance and disorderliness of life which is often associated with poverty and in which they had been raised, but there was also the difficulty of growing up and living between two cultures, of two different sets of values. Both Rose and Bernie had been born into families that were a mixture of English Protestant and French-Acadian Catholic. While such a blend might have worked out in some manner that would have been relatively harmonious, the most casual glance at the particular families and indeed neighborhoods in which they had originated made it plain that this had not been the case here.

What has been said thus far in discussing Figure 4 is overschematized, and some word of qualification is in order. In the first place, the difference between Figures 3 and 4, although conceptually convenient, is largely a matter of definition. This can be seen when it is pointed out that the problem of markets which confronted Tom could be represented by either diagram. That is to say, deterioration of markets may be regarded as an interference imposed between the person and his object, or as a defect in the object.

A second point is that Figure 4 may appear to equate object with person, that is, treat them as if they were the same order of "thing." As mentioned earlier, however, objects may be things or they may be relationships. More than this, whether things or relationships, the objects are not so external to the person as the diagram suggests. Their existence for him (representation in his mind) is what counts, and this is a part of the functioning of his personality.

Most of the objects of striving sentiments which a person comes to incorporate in his personality have, however, been acquired from the sentiments which prevail in his family and in the society in which he grows and lives. Many of these were held by others and expressed by others before he was born, and in this sense the objects existed apart from him. In his life he has found available a range of striving sentiments presented by the other people who are his social environment, and from these he has acquired and is acquiring his own particular collection. In this sense, then, one may speak of the social environment as providing the individual with objects, and hence as providing effective or defective objects with reference to maintaining his essential psychical condition.

Propositions Relating Disorder and Environment

153

A defect in the functioning of a given personality may result in failure, or the perception-anticipation of failure, in one or more of the essential patterns of striving. This is shown schematically in Figure 5.

FIGURE 5: *Interferences located primarily in the person*

The irregular margins of P are intended to represent a deficiency in the function of a given person, while the direction of the arrow (missing the object O^e) is intended to indicate functional failure of relevant sentiments in the personality system.

Mental deficiency as exemplified by Goofy Field who helped wreck the *Westway* illustrates such a defect in personality. While this type of psychiatric disorder is not in its origin thought to be primarily consequent on interference-with-striving, it can be instrumental in the failure of one or more of the essential striving sentiments such as those pertaining to physical security, obtaining recognition, or orientation as to one's place in society, and thus lead to disturbance of the essential psychical condition. This in turn may lead to other symptoms of psychiatric disorder, over and above those inherent in mental deficiency. In Goofy's case this took the form of a chronic anxiety state, similar to Tom Young's condition, but lacking the feature of acute episodes. He chewed his knuckles and bit his nails, and sometimes cried, but paid little attention to his racing heart.

I would like to suggest it as probable that there are hereditary defects of affect somewhat parallel to the cognitive defects of mental deficiency. An inborn tendency to excessive fear, as may have been the case with Tom's mother, for example, might produce inaction or exaggerated behavior so as to interfere seriously with the development and functioning of one or more of the essential sentiments. The same might be said for other kinds of emotions, for lability and instability of emotions, and for speed of responses. It may be noted, furthermore, that *too little* may be as damaging as *too much;* too little flexibility of emotions may also interfere with the development of the essential sentiments.[13]

Thus it could come about that some personalities have not merely malfunctional essential striving sentiments, but lack some of the categories altogether.[14] It is conceivable, for instance, that a person might have little or no basic urges of a sexual character. Such a condition would be bound to affect the whole organization of his personality. He might be compared to one who is tone-deaf and has the problem of adjusting to a world of music and of people who are not tone-deaf, or one who is color-blind but must live among those who have sensitivities and enthusiasms for color. One can posit constructive adaptations to a lack of sexual urge as well as others which might lead to some form of psychiatric disorder.

Incapacities besides the absence or near absence of sexual interests may also occur. The ability to give and receive love might be such another example. Here it is almost certain that some kind of sociopathic behavior would result.

What is being said in effect is that there can be some kinds of psychiatric disorder (as defined in Chapter IV) without antecedent disturbance of the essential psychical condition. When such disorders occur, however, they are apt to bring with them disturbance of the condition and hence lead to the development of further disorder and further symptoms.

The kinds of defect represented in the diagram are not limited to those that are inborn. It is possible for defect to be acquired, at some point in life, and to act thenceforward in the same manner as one that is inborn. An obvious and parallel example to mental deficiency is the loss of cognitive function due to brain damage, but acquisition can take place at more subtle, physiological levels as well, as in the case of the man who killed horses as a result of encephalitis.

Trauma to personality can also be psychological. If an upset in the essential psychical conditional leads to a chronic malfunction of the personality (e.g., excessive suspiciousness), by any of the means to be discussed in the next section, this defect can then act in much the same way as has been outlined for the hereditary or the acquired physiological defects, namely, interference with the formation and adequate functioning of one or more of the essential sentiments. Thus the process of symptom formation and symptom persistence can become circular, or spiral, cutting deeper and deeper, once having been set going by a particular set of circumstances, even though the original conditions later disappear. Pathology or malfunction of the circular type based on misfiring adaptations is exceedingly common in nature,

Propositions Relating Disorder and Environment

in all sorts of different contexts from cell physiology to social processes.[15]

Looking at interpersonal relations in terms of roles suggests still another manner whereby a defect in personality may occur. As noted in Chapter III, page 72, this view conceives personality as composed of roles derived from other people. The self is a composite or "internal community" made up of appraisals from the "significant others" encountered in the course of life. The functional capabilities of each personality are therefore profoundly influenced by the quality and quantity of these interpersonal experiences. In order to have an opportunity for optimal development, a personality must interact at least during the steep curve of the life-arc with a fair cross-section of people representing the normal range of roles. Damaging consequences may occur if the individual has limited opportunity in this regard, or if among the range of his significant associates there is a weighting with persons who themselves suffer from psychological disorder.

An only child, to take an extreme example, who lives most of his life before adulthood in a socially isolated family will be cut off from his age-mates and may, because of the deprivation in his interactions, fail to develop a repertoire of roles for dealing with his peers. This may be carried into later life and lead to emotional problems. A child in this position is also likely to find trouble in his relationships with authority figures because his experience with them has been largely limited to his parents and hence too restricted and too specialized. If, in addition to all the above, one or the other of the parents is himself peculiar, the child's likelihood of psychological malformation is correspondingly increased through the incorporation of these peculiarities as part of the role. Personalities which are defective because their role relations have been defective may therefore be expected to have difficulties in the development of some of their essential striving sentiments. These in turn lead to instability of the essential psychical condition.

Although Tom Young's life story was not extreme in this regard, it contained nonetheless some of the elements. He was an only child, raised on a backwoods farm, and there had been some inadequacies in the mother role due to her fearfulness and anxieties.

Life history, therefore, is relevant to Figure 5, since the diagram represents the person (P) at some point in the course of his arc and includes both inborn difficulties of personality and those acquired at an earlier time.

With these observations in mind, an additional set of propositions can now be stated. The reader may be bothered to find this designated as Series D, following immediately on Series A. I suggest that this matter be ignored for the present. It arises from the fact that the most convenient order of presentation is not the best for arranging the propositions once they have been explained. The letters and numbering refer to those employed in the final arrangement as found in Appendix B.

SERIES D. PROPOSITIONS CONCERNING INTERFERENCE WITH THE ESSENTIAL STRIVING SENTIMENTS

D1. Given Proposition A2 (page 146), certain striving sentiments may be designated as "essential" because maximally concerned with the maintenance of the essential psychical condition.

D2. Essential striving sentiments may fail in this function due to interference imposed by the environment.

D3. Essential striving sentiments may fail in this function due to defects inherent in the objects of striving.

D4. Essential striving sentiments may fail in this function due to defect, inborn or acquired, in the personality.

VI ESSENTIAL STRIVING SENTIMENTS AND SOCIOCULTURAL ENVIRONMENT

A restatement here of the points developed thus far may be useful. It has been postulated that there exists in every personality an essential psychical condition the disturbance of which may lead to the appearance of psychiatric disorder. The essential psychical condition is said to depend on a number of essential striving sentiments which have been described in ten major categories. The disturbance of the striving is pictured as occurring under three primary conditions: interference by the sociocultural environment in the striving, defect in those objects upon which the essential striving sentiments are focused, and defect in the already existing personality.

In the course of presentation, distinctions and categorizations have

Propositions Relating Disorder and Environment

been made for ease in conceptualization and analysis. In nature, however, boundaries are indistinct and overlapping. It would be rare, indeed, to find pure interference in striving, pure defect in object, or pure defect in personality in any given instance. It is supposed here that the three generally occur together, but the relative weight may vary a good deal from personality to personality, at different points on the life-arc, and from one set of circumstances to another. Many pastries, in short, have the same ingredients, but because the proportions differ, and the way of cooking, the results also differ.

Some of the environmental influences that can be significant for the production of psychiatric disorder may now be expressed in terms of the essential striving sentiments. Sociocultural situations can be said to *foster* psychiatric illness if they *interfere* with the development and functioning of these sentiments, since the latter in turn affect the essential psychical condition.

The sense in which *interfere* is employed has already been discussed. The word *foster* is used to indicate a preparation of the ground for some kinds of psychiatric disorder, but without the further assumption that such disorder necessarily follows. As noted previously and as will be elaborated later, the disturbance of the essential psychical condition can be resolved without the appearance of those patterns of behavior commonly regarded as illness.

The relationship of environment may be put in terms of the following propositions.

SERIES E. PROPOSITIONS RELATING ESSENTIAL STRIVING SENTIMENTS AND SOCIOCULTURAL ENVIRONMENT

E1. Sociocultural situations which interfere with sentiments of physical security foster psychiatric disorder.

E2. Sociocultural situations which interfere with sentiments of securing sexual satisfaction foster psychiatric disorder.

E3. Sociocultural situations which interfere with sentiments bearing on the expression of hostility foster psychiatric disorder.

E4. Sociocultural situations which interfere with sentiments of giving love foster psychiatric disorder.

E5. Sociocultural situations which interfere with sentiments of securing love foster psychiatric disorder.

E6. Sociocultural situations which interfere with sentiments bearing on obtaining recognition foster psychiatric disorder.

E7. Sociocultural situations which interfere with sentiments bearing on the expression of spontaneity (positive force, creativity, volition) foster psychiatric disorder.

E8. Sociocultural situations which interfere with sentiments of orientation in the person regarding his place in society and the place of others foster psychiatric disorder.

E9. Sociocultural situations which interfere with the person's sentiments of membership in a definite human group foster psychiatric disorder.

E10. Sociocultural situations which interfere with sentiments of belonging to a moral order and of being right in what one does foster psychiatric disorder.

This schematization contains, but perhaps does not make self-evident, most of what has been said about roles and personality malfunction. Considering roles as focal points in the sociocultural fabric and recognizing that any given individual fulfills many roles, it is usually possible to analyze interference with essential striving sentiments in terms of role conflicts, role incompatibilities, and role failures. One can also visualize the successive effects of such role conflicts with the movement of personality along the life-arc from childhood onward.

In particular, attention may be directed to the childhood experience with roles which become incorporated in a personality and which thus exert an influence on the capabilities of that personality in later life. Early encounters with defective, too few, or too many roles may thus result in a malfunctional person, not so much from interference with essential striving sentiments at this time, as through lack of experience with appropriate relationships. A person with such defective experience might encounter interference with essential sentiments later in life due to his inability to perform adequately the necessary roles.[16]

This last point may be cast as a supplementary proposition since it is not wholly contained in the previous series.

SERIES F. PROPOSITION RELATING INTERPERSONAL PATTERNS AND SOCIOCULTURAL ENVIRONMENT

F1. Sociocultural situations which expose a growing personality to defective role relationships foster psychiatric disorder.

The discussion thus far has led to aspects of the sociocultural environment which may, through disturbance of the essential psychical

Propositions Relating Disorder and Environment

condition, foster psychiatric disorder. It has been said a number of times that a disturbance of this condition does not necessarily lead to disorder. It remains, therefore, to trace the connections between such a disturbance and the occurrence or nonoccurrence of disorder, with continued emphasis on the influence of the environment in these further steps.

VII ALTERATION OF SENTIMENTS THROUGH THE SUBSTITUTION OF OBJECTS

I wish to suggest now that an upset of the essential psychical condition, once it has passed a certain threshold, is felt by the person as disagreeable. A variety of words are commonly employed to represent this feeling, such as "anxiety," "tension," and "depression." Whatever the technical language the central idea is widespread in clinical psychiatry and may be stated as an addition to the fundamental propositions:

SERIES A. FUNDAMENTAL PROPOSITIONS

A4. Disturbance of the essential psychical condition gives rise to disagreeable feelings.

An objection can be made to this on the ground that in many instances of interest to psychiatry the process takes place at an unconscious level, and hence there are no conscious feelings. I would agree with this in part and accept that much of what is going on is in fact commonly outside the area of awareness. In particular, the source of the disagreeable feelings is not apt to be apparent to the person concerned, as has been illustrated in the case of Tom Young. Furthermore, due to malfunctional adaptations to be discussed presently, the disagreeable feelings may be diminished and masked without an accompanying restoration of the essential psychical condition. On the other hand, it is my assumption that at some time on the life-arc and in some form, disagreeable feelings are involved and their imminent return remains a factor of importance in the functioning of the personality system.[17]

Given the disagreeable feeling—or the prodromal feeling of its possible breakthrough to consciousness—the personality reacts in the direction of getting rid of it. One form of this consists in altering the focus of the relevant essential striving sentiment, namely, changing the specific object. If, for example, an essential striving sentiment concerned with physical security, love, or recognition meets with interference, the latter may often be eliminated by shifting to another object. This may take the form of a change of job, a new person to love, or an attempt to seek membership in a group where recognition can be obtained, and so on. The possible specific illustrations for all ten of the essential sentiment clusters are, of course, virtually endless.

Thus, substitution of objects to eliminate perceived or anticipated interference in essential sentiments, without altering the essential functions of the sentiment, may be regarded as the personality's first line of defense—as prevailing, continuous, and on the whole successful in maintaining the essential psychical condition. It can be compared by way of analogy with man's ability to maintain his body upright while walking over uneven ground.

These points are worth emphasizing since in psychiatry we have had some tendency to overlook the resource of object substitution. This is perhaps because the problems of the patients we see draw attention to instances in which such substitution is ineffective and other processes are in evidence. It seems to me, however, that the matter is worthy of careful exploration, particularly with regard to defining successful psychological function and building concepts of mental health that encompass more than the absence of psychiatric disorder.

It is pertinent to note that a common characteristic of objects with relation to the essential clusters of sentiments often favors substitution. This is because a great many discrete and specific objects may be encompassed in any given cluster of sentiments, so that the blocking of one has little effect on the system as a whole, and hence on the essential psychical condition.

Gordon Chauncey is an example of one who had been particularly successful in the manipulation and substitution of objects so as to maintain his essential striving sentiments and hence his essential psychical condition with changing circumstances. This pattern is obvious in the history of his work and his economic enterprises, which of course contributed to his physical security, means of expressing aggression, recognition, spontaneity, orientation in society, and membership in a human group. He also employed object substitution successfully in many other aspects of life besides those connected with earning a living, however. This was manifest, for instance, in his behavior as the socio-cultural characteristics of the town altered rapidly after the 20's, with the change in many traditional class values and related social patterns and the marked increase in the size of the French-speaking population. It was also shown in his interpersonal relations and in his ability to deal with the progressive restrictions on his capabilities that came with the advance of age.

VIII   STEPS IN THE DEVELOPMENT OF PSYCHIATRIC DISORDER

A disturbed essential psychical condition may lead toward the emergence of a psychiatric disorder because object substitution is not successful and the interference with essential sentiments continues. Again, it may be noted that common relationships between objects and essential sentiments can favor this state of affairs. Some objects are by their nature not readily replaceable for most personalities. In this class belong those objects which occupy a key position in serving several different clusters of essential sentiments. A partner in love, for example, may also bring physical security, recognition, and a place in a definite human group. Such multifunctional objects, with a crucial position in many essential sentiments, are of great significance in the maintenance of the essential psychical condition.

Other factors also deserve consideration, of course, besides the nature of the object, such as the cognitive and affective equipment of the person and his basic urges, together with the various precipitates of his life-story. Thus, the over-all organization of personality may incline the individual to the flexibility displayed by Gordon Chauncey, or to the rigid clinging to certain objects no matter how difficult or impossible, as in the case of his wife, Lucy. In the course of her life-arc her personality had become organized around relatively few objects which thus occupied a central position in most of the essential clusters of sentiments. Her pursuit of gentility and her difficulties with the changes in society occurring after the 20's illustrates this. She remained year after year with a chronically disturbed essential psychical condition, manifest in her behavior and consciousness as a state of gnawing, resentful, depression.

At the opposite pole from inability to achieve object substitution, is the state of too great fluidity in this regard. Here, again, it may be a question of the nature of the objects, the nature of the personality, or both. A person can keep shuffling the objects relevant to his essential sentiments at a rate that amounts to disintegration of the sentiment system, and hence to failure in the integration of cognition, affect, basic urges, and unconscious processes. In such a state there can be no maintenance of the essential psychical condition, nor the cohesiveness and consistency as a unit necessary for adaptation to environment. Underlying Bernie Chiason's alcoholism was a turmoil of weak and unstable sentiments which approached this state. As a result, he appeared to others as spineless and shiftless, and his own opinion of himself was not much better.

Object substitution may also turn out malfunctional due to the nature of the replacement selected. This, of course, brings us to the considerations already discussed in the present chapter in connection with inadequate objects and the diagram presented in Figure 4, but it suggests one reason why people may select inadequate objects. It may be a desperate choice.

There is a crab in the North Atlantic which habitually covers itself with sponge as a means of self-preservation through concealment.[18] If the sponge is removed from the shell, the crab will search about for another piece and replace it. If sponge is not available, it will try other materials. Most of the time the system of defense works very well. Occasionally, however, the crab may not replace the sponge; or it may keep changing and piling on sponge with the result that the activity fails in its function of hiding the animal from its enemies; or it may use inadequate materials such as paper. These failures can come about for two main reasons: defect in the supply of materials in the environment, and defect in the crab, acquired or inborn.

The manipulation of objects by the personality as a result of disturbance to the essential psychical condition may be considered somewhat parallel. In general, the substitution of objects works well as part of the ever changing and exchanging process of a personality in its course along the life-arc. Malfunction can occur, however, from one or both of two main sources: defect with regard to objects available in the sociocultural environment, and defect, inborn or acquired, in the personality.

To mention the latter at this point may seem an instance of circular thinking, since the purpose of the discussion is to explain at least in part the evolution of defect. What is meant, of course, is that characteristics of personality antecedent to a given disturbance of the essential psychical condition may handicap the personality in using object substitution as an adequate defense or means of restoration. Hence the reasoning is circular, or spiral, only in that it reflects a process, psychopathology, which has this characteristic. The antecedent defects may belong in any of the categories already discussed under the headings of heredity and life experience, both physiological and psychological. The latter are notable for their capacity to develop progressive malfunction in which each step leads to the next, cumulatively, toward ultimate major disaster. One is reminded of the sequences by which the erosion of land sometimes occurs. A wheelrut on a slope will start the water cutting, and, as it cuts, the slope becomes steeper and the erosive power of the water and its silt increases.

The primary type of defective object from a psychological point of view is one that fails to restore the essential psychical condition. This is particularly so if the object selected is such that it eliminates, reduces, or disguises the perception of disagreeable feeling without having sufficient constructive effect on the underlying factors. For example, discomfort may be mitigated or removed, at least temporarily, by such agents as alcohol and drugs. A given personality may thus form a sentiment with one of these substances as the object, and this sentiment may come to occupy a central position in the personality, much as if it were one of the essential sentiments. In effect it is such a sentiment, but one which is self-defeating because the disturbed essential psychical condition continues. More than this, the persistent expression in action of the sentiment may lead to physical depletion and interpersonal difficulties which directly and indirectly further increase the disturbance of that condition.

Excitement by means of sex and adventure can be employed in a similar manner to fill consciousness and crowd out awareness of suffering. The fact that sex itself constitutes a focal point in one of the essential clusters of sentiments introduces no contradiction, because in the instance suggested it is not a matter of fulfillment and hence maintenance of the essential psychical condition, but of using sex to mask feelings while leaving a disturbed essential psychical condition untouched, or making it worse.

Various other psychological processes commonly present in personalities can also be employed to modify disagreeable feelings without an underlying constructive effect. A person can, for instance, turn to daydreams while disengaging himself from interactions with other people that disturb the dreams. Fantasied objects and fantasied achievement are thus substituted for real life objects and real life acts and by this means the disagreeable feelings are masked.

As one variant in this process, a person may strive to establish the blame on someone else and become absorbed in elaborating and maintaining this view. Another possibility is to blame his body and find relief in preoccupation with his health. This can be diffused as general ill health, or focused on some organ or system such as the digestive tract. It may also take the form of a difficulty in using an arm or a leg, or even a sensory system, as for instance vision.

Forgetting, that is, direct removal from consciousness, is also a psychological device by means of which to escape disagreeable feelings; in particular, painful memories and painful anticipations may be eliminated. Relief may be obtained, too, by attributing the disagreeable feelings to causes which, though false, are controllable, or seem controllable, such as germs. In this case, hand-washing and other ritual practices may constitute objects and focal points in sentiment systems which bring a sense of satisfaction.

The beginning of a trend in any of these directions may well be within the limits of behavior it is possible to consider normal. It may in some instances be of considerable functional significance in providing an immediate relief from the pressure of the disagreeable and thus enabling the personality to gird itself for a solution of the long-range problem through finding adequate objects. Taking a drink to cheer up, or a sleeping pill to get a good night's rest in the midst of one's worries, may not, in themselves, be malfunctional.

In many instances, however, there is a progression. Clinical observation suggests the occurrence of a series of steps in which each facilitates its successor toward one or another among the disorder patterns recognized in psychiatry and discussed in Chapter IV. Thus, the trends noted above may go on to a sociopathic condition such as alcoholism, sexual promiscuity, and delinquency; or a schizophrenic type of psychosis; or a paranoid state; or such psychoneuroses as hypochondriasis, hysteria, amnesia, and obsessive-compulsive disorders. Since these various adaptations generally fail in completely masking or removing from consciousness the disagreeable sensations, there is commonly evident some mixture of anxiety, tension, depression, bitterness and anger.

Propositions Relating Disorder and Environment

These progressive steps toward the formation of disorder have been described with the adult portions of the life-arc in mind. The principle they illustrate, however, applies equally well to the earlier years, even though the content of the patterns is different. For example, in childhood the disturbance of the essential psychical condition might be due to deprivation in a basic urge for mother love. Despite the fact that at this stage of its development the personality has limited resources and alternatives immediately available compared to the potentiality of later years, it will, nevertheless, make vigorous effort to shed the disagreeable feeling and restore the essential psychical condition. This could take the form of object substitution with sister, brother, or aunt, and it might, or might not, in the long run prove functional. The personality could also turn toward psychological satisfactions divorced from reality, that is, through the overdevelopment of autistic escapes, as with a dog or a toy. Diversions can also play a role through food, sexual pleasures, and emotional outbursts such as temper tantrums. Or, the environment may be manipulated through negativistic behavior, refusals to eat, and other devices in order to promote attention as a substitute for love. The ramifications and variations are many, but they can be summarized as disturbance of the essential psychical condition with malfunctional patterns of restoration. Furthermore, such occurrences in early childhood may be, and perhaps usually are, the initial steps in progressive, cumulative development of psychiatric disorder which does not appear as overt symptoms until the adult years.[19]

It should be noted that, for the purposes of this book, there is no need to explain the existence of fear, hate, love, sexual desire, depression, elation, aggression, suspiciousness, emotionally distorted thinking, retreat into imagination, and other patterns commonly evident in persons suffering from psychiatric disorder. These nouns apply to combinations and configurations of cognition, affect, and basic urges that are components of all personalities and are instances of the subsystems or parts which go to make up the self-integrating unit. The unit is, however, integrating and in people not suffering from psychiatric disorder these components participate in the integration. Disorder therefore consists in distortion and disproportion in the functioning of such parts, and this is where explanation is sought.

From this point of view it can be seen as plausible and almost self-evident that some of the initial steps outlined as methods of seeking quick relief from the disagreeable consequences of a disturbed essential psychical condition will be employed from time to time by most personalities. Particular selection will be a matter of heredity, physiological experience, and psychological experience. The critical issue is that some people continue far into the progressive spiral of psychiatric disorder, while others stop or pull back. Our interest is in the degree to which sociocultural factors, mediated through psychological experience, can determine one rather than another outcome.

It remains to consider the psychophysiological disorders such as headache, nausea, indigestion, peptic ulcer, hypertension and asthma. As noted in Chapter IV, this category encompasses symptoms of an organic type which have psychological factors as a major element in their origin and maintenance. Many of these same symptoms also occur primarily on an organic basis. Even when the psychological factor is the chief influence, organic agents may also be significant contributors, as for instance house dust in some cases of asthma. The central idea, however, is that a disturbance of the essential psychical condition can extend to a disturbance in the equilibrium of the whole organism. This amounts to a stress and response-to-stress complex in which there are many physiological ramifications, including reactions to organic agents.[20]

That physiological changes accompany emotional states is self-evident on the basis of everyday experience. We flush with joy and grow pale when frightened, to take as examples two acts which involve changes not only in the blood vessels of the face but in much more of the circulatory system, including the contents of the blood, together with widespread endocrine and autonomic activities. It seems probable, therefore, that a disturbance of the essential psychical condition would produce physiological alterations of some kind. Clinical investigations support such an expectation, but they go further and uncover many patterns of response that are not self-evident. Some persons, for instance, have a tendency to react to emotional disturbance with an outpouring of acid in the stomach. Among these, a number have such high and prolonged acidity that a relatively unprotected area below the stomach (the pylorus) becomes eroded, constituting an ulcer.

Before leaving this topic, it is worth noting that in addition to conditions placed under the heading of psychophysiological, some of the disturbances considered organic brain disease may have major psychological components in their origin. This applies particularly to the early onset and rapid advance of senility and arteriosclerosis.[21]

The central points of the preceding discussion may be summarized in the following propositions:

SERIES B. PROPOSITIONS CONCERNED WITH THE EVOLUTION OF PSYCHIATRIC DISORDER

B1. Given a disturbance of the essential psychical condition, a personality may adopt patterns of sentiment and action which lead to some relief from the resultant disagreeable feelings (A4, page 160), but which fail to restore adequately the essential psychical condition.

B2. Because of the relief, each response facilitates its repetition: hence there is a tendency for a personality to persist in a maladaptive direction (B1) once this has been started, leading ultimately to the occurrence of psychiatric disorders.

B3. Given a disturbance of the essential psychical condition (A4), physiological symptoms may appear as part of a general disturbance of dynamic equilibrium in the organism.

B4. Given a disturbance of the essential psychical condition (A4), pre-existing defect in personality may contribute toward the development of psychiatric disorder and/or the appearance of physiological symptoms.

IX STEPS THAT AVOID PSYCHIATRIC DISORDER

The substitution of objects so as to enable the essential clusters of sentiments to function, and hence lead to restoration and maintenance of the essential psychical condition, has already been mentioned in the first section of this chapter. This is indicative of the main processes by which interference with striving is eliminated and the essential psychical condition restored without the appearance of behavior likely to be called psychiatric disorder. The disagreeable feelings are corrected at their psychic sources and no crippling spiral is begun through immediate but superficial relief. The person selects new objects and maintains his essential striving sentiments in a manner compatible with both the needs of the personality system and the realities of the environmental situation. Since such behavior is also in the long run rewarding due to the reduction of disagreeable feelings, there is repetition of the constructive pattern in a manner similar to that described for the development of pathological patterns.

Beyond this, it is possible that out of this action something more effective than the previous level of functioning may evolve. The magnitude of the disturbance and the characteristics of the situation may result in the mobilization of capabilities in the personality that had not hitherto been active. Hence superior integration or productivity on the part of the personality can emerge and it may be noted parenthetically that both pathology and unusual gifts can have their roots in disturbance of the essential psychical condition. This possibility is in keeping with the frequent observation in nature that damage to a system results not merely in restoration but also in a strengthening of some aspect of the system. The point at which a bone has been broken, for instance, generally becomes more calcified and stronger than the bone adjacent.[22]

With regard to the psychophysiological types of disorders, it is evident that a restoration of the essential psychical condition would produce a more optimal state of the dynamic equilibrium of the whole organism. Hence one would not expect the appearance or persistence of disturbance to the vascular, digestive, and other systems—at least so far as psychological factors are concerned.

These several points can be assembled in a series of propositions parallel to those having to do with evolution of psychiatric disorder (B series).

SERIES C. PROPOSITIONS CONCERNED WITH THE NONOCCURRENCE OF PSYCHIATRIC DISORDER

C1. Given a disturbance of the essential psychical condition, a personality may adopt patterns of sentiment which lead to relief of the resultant disagreeable feelings (A4, page 160), by means of restoration of the essential psychical condition.

C2. Because of the relief, each response facilitates its repetition, hence there is a tendency for a personality system to persist in the constructive direction (C1) once this has been started, leading to adequate, or even superior functioning.

C3. Given a resolution of the disturbance to the essential psychical condition, and a consequent improvement in dy-

Propositions Relating Disorder and Environment

namic equilibrium of the organism, the nonoccurrence or disappearance of psychophysiological disorders will take place.

C4. Given a disturbance of the essential psychical condition, (A4), pre-existing resources of the personality may contribute toward the development of adequate or superior functioning.

The reader will note that the sequence of steps involved in the nonoccurrence of psychiatric disorder has much briefer treatment than is the case with the steps concerned in the evolution of such disorders. This apparent slighting is not a matter of interest, but of knowledge—indeed, of conceptual tools. It highlights the fact that we are far better equipped to define and explore illness than wellness. As noted in the general introduction and as will be mentioned again in later chapters, one of the ultimate aims in the present research is to find means for altering this situation and developing a body of knowledge with regard to the processes of health which will be comparable with our knowledge of the processes of illness.

For the sake of presentation, the malfunctional and functional or healthy trends that may flow from disturbances in the essential psychical condition have been discussed and presented in propositions as if they were mutually exclusive. It remains to be said that they can, and do, occur in the same personality at the same time. This may be stated as a combined proposition.

BC1. The trends indicated for the development of psychiatric disorder (B1, B2, B3, and B4) and for the maintenance of health or increasing capabilities (C1, C2, C3, and C4), can occur simultaneously in the same personality.

This proposition may cause some readers to wonder whether the essential psychical condition is supposed to be both present and not present at the same time. For, if the constructive restoration indicated in the C series occurs, there is presumably no disturbance and hence no disagreeable feelings to induce the destructive spiral of the B series. Or, is more than one essential psychical condition being posited?

Although it is true that the words "essential psychical condition" stand for a multidimensional process that could be considered in plural terms, this is not the point of the proposition. It seems more useful to emphasize restoration of the essential psychical condition as having qualities of degree and stability. Thus a constructive trend may be only partially successful, leaving still considerable discomfort as a focal point for the more or less destructive types of immediate relief. Or, conversely, the existence of the immediate types of relief may handicap rather than eliminate the more long-range processes.

Stability implies restoration that is continuously effective along a major portion of the life-arc. Instead of this, however, the restoration can be interrupted frequently, thereby giving the more destructive patterns opportunity for coming into play. Hence a segment of the life-arc may contain alternating constructive and destructive trends.

This view says more than the generalization that people are complex and contradictory. It also does more than indicate again that personality, as the functioning of a human unit, constitutes the integration of many trends, some of them divergent. Stating the coexistence and alternation of effective and crippling processes with regard to the restoration of the essential psychical condition suggests that health and illness, however defined, must be regarded as states which consist in a kind of algebraic sum of opposite processes. Many combinations are possible, with marked qualitative differences between them. It is a commonplace, of course, to visualize psychiatric disorder in a variety of categories, whether or not the particular groupings of Chapter IV are accepted. Less often is it suggested that there are also many different healthy patterns. This combined proposition points away from a unitary concept of health and toward the idea of numerous patterns of psychiatric wellness. It points to mental *healths*, rather than mental health.[23]

X SOME NOTES ON CAUSES

The question as to what are the crucial factors which determine why some people develop psychiatric disorders while others remain well is not, of course, answered in the descriptions and discussions of these chapters. Were this the case, there would be no need for the research with which our frame of reference is concerned. The aim has been rather to lay out alternatives, with emphasis on the sequential relationships that seem to be characteristic of life. Since our main interest is in the influence or lack of it on the part of sociocultural environment, the organization and presentation of the alternatives has been such as to expose this aspect for scrutiny as much as possible.

Let me say again that this should not be taken to imply either overlooking or rejecting heredity, physiological factors, or innate unconscious psychic processes. It is allowed that such factors may be critical regarding who does and who does not, in given circumstances, develop a disturbed essential psychical condition, and who, having developed this condition, does or does not go on to psychiatric disorder. Although there has been emphasis on progressive symptom formation in which each step, together with environmental circumstance, leads to the next, this is not to deny that the patterning of the illness may be under the influence of the particular kind of disturbance that is affecting the essential psychical condition. Nor does it deny the possibility that the crux of the matter may often be a malfunctional process that gets firmly fixed at an unconscious level very early in life, with symbolic representation in the objects of sentiments and in the verbal and other expressive patterns of the disorder.

On the other hand, the question is asked as to how often and under what circumstances more or less rigid fixation of a particular maladaptive pattern early in life is the essential feature. Given a number of people who have roughly the same resources in terms of heredity, physiological factors, and innate, unconscious psychic processes, can sociocultural factors determine who does and who does not develop a disturbed essential psychical condition, and of those developing the condition, who does and who does not go on to manifest psychiatric disorder? Are the cumulative experiences along the life-arc major influences, and can alteration of environmental circumstances affect outcome? Is the rigidity of the patterning seen in psychiatric disorders always and entirely due to some more or less single underlying unconscious configuration or is it due to the organization of the personality as a whole?

By the latter I have reference to the fact that, in an extensive and complex system, a change in one part has wide ramifications, and, as has been noted earlier, the self-integrating unit which constitutes personality has the general tendency to resist major alteration at any given moment on its life-arc. To alter the disadvantageous aspects of a disorder may involve drastic reorganization of the whole sentiment complex of the system. Since this complex is the precipitate of past experience as well as the interactions at the cross-section of the moment, such change amounts to rewriting the past history of the organism, an obviously difficult matter. Thus, for example, the person whose sentiment system has never evolved qualities of foresight with regard to the consequences of some kinds of immediate pleasures and immediate pains is not apt to change easily but rather may tend to progress deeper into neurotic patterns which bring prompt relief, even though they are self-defeating in the long run. Conversely, a personality with a sentiment system inclined to look ahead with regard to most aspects of living has some advantage in resisting immediate satisfaction. The sentiment systems which characterize personality, in short, are not developed overnight. The response to the situation of the moment has to be within the opportunities and limits set up by the preceding life-story.

If we look back now on Tom Young and the discussion of the derivations of his illness in Chapter III, it is seen that the various possibilities discussed there can all be considered illustrations of the way in which his essential psychical condition may have become disturbed. The further step to the appearance of symptoms can be considered as a response (anxiety, pounding heart, difficult breathing) to that disturbance (B3), with, however, the immediate perception of this in terms of his current sentiments leading to a new sentiment, "I have heart failure." Whether or not these current sentiments were themselves colored by the disturbance of the essential psychical condition with tendencies toward guilt and self-punishment, the fact remains that such perceptions at once give a particular place to the experience in his awareness. He perceives it as the advent of a more or less permanent danger and is confirmed in this by the sentiments and responses of people around him.

Thus the patterning of the anxiety attack is developed and perpetuated. It could progress to psychoneurotic invalidism, especially if that state were to relieve Tom of some of the inner and outer pressures contributing to the interference with his striving and hence the disturbance of his essential psychical condition. If, for instance, having heart failure through no fault of his own were to relieve him of responsibility for the two families and the consequence of economic failure, or if it increased his security in relation to his wife by making it necessary for her to accept his dependence, much like that of a little boy, and so on, then there would be additional impetus for confirming himself in this kind of sick role. This could obtain, even though there was incomplete restoration of the essential psychical condition and he continued to have miserable and frightening attacks. His condition would be one that was to some extent protection against worse. Hence, a problem for the doctor, coming on the scene early in the formation of symptoms, was to prevent, if possible, the development and confirmation of a recurring illness pattern with all these supporting inducements (or "secondary gains"), while at the same time exploring the factors responsible for the essential psychical condition becoming upset, and seeking a way of dealing with them.

Reverting once more to some general points about the process of symptom formation, it may be noted that there are a number of explanatory ideas that have bearing on the appearance of both psychological and psychophysiological symptoms once the essential psychical condition has been disturbed. If we view each personality as a system in dynamic equilibrium, it can be supposed that, under stress, each tends to develop malfunction in that part of the system which has the least stability, or the least resources for restoring stability. This may be the imagination for one, the balance of different affects for another, digestion for a third, the vascular system for a fourth, and so on. The location of the weakness may vary from person to person according to heredity and previous life experiences, particularly those of a physiological character.

A recurrence of the stress, however, has a slight tendency to evoke the same pattern, everything else being equal. This could be because the first activation of the pattern renders the neural pathways and connections it involves a little more susceptible to response than alternative routes. With each successive activation the effect is cumulative. Hence the tendency of one individual to react to disturbance of the essential psychical condition with his stomach and another with some aspect of his emotional system can be the end result of a kind of progressive organic habit formation.

Another concept utilizes the idea of the conditioned reflex. According to this, the organism acquires a characteristic pattern of responding to emotional disturbance through reinforcement. The beginning may be a matter of chance, but the persistence of the pattern is due to some kind of reward. Since no such rewards are usually evident at an obvious level, theories of unconscious psychic processes and basic urge gratification have to be invoked.

A closely related view attaches importance to the possibility of *sym-*

bolic meaning in the symptoms. Thus, to take a simple example, vom‑iting may be a way of expressing unconscious rejection. This, like the previous, not only suggests that unconscious factors may play a role in the disturbance of the essential psychical condition but conforms with the view that they also influence the selection and shaping of some of the resultant symptoms.

As is the case with many other categories discussed in this book, these points of view are not mutually exclusive. All the processes indicated may be commonly involved in the appearance of psychiatric disorders.[24]

XI   THE INFLUENCE OF THE SOCIOCULTURAL ENVIRONMENT

As noted already, the formulations of this and preceding chapters do not yield any succinct or key-to-lock type of explanation as to why some people develop psychiatric disorders and others do not, or why, among those who do develop disorders, some have one pattern of ill-ness while others have another. Rather, starting with heredity, they postulate a range of factors, each of which is capable of exerting some influence on the outcome of a disturbance to the essential psychical condition in a given personality. These factors help toward an answer by being targets of inquiry. When they can be reduced to researchable questions one can hope, in time, to discover their relative importance in various circumstances. Since our focus of interest is the influence of the sociocultural environment, discussion here will be limited to that kind of factor.

Having considered how the sociocultural environment may play a part in the disturbance of the essential psychical condition, the con-cern now is with its effects, once such a disturbance has taken place. Even so, however, there is some overlap of topic, for what was said earlier about the kind of objects offered by the environment to the un-folding personality also applies when it comes to the substitution of objects. Depending on its patterning, the sociocultural environment can steer a personality toward the development of disorder (the B Series) or toward nondisorder (the C Series). More than this, if the trend is toward disorder, the environment can exert an influence as to which type of adaptation occurs and hence have a differential effect

Propositions Relating Disorder and Environment

on the patterning of the disorder, including its most obvious symptoms. On the other hand, if the trend is away from disorder, the environment can equally well exert a selective effect on which of many possible patterns of functioning, or mental health, is actually adopted.

To illustrate, in a society that lacks farms, markets, guns, and competitive sentiments, Tom Young could not have developed many of the characteristics of his illness, including the symbolic elements. He might have had an anxiety attack, but the ideational content, the symbols and manifestations, would have been different. In a society that lacks alcohol, Bernie Chiason could not have developed his particular sociopathic type of disorder. In a society that does not have sentiments of cleanliness and link them with Godliness and social prestige, as does the Northeast, there is less encouragement for developing those obsessive-compulsive patterns which emphasize germs and lead to rituals of hand-washing and turning door handles with sterile bits of paper. On the other hand, a rigidly structured society that permitted little change of role on the part of its members would not have given Gordon Chauncey the opportunity to develop his kind of successfully functioning personality.

Environment can exert this type of selective effect, not only on the more purely psychological disorders but on the psychophysiological illnesses as well. Thus, reactions such as headache, nausea, palpitations, diarrhea, and many more may be heightened or diminished by prevailing sentiments both toward the symptoms and toward the person who exhibits them. Apprehension about and efforts to conceal nausea, for example, may increase the sense of discomfort and thus adversely affect the total equilibrium, with the result that nausea becomes vomiting. On the other hand, in a culture where headaches are a cause for loving concern and even a little prestige as a mark of driving oneself hard and being a bit of a martyr, there is apt to be some encouragement toward their emphasis and prolongation.

Sociocultural environment may also exert an influence on psychiatric disorder through the presence or absence of therapeutic resources, and in cases where these are present, through their nature and effectiveness. Where resources are numerous and effective one may expect a smaller load of morbidity as compared to a similar situation in which these facilities are lacking. In speaking of resources, I include, of course, the formal therapeutic systems such as hospitals, out-patient clinics, and private practitioners. But there is also need to recognize the importance of other institutions such as schools, churches, welfare agencies, and police, and of informal resources in wise men and women who, whatever formal roles they occupy, constitute advisors, therapeutic listeners, and confidants for their friends, neighbors, and relatives. It seems likely that many communities which lack all formal psychiatric treatment and in which the very name psychiatry is little known and less understood may, nevertheless, have numerous indigenous and valuable resources of a therapeutic character.

These environmental considerations may be stated in two additional propositions, one in the B series and the other in the C.

SERIES B. PROPOSITIONS CONCERNED WITH THE EVOLUTION OF PSYCHIATRIC DISORDER

B5. Given a disturbance of the essential psychical condition (A4), sociocultural conditions have a selective influence on the emergence and persistence of malfunctional patterns of personality leading to psychiatric disorder (B1, B2, and B3).

SERIES C. PROPOSITIONS CONCERNED WITH THE NONOCCURRENCE OF PSYCHIATRIC DISORDER

C5. Given a disturbance of the essential psychical condition (A4), sociocultural conditions have a selective influence on the emergence and persistence of personality patterns which do not lead to psychiatric disorder and which may lead to superior functioning (C1, C2, and C3).

XII SUMMARY AND CONCLUSION

The present chapter has dealt with various ways in which the sociocultural environment can enter, directly and indirectly, into the process whereby a personality develops one or more of the disorders subsumed by the field of psychiatry. Since it is convenient to have a single term by which one can refer to this aspect of environment, the word *noxious* will be employed henceforward together with *benign* as a contrasting tendency. These terms have wider meaning in medicine, encompassing physical as well as psychological factors. Although "psychonoxious" and "psychobenign" might be more explicit, this hardly seems sufficient reason for perpetrating such a combination of sounds. It is thought that in the context of this frame of reference the special meaning of the shorter words will be self-evident.

Since all environments must inevitably have both noxious and benign influences, they cannot be classified in a twofold system as either one or the other. We may, however, think of them as more and less noxious and compare one with another in these terms. According to what has been said so far, the main characteristics of the more noxious environments may be summed up as follows:

1. High degree of apparent risk with regard to physical security, sexual satisfaction, expression of hostility, expression of love, securing love, obtaining recognition, expression of spontaneity, orientation in society, membership in a human group, and a sense of belonging to a moral order.

2. Sociocultural conditions which permit or foster the formation of those behavior patterns (intrapersonal and interpersonal) which lead to psychiatric disorder rather than to more constructive forms of adaptation.

3. The absence of therapeutic and remedial resources, both formal and informal.

Obviously all the above features will rarely be found to a really extreme degree in any environment. As main characteristics, however, they offer a basis in terms of which to examine environments in order to see if some appear to be outstandingly noxious as compared to others. These are matters of qualities as well as degree. If such contrasts can be found, then we have an opportunity to explore through experimental observations our theories regarding the relationship between sociocultural environment and psychiatric disorder.

CHAPTER NOTES

1. For going over the ideas set forth in this chapter and for numerous helpful suggestions, appreciation is expressed to Jerome D. Frank, Theodore Lidz, and John C. Whitehorn.

2. For an illuminating yet brief comment on the problem of interrelatedness, of fields, systems, and subsystems as bearing on the study of human behavior in health and disorder *see* A. W. MACLEOD, E. D. WITTKOWER and S. G. MAR-GOLIN, "Basic Concepts of Psychosomatic Medicine," in

ERIC D. WITTKOWER and R. A. CLEGHORN (Eds.), *Recent Developments in Psychosomatic Medicine* (Philadelphia: Lippincott, 1954), pp. 3-9.

3. *Webster's New International Dictionary of the English Language,* 1957, defines an object as "That which is set, or which may be regarded as set, before the mind so as to be apprehended or known; that of which the mind by any of its activities takes cognizance whether a thing external in space or a conception formed by the mind itself; as an *object* of knowledge, wonder, fear, thought, study, etc." In the light of this definition "object" is taken as referring to a wide range of different phenomena and includes relationships and feelings as well as material entities. Consider, for instance, food, recognition, and love. Furthermore, the gratification which comes from object striving may arise on the basis of direct sensory stimulation, of psychological states induced by symbols, or through some mixture of both.

4. The illustrations given in the text as to the kind of process meant by essential psychical condition are negative, and this reflects much psychiatric theory. For example, Freud thought of the reduction of excitation, Horney and Sullivan emphasized escape from anxiety, Adler spoke of overcoming feelings of inferiority, and Fromm of decreasing the inhibitors of spontaneity.

There are some, however, who have emphasized the optimal state as having the positive component which is included in the notion of the essential psychical condition. Taking "tension" to illustrate the point, I would say that the optimal state is not the absence of tension, but some degree that is intermediate between too little and too much. This is quite different from Sullivan's "euphoria" as a state of "tensionless bliss."

In broad terms I conceive the personality system as sensation seeking, as striving to function and to exercise its capabilities and find expression for many of its potentialities. Such a tendency is part of a general impulse to look for experience that has its basis in the genes of the organism. Meyer had this kind of thing in mind when he spoke of spontaneity; the existential psychiatrists give emphasis to it; as did McDougall when he pointed to dynamic striving

Propositions Relating Disorder and Environment

as a basic characteristic of the personality system. Murray stresses the significance of "zest" and the "need for activity," and, with Kluckhohn, he has formulated the concept of "proaction" in contrast to "reaction." Similar orientations emphasizing the self-actualizing potentials of personality have been presented by Maslow, Goldstein, and Rogers.

See: ROLLO MAY, ERNEST ANGEL, and HENRI F. ELLENBERGER, (Eds.) *Existence, A New Dimension in Psychiatry and Psychology* (New York: Basic Books, 1958); WILLIAM MC-DOUGALL, *An Introduction to Social Psychology* (London: Methuen, 1936), pp. 304-310; HENRY A. MURRAY, *Explorations in Personality* (New York: Oxford Univ. Press, 1938), pp. 129-134; HENRY A. MURRAY and CLYDE KLUCKHOHN, "A Conception of Personality," in *Personality in Nature, Society, and Culture* (New York: Knopf, 1953), pp. 10 and 36; A. H. MASLOW, *Motivation and Personality* (New York: Harper, 1954); KURT GOLDSTEIN, *The Organism* (New York: American Book, 1939); CARL ROGERS, "A Theory of Personality and Behavior," in *Client-Centered Therapy* (New York: Houghton Mifflin, 1951), pp. 481-533.

Recently Olds has reported experimental work in which rats are seen to seek cerebral excitation by means of electric shocks. He feels that these studies call in question all theories that base motivation primarily on tension reduction or similar process. See: J. OLDS, "Self-Stimulation of the Brain," *Science,* Vol. 127, no. 3294, 1958, pp. 315-324.

5. A quantitative concept of psychic energy was central to much of Freud's thinking and has been an important reference point for many of his followers. In recent times, however, there has been some change in viewpoint. E. Pumpian-Mindlin has written an interesting review suggesting some changes in Freud's thinking during his later years. Colby has developed a concept of psychic energy along lines that are in harmony with this frame of reference.

See: EUGENE PUMPIAN-MINDLIN, "Propositions Concerning Energetic-Economic Aspects of Libido Theory: Conceptual Models of Psychic Energy and Structure in Psychoanalysis," in LEOPOLD BELLAK (Ed.), "Conceptual and Methodological Problems in Psychoanalysis," *Annals of the New York Academy of Sciences,* Vol. 76, Art. 4., 1959, pp. 1038-1052;

KENNETH MARK COLBY, *Energy and Structure in Psychoanalysis* (New York: Ronald, 1955).

My own notions along this line stem from studies in neurophysiology from 1932 to 1934. These led to thinking in terms of controlling electro-chemical patterns in the central nervous system. The respiratory center served as a model, but with the additional consideration that such controlling patterns could be acquired through experience and could furthermore lie dormant or disconnected from consciousness and action, but capable of coming into play from time to time according to circumstances. This orientation made it difficult to accept the concept of psychic energy when this was later encountered in the course of studying psychiatry.

6. The reader may note in this and subsequent diagrams some similarities to the topological ideas of Kurt Lewin. Although they have not been derived specifically from a study of his work, it is likely that there has been some influence through conversations with Lewin and with several of his students. It is important to note, however, that the arrows in my diagrams do not correspond to Lewin's vectors, nor is personality to be equated with "life-space," although there is overlap in these concepts. Furthermore my diagrams are not intended to be mathematical representations following Lewin's patterns, but are merely illustrations of the type he described as holding "only in so far as the analogy holds, i.e., really only as long as it is convenient. As soon as consequences ensue which do not agree with the real facts, one evades the difficulty by asserting that it is after all only a model or an illustration. One says, 'A comparison is not an equation.'" *See:* KURT LEWIN, *Principles of Topological Psychology* (FRITZ and GRACE HEIDER trans.) (New York: McGraw-Hill, 1936), p. 79.

7. Another way of describing Mr. Young's behavior in this instance is to say that he had a different "reference group" than his son in the matter of farm practices. This brings to bear a mode of conceptualization and a body of theory which has been comprehensively discussed by Merton. *See* ROBERT K. MERTON and ALICE S. ROSSI, "Contributions to the Theory of Reference Group Behavior" and ROBERT K. MER-

Propositions Relating Disorder and Environment

TON, "Continuities in the Theory of Reference Groups and Social Structure" in *Social Theory and Social Structure* (Glencoe, Ill.: Free Press, 1957).

Some additional references are: MUZAFER SHERIF, "The Concept of Reference Groups in Human Relations," in M. SHERIF and M. O. WILSON (Eds.), *Group Relations at the Crossroads* (New York: Harper, 1953); THEODORE NEWCOMB, *Social Psychology* (New York: Dryden, 1950); CHARLES C. HUGHES, "Reference Group Concepts in the Study of Changing Eskimo Culture" in *Cultural Stability and Cultural Change*, Proceedings of the 1957 Annual Spring Meeting of the American Ethnological Society.

8. The discussion of unconscious processes given in this chapter is, of course, only an outline of selected aspects considered as having a part in the frame of reference. The effort is toward simplified presentation of relevant ideas and not toward the summary of a very large body of complex theory. While "conscious" and "unconscious" are given emphasis as being connected on a range and as being under the influence of multiple factors, it has not been thought necessary to introduce the "preconscious" and other technical terms which in effect result in a more elaborate schematization.

In a book devoted to this topic, for example, Miller lists as meanings of "unconscious": "unresponsive to stimulation" due to hypnosis, sleep, being knocked out and daydreaming; "unsensing" because of deficiency in sensory tract and because of weak stimuli; "unnoticing (unattending)"; "insightless"; "unremembering"; "unable to communicate"; "acting involuntarily"; and the psychoanalytic meaning. *See* JAMES GRIER MILLER, *Unconscious* (New York: Wiley, 1942); *see also* LEOPOLD BELLAK, "The Unconscious," in "Conceptual and Methodological Problems in Psychoanalysis," *Annals of the New York Academy of Sciences*, pp. 1066-1097.

9. The main basis for this compilation is experience and theory in psychiatry. I am particularly indebted to Urie Bronfenbrenner for a review he made about the time the frame of reference was being developed. *See* URIE BRONFENBRENNER, "Toward An Integrated Theory of Personality," in ROBERT R. BLAKE and GLENN V. RAMSEY (Eds.), *Perception, An Approach to Personality* (New York: Ronald, 1951).

Impressions have been drawn in addition from psychology, social psychology, and cultural anthropology, though it would be hard to give specific references.

Other influences stem from personal experience, not only in clinical psychiatry but also in morale assessment and in conducting personality studies of nonpatients in several cultures and under a number of different kinds of stressful circumstances. *See:* ALEXANDER H. LEIGHTON, *The Governing of Men* (Princeton: Princeton Univ. Press, 1946) and *Human Relations in a Changing World* (New York: Dutton, 1949).

10. A word should perhaps be said here with regard to the term "instinct." Although there are some current signs of its revival, it is a word which fell into disrepute many years ago apparently because invoked too readily as an explanation of behavior. Many instincts were postulated with concomitant disregard of the effects of experience and learning by the organism in the course of growth. I have retained it because it is simple and useful if not overworked, and it conveys to most people a general idea of inborn disposition.

"Drive" is a possible alternative term, but I have avoided it because of its specificity. For the purposes of this frame of reference, it means too much and that much too precisely. For example, Allport says: "A drive is defined as a vital impulse which leads to the reduction of some segmental organic tension. It has its origin in an internal organic stimulus of peculiar persistence, growing characteristically stronger until the organism acts in such a way as to alleviate the accumulating tension." (GORDON W. ALLPORT, *Personality, A Psychological Interpretation* [New York: Holt, 1937], p. 113.)

And Murphy defines the concept as: "Basic tendency to activity; the action tendency, initiated by shifts in physiological balance ('restlessness'), is accompanied by sensitivity to particular types of stimuli so that eventually a consummatory response occurs." (GARDNER MURPHY, *Personality, A Biosocial Approach to Origins and Structure* [New York: Harper, 1947], p. 984.)

11. In a personal communication, Talcott Parsons has pointed out that the ten essential striving sentiments can be seen as falling in three groups that have bearing on concepts of personality development and organization.

"The first two are closest to the organic level of integration. The third, fourth, fifth and sixth belong together with reference to deep-rooted motivational systems taking origin in child-parent relationships. Your 'love' and 'recognition' are close to W. I. Thomas' 'response' and 'recognition.' The last four are more differentiated relational needs, the products of later phases of socialization. They come very close to what I have been calling 'structurally generalized goals.' Those I consider post-oedipal as contrasted to primary need dispositions which are pre-oedipal."

12. The incompatibility of objects is not purely a matter of logical relationships. It is possible for the sentiment system of a personality to incorporate objects which are by rational standards in conflict or mutually exclusive without producing disturbance of the essential psychical condition. This occurs when the nature of the objects, the environmental situation, or the personality is such that the incompatibility reaches awareness only vaguely or not at all. This can be accidental, as when the sentiments containing opposed objects crop up at such different points in the weekly or monthly round of existence as to make the conflict difficult for most persons to perceive, or the lack of recognition can be more motivated as for instance when an inhibition of conflict recognition serves to avoid disruption to the functioning of the sentiment system and hence the personality.
See ALEXANDER H. LEIGHTON, *The Governing of Men,* pp. 288-292.

13. Ginsburg reports that work with rats gives clear evidence of aggressive and nonaggressive behavior as being hereditary traits. See BENSON E. GINSBURG, "Genetics as a Tool in The Study of Behavior," *Perspectives in Biology and Medicine,* Vol. 1, no. 4, 1958, pp. 397-424.

14. This point, a significant one for the frame of reference, was not in the earlier drafts. It was drawn to my attention as an omission by Toshio Yatsushiro.

15. Indeed, many of the phenomena in nature which we consider disorder are in fact adaptive patterns out of phase with the larger system of which they are a part. Clotting of the blood, for instance, can be seen as having the function of preventing a creature from bleeding to death when it happens to get cut. This same clotting mechanism can, however, cause death by going off under the wrong circumstances as when it plugs an artery in the heart and so constitutes an instance of coronary thrombosis.

At the level of group behavior, an armaments race is probably a good example of adaptive mechanisms turned destructive due to alteration in the character of weapons today.

16. The reader is referred again to Chap. III, pp. 72 and 73, and particularly Notes 14 and 15 in that chapter.

17. There are both semantic and theoretical problems interlaced in this question. One could well say that all that comes through to consciousness is the threat of a disagreeable feeling, something that is pale by comparison to the discomfort the underlying "thing" would yield were it to become manifest. This still leaves, however, some awareness of the disagreeable as part of the process and this is all that proposition A4 says.

The possibility remains that the whole could transpire at an unconscious level so that at no time on the life-arc of a given person does any disagreeable feeling associated with a particular type of upset to the essential psychical condition appear in his awareness. Some psychiatrists would maintain this view and, indeed, insist that this is the really important part of the matter.

For the purposes of this frame of reference I do not find such a view necessary. It would be foolish, of course, in the present state of our knowledge to deny that it could be so. Some of the satisfied sociopaths one sees offer temptation for believing it. In general, however, the patients one observes clinically are not happy about their condition. They are as a rule deeply involved in a struggle with disagreeable feelings, however self-defeating this may be, and however limited their awareness of all the factors. Furthermore, in approaching the problem of case-finding in connection with an epidemiological study it is appropriate to anticipate that the same characteristics will be found in the bulk of cases it will be possible to identify.

Propositions Relating Disorder and Environment

18. *See* MAURICE BURTON, *Margins of the Sea* (New York: Harper, 1954), p. 162.

19. This view of progressive disorder formation with one step leading to the next is derived primarily from training under Adolf Meyer who was in turn influenced by William James's ideas regarding habit formation and personality. *See:* ADOLF MEYER, "Remarks on Habit Disorganizations in the Essential Deteriorations, and the Relation of Deterioration to the Psychasthenic, Neurasthenic, Hysterical and Other Constitutions," pp. 421-431, "Fundamental Conceptions of Dementia Praecox," pp. 432-437, "The Dynamic Interpretation of Dementia Praecox," pp. 443-457, "The Problems of Mental Reaction Types, Mental Causes and Diseases," pp. 591-603, in *The Collected Papers of Adolf Meyer* (EUNICE E. WINTERS, Ed.), Baltimore: Johns Hopkins Press, 1951), Vol. 2, "Psychiatry"; WILLIAM JAMES, *The Principles of Psychology* (New York: Holt, 1890).

For a recent presentation of a similar view, *see* NORMAN CAMERON, *The Psychology of Behavior Disorders* (New York: Houghton Mifflin, 1947).

20. For a review of theoretical orientations in psychosomatic medicine, *see* MEYER MENDELSON, SOLOMON HIRSCH, and CARL S. WEBBER, "A Critical Examination of Some Recent Theoretical Models in Psychosomatic Medicine," *Psychosomatic Medicine,* Vol. 18, no. 5., 1956, pp. 363-373. *See also:* ERIC D. WITTKOWER and R. A. CLEGHORN (Eds.), *Recent Developments in Psychosomatic Medicine;* HANS SELYE, *The Stress of Life* (New York: McGraw-Hill, 1956); HAROLD G. WOLFF, *Stress and Disease* (Springfield, Ill.: Thomas, 1953); FELIX DEUTCH, (Ed.), *The Psychosomatic Concept of Psychoanalysis* (New York: Internat. Univ. Press, 1953).

Although these books and the article were published after the development of this frame of reference, they provide a convenient summary of some general ideas which did enter into its formation.

21. See page 121.

22. This is an observation of interest but it is not an argument in favor of cultivating fractures. The same conservative view should apply to cultivated disturbance of the essential psychical condition, although one hears occasionally people advocating psychological traumata (for other people) on the grounds that it will toughen their fiber. I do not think we know enough about the processes involved to undertake inflicting emotional difficulties on any man for his own good.

23. For a previous discussion of the idea of "mental healths" *see* ALEXANDER H. LEIGHTON, JOHN A. CLAUSEN, and ROBERT N. WILSON, (Eds.), *Explorations in Social Psychiatry* (New York: Basic Books, 1957), p. 403.

24. This statement of several points of view regarding the development of symptoms is oversimplified, but one thought sufficient for the purpose of the frame of reference at the time of its construction. Some items of relevance dealing mainly with psychosomatic symptoms are given in Chapter Note 20. In addition, *see:* JOHN DOLLARD and NEAL E. MILLER, *Personality and Psychotherapy: An Analysis in Terms of Learning, Thinking and Culture* (New York: McGraw-Hill, 1950); W. HORSLEY GANTT, *Experimental Basis for Neurotic Behavior* (New York: Hoeber, 1944).

Chapter VI

The Sociocultural Environment

T HE PROBLEM for consideration now is—what type of sociocultural environment makes a difference so far as psychiatric disorder is concerned? Some criteria based on psychiatric experience and thinking for identifying noxious conditions have been outlined, but this is not enough. We require some way of conceptualizing and classifying environments as such; we need a typology before we can say, this type is noxious as compared to that. Thus, we have arrived at the position of one who has considered the characteristics that go to make up a dangerous animal (claws, teeth, poison), derived from marks found on victims, but until we have some conception of species we cannot say which kind of animals are dangerous and which are harmless, much less helpful. Raising the question of what kinds of environment make a difference brings us now to the problem of categories of environment.

This chapter will begin with a discussion of a few cautions bearing on concepts of personality in sociocultural environment. Having noted these, some ways of thinking about and analyzing sociocultural phenomena will be outlined with emphasis on community units and their components, including communication, coordination, and shared sentiments. At the end a number of propositions will be given (Series G) having to do with the nature of society and culture. The discussion of various sociocultural patterns as a basis for typing environments in order to explore for influence on psychiatric disorder will be postponed until Chapter VIII.

I PERSONALITY IN SOCIOCULTURAL ENVIRONMENT—SOME CAUTIONS

A first point for attention is that the concept of personality in a sociocultural environment is different from the everyday sense in which one speaks of an entity in an environment. Commonly, when we say "environment" we have in mind something like the relationship of the Antarctic to penguins. The referent here is not any given penguin, but all such creatures in contrast to all the nonpenguin characteristics of the region in which they live—the ice, the ocean, the cold, the food supply, and the predators. The environment is grasped by the mind as a set of factors apart from penguins. One can also, without danger of confusion, think of penguins as affected by these factors and suppose that, over millions of years, the factors have played a major role in the evolution of the species. The environment, in short, can do things to penguins and this can in common-sense terms be considered a fairly straightforward type of cause and effect relationship.

Turning from penguins in general to a given penguin, it is also possible to think of the effect of environment in similar terms. It cannot, of course, change him or her into a different species, but it can freeze or feed him, give a long or a short life, cause him to be sickly or well. One may also extend the idea of environment to include other penguins without radically changing the concept. The other penguins with whom he interacts are thus his social environment and as such they can have causal relationships to his life-story and his condition at any particular moment.

If, however, instead of a particular penguin one thinks of a typical penguin and so makes generalizations, and then talks about the influence of social environment, he is, in effect, talking about the influence of penguins in general upon penguins in general. This is not necessarily nonsense, but it is a problem of highly complex interdependencies in which the entities being examined have to be specified with particular care. The problem is of a different order from the question of the impact of the Antarctic environment on penguins.

Personality in sociocultural environment entails meanings and relationships of this latter type. "Environment" here is not physical, but a way of specifying the interactions of many personalities as seen from one point of view; its study in relation to personality is consequently fraught with semantic and conceptual entanglements. A major danger is that, due to the use of the word "environment," an implicit model will be employed of the species-in-nature type, like the penguin in the Antarctic. The environment is thus reified as separate from personality, and cause and effect relationships are easily postulated which are actually the same phenomenon stated in two different sets of terms. Speaking of a paranoid type of personality being produced by a paranoid culture can be an example of this sort of thing.

As long as the psychiatrist, psychologist, or other student of individual behavior and the student of society and culture are each working in his own field, the problem is not necessarily relevant. The investigator of personality can generalize about development and function and other processes implied in the life-arc without being troubled by the fact that some of what he deals with constitutes particular instances of group phenomena. The study and treatment of psychiatric cases is an example of this. The social scientist can similarly study the characteristics and functioning of human groups and uncover societal processes without concern for the fact that these are also personality processes.

When the two join, however, in an effort to study the influence of society and culture on personality, then these areas of overlap require careful discrimination. There is need for examination of concepts and terms in order to sift similarities and differences that exist in words from those that exist in phenomena. Otherwise one may be led to make statements which are very like saying, "Drops of sea water are salty because of the salt in the ocean."

One way of resolving the matter is to concentrate on the effect of sociocultural environment in personality formation. This places the newborn child in the foreground, together with the subsequent story of his personality development under the influences of the matrix in which he has appeared. The essential idea is to examine how the child in general is affected by the already existing adults in general, and an antecedent-consequent framework is thus possible. The framework has its difficulties, however, because the adults do not encompass the whole of the sociocultural environment. Siblings are apt to be important from a very early age and, with each succeeding year, the age peers in the society loom larger and larger as a major part of the environment. Here, obviously, the antecedent-consequent paradigm cannot be applied in any starkly simple form, but, rather, one is again confronted with complex mutual interdependencies. The paradigm has its uses for a given child, which is the usual clinical orientation, but it becomes hard to manage when one turns to children in general.[1]

The important point for our purposes is that an effort to keep the sociocultural environment as an independent variable clearly separate from personality as a dependent variable results in an emphasis on particular aspects of the sociocultural environment and a particular part of the life-arc of personality—the early years. These are undoubtedly of great significance in mental health and psychiatric disorder, but if one considers what has been said in this frame of reference about the various ways in which environment can exert an influence, about the susceptibility of personality to noxious and benign factors all along the life-arc, and about the dynamic equilibrium in the cross-section of the moment, it is evident that more is involved, and this "more" must not be lost from sight if we are to understand the nature of our problem. The fact that conditions of experimental design may limit one in a research operation to certain selected aspects of personality and environment makes it imperative for a frame of reference to provide orientation as to where and how such results may fit

The Sociocultural Environment

into the larger picture. One has to be vividly aware that, just because child socialization by adults is both an important and a comparatively researchable problem, it is by no means the whole story so far as the relationship between sociocultural environment and disorder, or the malfunctioning of personality, is concerned.

Another major consideration has to do with the fact that the margins of the unit for study in the case of personality are more or less definite, whereas in the case of the sociocultural environment they are by comparison indefinite. Personality as the word is used in this book refers to the functioning of a person, and hence the individual human being constitutes the unequivocal unit for investigation.[2] If one asks where the sociocultural environment is, the answer is not invariable as with personality but depends on purpose and viewpoint. One can say, of course, that it is lodged in a grouping of people called "a society," but this term represents a range from village to world.

The arbitrary character of margin and the possibility of having societies nesting within societies creates problems not found in the general conceptualization of personality. The fact that the unit of investigation (a society) can be specified according to numbers of alternative criteria raises the possibility that different apparent relationships to personality may be found according to the definition employed.

Closely related to the preceding is a difference in the relationship of the investigator to his subject matter and a difference in the way knowledge is gained in approaching the study of personality as compared with the study of society and culture. In the case of personality, particularly in the clinical studies of malfunctioning personality, it is possible to perceive the unit of investigation—the individual human being—acting as a whole, at least within limited periods and in particular settings, as for instance during the psychiatric interview, during a projective test, or while under observation in a hospital ward by nurses trained for the task. However obscure the underlying processes may be, such actions and appearances as the personality system manifests as a unit can be directly apprehended.

This fact has exerted a profound influence on the whole framework of psychiatric thinking with regard to the nature of personality and psychiatric disorder. The student of society and culture, no matter what definition is selected, rarely, if ever, perceives his unit of investigation acting as a whole, at least in terms comparable to those that can be applied to the clinician.[3]

Thus, while the student of personality can perceive some behavior of the whole, analyze this into components, and then build a construct which represents more of the whole than can be directly seen, the student of society has to begin his inferences with phenomena that are even further removed from the totality he wishes to grasp. He has to infer the behavior of the whole society and then with these inferences build still others regarding underlying societal processes. His position is much the same as an anatomist's would be if he were microscopic in size and faced with the necessity of inferring from the character of many individual cells the gross structure of the whole animal. Indeed, it is more difficult, for he has to infer not only the gross structure but the functioning as well.

There are two consequences of this situation that deserve mention. One is that the student of society tends to use indices to tell him about the behavior of his unit of investigation, whereas the psychiatrist *at a comparable level of study* is using direct observation of the phenomenon in question. The psychiatrist does not for example employ quantifiable indices when concerned with anxiety in a particular patient. Such indices have to be used, however, if one wishes to make generalizations about anxiety in a society. This raises certain problems of comparing and relating facts obtained in such a different manner. More important, however, it may involve different styles of thinking about phenomena and different modes of explanation that are not easily brought into relationship one with the other.[4]

The second consequence is that the student of society, not being able to perceive the target of his investigation directly, uses as the basis for his indices the same kind of phenomena employed by the student of personality, namely, the behavior of individual human beings. Different use is made of the phenomena, of course: the student of personality utilizes it to describe and explain person functioning, while the student of society utilizes it to describe and explain societal functioning. The fact, however, that indices bearing on the characteristics of the sociocultural environment are based on individual behavior again suggests caution in treating correlations as causal relationships. For not only is the sociocultural environment composed of interacting personalities as noted at the beginning of this section, but also concep-

The Sociocultural Environment

tions as to the nature of the sociocultural environment considered as a whole are largely derived from the same kind of raw material as are the concepts of personality—the behavior of individuals.

There is not of course total overlap of phenomenal focus, because each field of study tends to concentrate on different types of individual behavior. Nevertheless, this question of discriminating between personality-in-environment relationships that are in nature and those that are inherent in the instruments, names, and concepts used is of prevailing importance. Moreover, not only is it a significant question but it is also an obscure and difficult one. We do not know all the sociocultural factors that may be active in the total process whereby personality is defined or whereby a psychiatric diagnosis is made. Similarly, we do not know all the aspects of mental health and illness that may be implicit in the operations whereby the characteristics of society and culture are defined. Hence it would seem that a major target in this field is to bring about some clarification.

In many types of research it is considered something of a failure in design if one discovers that a postulated causal relationship between two supposed phenomena turns out to be merely the same phenomenon seen from two different viewpoints. One is expected to eliminate this possibility in the way the research is laid out. It would, however, be a mistake to hold rigidly to this view in our field, since it is one of the major problems in need of clarification and cannot be done by taking thought alone but requires research operations. The best approach would seem to be to seek, as a first stage and using the concepts we have, areas of high correlation between psychiatric disorder and sociocultural environment and then, secondly, to seek their meaning. In looking for meaning, part of the research target should be to discern and make explicit relationships that are hidden in the definitions and procedures. This is a necessary step toward a closer understanding of the relationships that are in nature.[5]

II A SOCIOCULTURAL UNIT

The term, "sociocultural environment" employed thus far in these pages betrays our concern with personality. We must recognize, however, that the phenomena designated have, for the most part, been studied by anthropologists and sociologists not as environment for something else, but as phenomena of interest in their own right—the behaviors of human groups. This viewpoint will be adopted in the rest of this chapter and consideration given to some main concepts employed by social scientists. The essential question, nevertheless, for our purposes is this: Do these concepts provide a framework for specifying sociocultural categories which can be organized on some kind of a scale that ranges between those that are noxious and those that are benign?

As a point of departure one type of sociocultural unit will be discussed in this section, while in the two sections which follow a number of its components will be treated. The aim is to delineate and discuss selected concepts and their relationships to each other. As noted earlier, the question of suitability as categories that have bearing on psychiatric disorder will be taken up in Chapter VIII.

If one flies over the Northeast and looks down, he can see human patterning very plainly. Here are towns, villages, and hamlets interconnected with rail and road, a physical manifestation of the network mentioned in the second part of Chapter I. Here, over and over again from one node in the network to another can be seen the reduplication of homes, stores, factories, schools, and church spires. These physical arrangements reflect the patterning of group living on the part of the people who inhabit the land below. This is patterning in the same sense as discussed at the beginning of Chapter I. It flows through time with innumerable simultaneous expressions that form interweaving and reciprocal themes. In Whitehead's terms, it is a succession of "durations." [6]

As noted earlier, its spatial margins are hard to define. Except for an edge at the Atlantic seaboard, it goes on and on like wallpaper design, north, south, and west until one flies out of the Northeast altogether. And precisely where the Northeast ends is equivocal.

The edges of the patterning in time are also unclear. Historical studies tell of the origin of European man in the Northeast and the changes that have occurred with the years since then, but the future is unforeseeable. There is no predictable arc that corresponds to the life-arc of the individual.

So there is patterning, and it is patterning that presents a baffling extensiveness. Yet there are apparent certain nodal points within the extension, the reduplicated communities with local countryside bound loosely to them. The extensive pattern has main features which are

The Sociocultural Environment

repeated. Despite the problems of overlap and lack of clear-cut margins, these nodes seem to suggest themselves as an approximation of units within the extension. Let us take one, therefore, as an instance of a sociocultural unit, a point of reference in discussing further the nature of the patterning. The Harbor Town and its environs that have been mentioned in connection with Tom Young, the Chaunceys, Dr. Coindreau, and the rest can serve this purpose.

A first item to note is that the town, as a community, and despite the difficulty of its space-time margins, is a self-integrating unit. It is a patterned and patterning system with functions and components. Moreover, although the whole is under the influence of its components, it has qualities and characteristics of wholeness which are the synthesis rather than the mere addition of the parts.[7] The town government provides one means of illustrating this. Although most persons contribute to it directly and indirectly (e.g., through taxes), government is not just the total of these actions, but a pattern composed of the total of their interdependencies. It is more like a baseball team than like four or five men trying to push a car out of the mud. In the latter case, the group effort is more or less the sum of individual effort, whereas with the team the results depend on patterns of reciprocity and integration, on a wholeness.

Government is a rather formal example of the kind of thing that makes it appropriate to speak of the town as a self-integrating unit. There are other formal instances, as in the school system and the community hospital, but there are also informal examples, as in the economy and the division of labor seen in the system of social classes. These are said to be informal because the pattern involves much behavior for which there are no written rules or laws, and it has many aspects that are not explicitly stated by the community members. It may be noted, however, that most of the action patterns of the unit have both formal and informal aspects, and this applies even to the more formal examples named above—government, school system, and hospital.

Although the town is a self-integrating unit, this does not mean that such integration is altogether based on willing cooperation between persons or between groups. Some forms of integrative action are founded on rivalry, struggle, and competition, as in politics, class relations, and many economic enterprises. Their net effect, however, is to contribute to the unit, somewhat as in sport, where it takes rival teams to create the whole pattern of a game.

The community is not only a unit; it is a living unit. By this I mean to emphasize that it is a system consisting in energy exchange, of dynamic equilibrium. However complex it may be, however subtle and refined the innumerable combinations and permutations of its patterning, every aspect of its existence involves energy in the biological sense and is part of a process whereby energy is taken into the system and given out again.

Subsistence activities are an aspect of this. Chief among these in the Harbor Town is the catching and processing of fish and the cutting and processing of timber. Other activities also relevant include farming and handling of farm produce, especially milk and butter, catering to summer tourists, and operating stores and services. Through such complex, interdependent patterns, energy sources are extracted from the sea and the land, partly used or stored within the unit and partly exported in exchange for energy sources and potentials for energy sources derived from other areas.

The consumption of energy by the community is not limited to feeding its constituent members but extends in many elaborations. Touching on only a few illustrative examples, it can be noted that energy is employed in work connected with securing the energy sources themselves, as in the use of boats, tractors, and trucks in order to carry on fishing, farming, and lumbering. Energy is also employed in activities having to do with protection against physical environment, disease and other forces which might damage or interrupt the life of the community. The use, however, goes far beyond these rather stark needs into all that might be grouped under culture or style of life in the community. Wherever there is work, wherever there is action, biological energy is in transit through the system.

Embedded in this patterning are activities having to do with promoting a satisfactory psychological state of existence among the persons who go to make up the community. Although a community unit can survive, at least for a time, under conditions which are thoroughly miserable for the members, as in a state of siege or severe economic depression, ordinarily it provides resources whereby the needs and desires of most of the individuals can be met to some degree. Prominent among such needs are those connected with the essential striving sentiments which have been listed in Chapter V (page 148), and which cover a range from physical security to less palpable characteristics such as spontaneous and creative expression. Part of the functioning of a community unit, in short, is concerned with making available a field for the expression of cognition, affect, and the basic urges.

The above may be restated by saying that an aspect of the acting of a unit such as the Harbor Town has to do with providing opportunity for the psychological functioning of the individual persons of which it is composed. More than this, the community system plays a part in shaping instincts through experience into basic urges and, ultimately, sentiments. Hence the community unit functions both to meet personality needs and to shape and even create them. This occurs as part of the process of replacement in the continuous loss and gain of individual death and birth.

As a system in a state of dynamic equilibrium, with many interdependent, complex parts, a community unit has a tendency to maintain the status quo and hence to resist forces making for change in its patterning, especially exogenous forces pressing for rapid and extensive alteration. The history of the Harbor Town contains many such resistances, including delays in the introduction of most improvements in the technology of fishing and lumbering, and in acceptance of more subtle shifts in values and philosophy of life. On the other hand, resistance is not absolute, but shows that plasticity of living things which leads to adaptation and modified pattern when the *status quo ante* is not restored.

Due to such capacity for change in the patterning of the self-integrating unit, the concept of dynamic equilibrium must, as in the case of personality, be treated in terms of an orientation rather than a set of laws. As a result of exogenous changes, new patterns constantly appear.

There is also endogenous change. This can be illustrated in connection with population increase. If the Harbor Town were to double its size, it would not only change quantitatively, but would obviously experience innumerable qualitative alterations as well throughout its patterning.[8] For instance, many transactions now accomplished informally on a face-to-face basis would have to be organized more systematically to assure their accomplishment. There would be an increase in rules and regulations and these would be more rigid than now—less susceptible to modification according to circumstances. Within the town government, subunits might be set up for administrative purposes.

Another point for consideration is the fact that the community has something which corresponds to a life-story. As noted before, this does not mean that it closely resembles the curve of the life-arc shown by personalities—and by a group of organisms such as a clone. Although it has, of course, an origin, the broad features of its course and outcome are much less predetermined than is the case with personalities. On the other hand, there is the orchestral flow through time, and its characteristics at any given moment are under the influence of the past events which have led up to that moment as well as to immediate circumstances. There is, in short, *life-story* and *cross-section*.

The reader will have detected by now that I have some kind of parallel in mind between a personality system and a community system. What I wish to suggest is that there are certain characteristics common to personality and to nodes in a social fabric such as the Harbor Town which are neither accident nor analogy, but fundamental to living systems. They are not chance similarities, such as may be seen sometimes between the outline of a cliff and a human face. On the contrary, units analyzable into levels of integration, dynamic equilibrium, adaptation to change, and endogenous change are thought to be characteristic of life in all its many forms around the globe.

As organisms such as human beings are self-integrating units composed of cells which are also self-integrating, so also to some degree the community is an organism composed of human beings. The fact that the individuals in a community are physically detached does not negate this, but rather reflects the type of integration. Physical connection merely facilitates the interchange of energy, the division of functions, and the flow of coordinating signals. Human beings have such capabilities of communication that they can achieve a high order of group integration without the physical attachment common in many forms of life. Nevertheless, there are other examples of this kind in nature, as for instance the colonies of bees and ants. Their systems are, of course, much more rigid and based on different principles, but they do constitute an organismic type of unity without physical attachment of the parts. The colony is the whole body and the insects are like independently moving constituent cells.

It is also of interest to note that one can find in nature many degrees of cohesion between independent entities and self-integrating units made up of these kinds of entities. There are independent cells such as amoebae and there are animals composed of cells such as human beings. Between these extremes are cell colonies of varying degrees of integration, with the Portuguese man-of-war representing something on the border between cell independence and cell union to form an individual. The slime mould, a more primitive form of life, moves back and forth across this border. At times it has a worm-like shape and crawls, with differentiation between a head-end and a tail, whereas at others all the constituent cells separate and spread detached over a surface, like a grazing flock of sheep.[9]

The organismic characteristics of communities such as the Harbor Town may be summed up by referring to them as quasi-organisms. "Quasi" is employed in recognition of the difficult problem of margins and of the fact that the degree of integration is not so complete as in many organic systems. The emphasis, however, is on "organism" rather than "quasi," and it is an emphasis which is very likely peculiar to this book. Although many social scientists take the community as a conceptual unit and stress the interdependence of its components, it is probable that relatively few today are willing to go as far as I do in the direction of considering it an organism. I should like to say, however, that there are limits to the comparison. It is not suggested that one can make inferences directly from organism to society, and Spencerian ideas of social evolution are not implied. It is rather a matter of looking at living processes in a certain way and within a framework that keeps in mind that they are living. Its usefulness lies not in enabling one to draw conclusions from organisms that apply to societies, but rather in enabling one to draw ideas and perspectives from organisms that aid in exploring the nature of community systems.[10]

The point is a major one in this frame of reference and it has influence on the selection and development of research design. Looking on the community as a quasi-organism keeps in the foreground the fact that energy is drawn from nature, distributed through the system and returned again to nature. This metabolic type of pattern is the core of the integrating action, the central theme upon which all functions depend. The view also writes large the word "integrate" and stresses the interdependence of constituent elements in the course of this process. Thus, an event in one part of the system is apt to have widely ramifying effects in other parts. Of equal importance is the expectation that the functioning of any given part or localized event is under the influence of the functional characteristics of the whole unit. This influence of the whole is of manifold character, some of it obvious, some of it subtle, and some of it in all probability as yet unknown to students of society. Hence, in examining the functioning of parts, discrete acts, or events, the problems of context are uppermost. One can, for instance, compare corresponding parts of two different communities with each other, but he cannot safely make inferences as to their meaning unless he understands that the communities as functional wholes are similar, or differ in some known manner.

To illustrate this more concretely, let us suppose that our attention is drawn to the local government part of the Harbor Town and we compare this with the government in another town across the bay. Suppose further that it is found that the other government functions much less well in collecting taxes, and hence in providing services and utilities. The organismic view would hold it as very unlikely that you would discover the main reasons for the difference so long as you confined your investigation to the town councils, by-laws, and other aspects of the governments. You would have at least to study the functioning of other main parts of the town with which its government articulates, and you would have to investigate the functioning of each town considered as a whole. The latter can well sound too ideal and too general to be feasible, just as may be the case in trying to work with "personality as a whole." The organismic view, however, would lead one to feel that the problem cannot be ignored because it is difficult, and that one must find standards in terms of which to estimate total functioning as it may affect the functioning of parts. Criteria would have to be sought in terms of relevance to the problem at hand.

These remarks on communities as quasi-organisms are introductory. A return will be made to the topic again in connection with selecting sociocultural units for investigation and in the development of research design (Chapter VIII, pages 279-289).

III SOME COMPONENTS OF SOCIOCULTURAL UNITS

The present section is concerned with amplification regarding components of the Harbor Town considered as a sociocultural unit. The smallest parts are, of course, the individual personalities of which it is composed. These are the basic units and have already been compared to the functioning of cells in relation to a body. We shall not, however, discuss these further but rather turn to configurations composed of the interactions of numbers of personalities, configurations which are functional with relation to the community unit and which tend to outlast the presence of any given personality. Referring again to an organism, these parts are more like organs than like individual cells.

One of the most obvious components or functional configurations in the Harbor Town is the family. At any given moment the biological unit consisting in mother, father, and children is found reduplicated throughout the community; although with the passage of time there is disappearance of particular families through the departure of members, new families are constantly being formed. Thus the families, as components of the community, are always present.

There is more, however, than the biological unit to be considered. There are interactions between nieces, nephews, uncles, aunts, cousins, grandparents, and grandchildren which make up a web of relationships that can be designated as "extended family." Most of the population of the Harbor Town and its countryside participates in such interlocking and overlapping extended families.

As a component of the quasi-organism, it can be seen at once that the family has a number of important functions. The most obvious of these are the creation of new members, their training and introduction to the social system, functions that are necessary for the survival of the self-integrating community unit in view of death and migration of individuals. It is also to be noted that the family as a sociocultural pattern has a functional relationship to the personalities of its constituent members. Physical security, love, sexual expression, the achievement of recognition, opportunity for expressing spontaneity, orientation with regard to one's place in society, the sense of belonging to a human group, and the sense of being right in what one does, are all encompassed in family patterning. Families may therefore be considered as having two dimensions: one contributing as a part to the total quasi-organism, the other providing opportunity for some of the functioning of individual persons. This dual characteristic will be found in varying degrees in other components of the community to be discussed.

Aside from kinship, there are clusterings based on neighborhood which often constitute functional parts of the whole. Dr. Coindreau lived in one of these, called "Hillcrest," at the western side of the town. Having its own stores, a church, and many recreational activities, the members tended to consider themselves as different from the rest of the community. Yet Hillcrest was administratively under the council and was continuous with the economic (subsistence) complex of the town.

There are many other less distinct neighborhoods that nevertheless have recognizable characteristics and could be considered as parts. The area around the mill where Bernie Chiason lived was known as tough and run-down; a new section on a road leading out of town had a "fast set"; while Princess Street where the Chaunceys lived, although rapidly losing its character, was still considered solid and respectable. Each of these geographic associations of people formed groups which made more or less functional contributions to the town as a whole and in addition provided more or less for the functioning of individual persons.

There are also associations built on friendship that do not necessarily have coincident geographic margins. These friendship clusters tend to be far less stable than the neighborhoods, sometimes disappearing when particular individuals disappear, and yet there are some fairly consistent patterns. For instance, there had been, for many years and through more than one complete turnover of members, a number of groups made up of unmarried young people and others composed of younger married couples. There was also a group of older, unmarried, or widowed women, most of them employed as teachers or clerks.

Clusterings, or interactive groups, of a somewhat different although overlapping character also exist with a focus on some particular activity. Lumbermen, fishermen, storekeepers, farmers, doctors—each of these were bound together in their respective occupations. Other focused patterns of association were seen in institutions such as industrial plants, the different religious denominations, in recreation such as baseball teams and card parties, in town government, in the school system, in the hospital, in the fraternal organizations, in the service clubs, in the Board of Trade, and in many more.

Cultural differences also involve patterns of interaction, the members of each group tending to have more frequent contact and a qualitatively different contact with their own kind. The major distinction in the Harbor Town along this line was between English- and French-speaking, but there was also a small Jewish group, and a number of Chinese who ran restaurants and a laundry service. In the environs were a few Indians who, since they still spoke their Algonquin tongue, could be considered as retaining at least a remnant of their culture.[11]

The socioeconomic classes represent another type of subpattern contributing to the total patterning of the town. In this case, as with culture, the idea of clustering or interaction has to be extended beyond people who do in practice interact, to encompass also those who do not actually, but would find it natural to do so should the occasion arise. The Chaunceys and the Chiasons illustrate individuals at contrasting levels in the socioeconomic classes.

Roles offer a still different view of sociocultural patterning in the town. This concept has been mentioned briefly in Chapter III, page 72, and again in Chapter V, pages 156 and 159. The concern now, however, is in terms of roles not as contributions to the malfunctioning of personality but as action and interaction patterns (doctor, nurse, teacher, mother, boss, brother, councilman), each of which is a unit in the total web of reciprocal relationships that make up the sociocultural system of the community. Any given person fulfills many roles and any given role may be occupied successively by many different persons.

Some of the main components of a sociocultural unit like the Harbor Town can now be summarized as: family, including extended families; neighborhoods; associations; friendship groups; occupational associations; institutions such as those concerned with industry, religion, government, recreation, and health; cultural systems; socioeconomic classes; and finally societal roles.[12]

It was noted earlier that such components of a sociocultural unit face two ways so far as function is concerned—one toward the community unit and one toward the constituent personalities. In some of the components, the service of personality needs appear to be predominant, with contribution to over-all community function being indirect through the maintenance of capable personalities; perhaps the friendship and recreational groupings exemplify this. In other instances the contribution to the functioning of the community predominates over contribution to personality functioning. This is most easily seen in government, which includes taxation, the handling of delinquency, and the treatment of the poor more from the viewpoint of community benefit than individual benefit.

These are extremes, however; at more subtle, yet more pervasively influential levels, all the subpatterns noted can and do have effects both favorable and unfavorable to personality and to community. This creates alternatives so far as over-all consequence is concerned: there may be consonance in that patterns which fulfill community function also fulfill personality function; there may be conflict, so that the more there is of one, the less there is of the other; and there can be all sorts of intermediate states and combinations.[13]

As one considers the functioning of these community subpatterns or components, he is led to suspect that psychiatry may have overstressed the conflict between community function and personality function. This could easily happen if the people we see as patients are precisely those who from infancy onward have suffered in this respect, while the others have little need of our services. If one looks at personalities in their community setting rather than exclusively through the window provided by viewing people with psychiatric disorder in a clinic or private practice, it seems that the subpatterns of the sociocultural unit are to a very large extent suitable for meeting the basic urges, for shaping and facilitating the essential striving sentiments and hence the maintenance of the essential psychical condition. This shifts emphasis from instinct or basic-urge frustration by a tyrannical environment to questions about the relationship between urges and sentiments shaped, and the urges and sentiments satisfied by the components of the sociocultural unit. Perhaps this kind of question is an opening into the nature of mental health and the development of a positive rather than a residual concept.

IV COMMUNICATION AND COORDINATION

In speaking of the sociocultural self-integrating unit and its parts, it is evident that the functioning of both the whole and its subsystems requires communication and coordination, the first being a necessary condition for the second.

The elementary characteristics of communication are so well known as to require little more than mention. The most basic fact is that through the use of particular kinds of patterns called symbols, human beings can transmit meanings to each other and store the symbols and meanings in memory.[14] The physiological foundation for this is the nervous system, where the symbols may be assumed to have a phenomenal existence in the patterning of electrochemical impulses.

Spoken words as symbols by which one individual reaches one or more others are the prototype of communication. In this, a patterning of nervous system impulses is transferred between individuals through the medium of correspondingly patterned sound waves. There are, however, other forms of communication, such as facial expression, posture, and gesture, involving transmission through patterns of light waves and through direct touch. The written word and pictures add greatly to the capacity for both the transmission of meaning and its storage for future reference. Printing, telephones, photography, radio, and all such other technological developments are steps toward greater range and efficiency. Roads and paths and means of transportation such as automobiles must also be considered in this light, since they facilitate the movement of both objects and people carrying meaning.

The Harbor Town, therefore, may be seen as containing a number of different kinds of networks along which communication flows. It is also evident that these networks are essential to the functioning of components and whole. Without them the self-integration would be impossible.

On the other hand, the networks alone are not enough. The symbols that are transmitted are not necessarily coordinative. It would be altogether possible for these channels of communication to be traveled by symbols that are meaningless or that resulted in confusion, incoordination, and disintegration of functions. If the patterns of the quasi-organism are flowing through time like orchestral music, there has to be something which maintains functional integration and avoids chaos, something which persists while individuals come and go, something which those already present hand on to newcomers.

It would be possible to suggest that the "something" is culture. Culture, however, is on the whole a broader concept, including material objects, practices, and the networks of communications themselves. It includes the coordinated as well as the coordinating. For the purposes of our frame of reference, there is need to emphasize a selected aspect of culture, namely *shared sentiments*.

The nature of the concept of sentiments has been sketched and utilized in previous pages in connection with personality and in relation to the influences at work contributing to mental health and disorder. The focus then was on sentiments that are concerned with the integration of the cognitive, affective, basic-urge, and other aspects of personality—whether or not they were shared between persons being a secondary matter. The interest now, however, is precisely with those sentiments that are shared or reciprocal so as to constitute an interpersonal system, and with their relationship to the functioning of a sociocultural unit such as the Harbor Town.

It will be recalled that sentiments are considered to be ideas charged with affect, with roots in basic urges. Analytically, three general characteristics may now be noted: ideas concerned with *what is,* ideas concerned with *what ought to be,* and ideas concerned with *what is desired.* These characteristics are not categories of sentiments, however, since most sentiments are combinations. The shared feelings of how the world is and how things ought to proceed for self and others make possible the ongoing patterns of family, neighborhood, class, government, and all the other components of the community unit, as well as their coordination into the whole.

In order to bring out some of these relationships, let us visualize the Harbor Town at a particular cross-section of the moment, one that is just long enough to render the sequential patterns discernible—rather like a short run of movie film that is able to show any and all aspects of the community simultaneously.

Let the moment in question be about 9 o'clock on the same evening of September 20, 1950, on which Tom Young had his anxiety crisis. It will be recalled that at this time, an equinoctial gale is blowing over the town and harbor and over the countryside linked socially and economically to it. Rain drenches the wharves and the roar of the wind combines with the splash and sucking of the waves around the pilings. The sheds and offices are closed for the night and stand against the gale, cubes of dark and quiet. In the desks and files, however, lie ledgers, orders, and lists filled with symbols which will guide and inform the clerks, foremen, and stevedores when they return in the morning to begin another day's work. These shared symbols are major determinants of the life tomorrow on the wharves, and their importance can be realized by supposing the difference it would make were they all destroyed during the storm.

The Sociocultural Environment

Of importance equal to the symbols and meanings stored on paper are the symbols and sentiments stored in all the people who participate in the business of the wharves. These personalities are scattered now throughout the town, doing many different things, although on a night like this the greater part are in their homes, in one or another of these houses lit like lanterns on the hillside in the gathered dusk. The shared sentiments which they contain at this moment will direct them in the morning to the wharves to pick up the work of the day, just as other shared sentiments have led them to leave the wharves closed and deserted for the night and to turn their attention at the present time to activities not connected with work.

Yet the absence of work is not universal. There are night watchmen making their rounds, more than usually alert because of the wind and rain and the possible damage to goods through leaks in roofs and around doors. There is also a steamer tied to one of the wharves, lighted and quick with the hum and mechanical pulsations that betoken the biological beings she contains and expresses. The shared sentiments designate these necessary protective and maintenance activities and the alternation of work between persons, so that those who are busy now will rest in the morning.

Along the business streets of the town the stores, like the wharves, are shut, their current status and their opening tomorrow similarly determined through shared sentiments and organized schedules of symbols. Yet not everything of relevance and importance is predictable about or to the people of the stores. They cannot know, for instance, the exact nature of tomorrow's business. This lies in another body of sentiments, formed and particularizing in people here and there throughout the town and adjacent countryside who will be led by these to be tomorrow's customers. The sentiments of commerce set the stage, set general themes, and set limits, but there remains the unpredictability of specific events, of specific combinations of sentiments, and of thoughts and feelings too transient to be considered sentiments.

This mixture of specification and flexibility in determining human group behavior is characteristic of many other systems of sentiment besides those of commerce. Again we may recall games and note that sentiments are like their rules and associated feelings; this is probably not accident, since games are derived from life and often constitute aspects of life in the microcosm.

Not all the stores are closed. As in the case of the watchmen and the watch on shipboard, some aspects of the town are marked by shared sentiments for continued functioning at this time. One of the two drug stores is open in view of possible medical needs. The same applies to one of the six gas stations, since transportation goes on at night. The garages are closed, but one has a mechanic on call. All three of the restaurants are doing business, even on such a bleak night, their neon lights gleaming on the wet windows and the wet streets. According to shared sentiments, people should be able to eat and take refreshment at night, particularly travelers away from home; and so it is appropriate for restaurants to stay open when other businesses are closed—even on Sundays.

The industrial life of the town, like its commerce, is also at a low level of activity. The fish processing plants, the sawmills, the dairy, the forges are at a maintenance level, operating according to sentiments which existed before our moment of observation and which govern it and will govern the surging up of action in the new day.

The case is similar with the town government. Its books lie shut on the symbols which record its knowledge and dispositions. It exists mainly now in the sentiments of the town people, including the mayor, councillors, and clerk and fanning out to every voter. Yet even here, all is not quiescent. The night policeman, having a cup of coffee in one of the restaurants while his slicker drips on a hook near the door, is about to resume his rounds. A skeleton road crew is going over the streets checking the culverts and trying to prevent flood.

The educational system is also inactive, except for one class in painting in the division of adult education. Yet if one knew all the sentiments bearing on education in the teachers, mothers, fathers, taxpayers and children that make up the community, he could foretell the movement of the yellow busses, the trooping in, the classes, cafeteria, athletics, and all the rest that constitutes school.

The health system, like the telephone exchange, is in full operation. All the doctors are either in their offices, out seeing patients, or in the hospital. And the hospital itself, as a focal point in contrast to factories and commerce, is full of light and the movement of an emergency operation. There has been a car accident in the storm. Illness and injury must be treated as they occur.

Thus does the sentiment system move, drawing events after it, in a sense keeping everything going, including the town clock.

The Sociocultural Environment

This illustrative glimpse could be extended much further, but enough has been said to point up the fact that in the cross-section of this moment the people of the community, for the most part, act in unison and reciprocally according to pre-existing sentiments they contain within them, which are activated and deactivated by symbols traveling the communication network. The systems of sentiment formulate for each person what he ought to be doing, what he wants to be doing, and what he can be doing; and how to perceive, interpret and react to events and to the behavior of others. They enable him to take meaning out of the symbols that reach him through the network of communication. His perception, reason, and behavior are thus guided; there is no full expansion into all possible types of those acts, but rather selected blind spots, selected deafness, and selected emphases and preferences in which the patterned functioning of the parts and the whole of the community has its existence.

If we look at a family instead of the whole town—any family—it can be seen that each member has some sort of schedule of ideas and feelings with regard to how he ought, can, and wants to comport himself with relation to the other members, whether he is taking the initiative, or they. There are feeling-toned specifications for brothers, sisters, mother, father, children, husband, wife, and for each of these in relation to the family unit considered as a whole.

The same characteristics obtain with regard to the rest of the components of the quasi-organism—the associations, the institutions, the socioeconomic levels, and the cultural groups. Sentiments having to do with group identity, characteristics, and worth are of major importance in some of these and have much to do with intragroup cohesiveness—or the lack of it. This is prominent particularly in class levels, religious associations, and cultural groups. Numbers of these have distinctive systems of sentiment which, together with the relevant symbols, are the hallmark of the group and set them apart in some respects from the rest of the community. The Salvation Army furnishes one example of this, with the uniform as a particularly obvious symbol.

While the cross-section of the moment makes it possible to visualize schematically the relationship of pre-existing systems of sentiment to the coordinate and integrative character of the unfolding time edge of community behavior, questions remain as to the origin and maintenance of the sentiments and as to their modifiability.

Any sentiment to which we turn our attention has antecedents, but the ultimate origin of sentiments as a class of phenomena is, of course, out of sight beyond the backward reach of human history. If, however, we widen the cross-section of the moment to a span of a few years, it is possible to visualize something of what is at work. Each new individual born into the community can be seen as acquiring a portion of the pre-existing sentiments. This is an integral part of the development of personality as outlined earlier, for the acquisition and differentiation of sentiments are tied to the satisfaction of basic urges. Since for the most part the satisfactions can only be achieved directly or indirectly through other human beings, the sentiments developed by each person tend to be those already available and operative in the society. They are acquired in part by deliberate inculcation from elders, but also largely from the experiences of living and growing amid the pre-existing sentiments and finding out how to grasp the meaning and in turn manipulate the innumerable symbols constantly flying along the communications network. Partly taught and partly self-taught, each person learns the rules of the game of living in the community.

People who move into the Harbor Town, rather than having been born there, bring with them their complement of sentiments and symbols already formed. If they come from a similar unit, there is ordinarily little difficulty in adjustment, but if they come with a set of sentiments which are not shared and which do not fit reciprocally with the greater part of those already in the community, then there is apt to be trouble. As a rule such people succeed in modifying their sentiments, particularly through object substitution, so that some fitting is achieved. Occasionally this does not occur to any appreciable extent, in which case they for the most part either move elsewhere or become isolates. A few may succeed in changing the sentiments of the community.

Sentiments, then, are perpetuated in the course of the gradual erosion and replacement of community members. Each new individual acquires a portion of the pre-existing sentiments because they are essential to his functioning as a person, his striving with regard to objects and motives.

Nevertheless, the community's web of shared sentiments is plastic rather than rigid, and, when viewed over a still longer time span, considerable change can be seen. Some of this is inevitable in the course of the population turnover. Transmission cannot be perfect and hence each new individual brings with him some variation in the systems of sentiment he develops as compared to what existed before. Such minor variations can become mutually reinforcing and cumulative rather than purely random and hence one could expect some drift in the systems of sentiment in quasi-organisms through time, even if there were no other factors at work.

There are, however, other factors at work, and the main changes of sentiment are reactions and adaptations. Some of those factors may be endogenous, such as alterations in social integration made necessary by increased population or alterations in economic base as when the forest is overcut or when a new mineral resource is discovered. The greater part of the factors, however, for units like the Harbor Town come from outside; and their number and effects are staggering.

In order to illustrate this process, let us go back not a few, but fifty, years, and sketch briefly a moment in 1900 for comparison with the picture just given of an autumn evening in 1950. Starting as before with the wharves and shipping, two things are at once evident: first, there are far more boats and piers, and second, although there are steamers and steam tugs, the main reliance for locomotion is on sail. With these two facts go a host of sentiments which have since changed or vanished over fifty years, or linger only as memories. In global terms, the life of the town was much more sea-oriented than it is by the middle of the century and numerous sentiments prevailed in relation to this. The captain and the merchant-trader, both of whom often owned ships or shares in ships, occupied positions of high prestige. Their houses stood along Princess Street, many with cupolas from which to view the sea and the coming and going of vessels. These men, together with their families, dominated the social, political, and economic life of the community. Many a family, many a business, and many a church was run with sentiments largely based on those suitable for running a ship.

Not only have these individuals died and their several personalities vanished, but the whole system of sentiments that guided and coordinated their behavior has likewise gone—their knowledge, their desires, and their values. Gordon Chauncey had been of their number, and his keeping the *Westway* was an expression of surviving sentiments in him, yet even he had drastically altered his ideas and practices so that he could scarcely be considered a vestige of this past. He had known it and participated, but he had not struggled as had some others to keep it alive when the decline set in.

If one turns from commerce to fishing, similar contrasts are evident. In 1900 one could at times see thirty vessels anchored in the harbor, making ready for the Grand Banks. Today, the fishing is done in smaller boats and close enough to home so that the fishermen, for the most part, come back each night. With this change have come interdependent changes in sentiments pertaining not only to the work of fishing as such but to the families and the family life of fishermen.

Moving in from the waterfront to the town itself, it is evident that this was a steam and horse-powered society. The railroad offered competition to ships so far as commerce was concerned, but the road system was rough and haulage by horse was a bare trickle in comparison to what moved by ship in 1900 or what moves by truck and automobile on black-top in 1950.

The stores were fewer in number and more general in character, and they stayed open every night, except, of course, Sunday. There were no chain stores and no restaurants, only hotels and boarding houses where the serving of food was limited to regular meal hours. There were no garages, gas stations, or offices for mail-order houses. On the other hand, there were some thirty small and medium-sized factories as compared to six factories of today. These vanished industries included a tannery, an abattoir, a harness-making plant, two carriage shops, three shipbuilders, two foundries, a stove-making plant, a stove polish plant, a glue factory, a sail-making loft, a shingle mill, a shoe factory, three grist and two carding mills, a factory for making window frames and molding, a freight-car-building factory, and a pencil-making plant, besides the sawmills and fish plants which have come down to the present time. These various institutions employed anywhere from five to one hundred persons and all were locally owned. This is in contrast to the factories and most of the stores of today, which are owned in whole or in part by outside corporations.

There were more doctors, some of them very well trained in places like Harvard and Edinburgh, but there was no hospital, and life was prey to sudden onslaught from "dread diseases" such as pneumonia, and killing epidemics of diphtheria and typhoid fever. Occasional cases of smallpox occurred, sending waves of fear through the community. "Consumption" was a constant and insidious killer, sometimes wiping out whole families.

The changes have come about through a series of interlocking technological advances. On the one hand there has been progressive centralization of industry and the development of mass production. The cities have poured cheaper and often better consumer goods into the town, thus destroying through their effective competition the local, independent industries. On the other hand, there has been the invasion of the small town by technological innovations which have directly changed its way of life. Chief among these is the internal combustion engine, in the form of automobile, truck, tractor, and motor boat. As a result of the opportunities and facilities derived from this new source of power, the working conditions of farming, fishing, lumbering, and manufacturing have been extensively altered. Similar remarks hold for other innovations having to do with electric power, modern highways, radio, and television. The effects of all of these together have had repercussions which leave no aspect of life in the quasi-organism untouched. It is not just the working conditions, or the complement of household conveniences such as washing machines and "fridges," that have to be considered, but alteration in the way man, woman, and child spend all of the twenty-four hours of the day.

The important point in all this for our purposes is that these innovations produce alterations in the systems of sentiment. The technological and commercial changes bring with them not merely alterations in knowledge and skill, but widely ramifying alterations in the system of ideas and feelings about what is, what ought to be, and what one desires. Systems of sentiment pertaining to man's relation to nature, to man, and to the supernatural are all affected. Ideas and feelings of independence, for instance, of self-determination, and of class distinctions could flourish more easily in a town that supplied most of its own wants and had both its industry and its ships operating according to the values and practices of captain, officers, and crew.

The effects of technological innovations are only a part of the tendencies toward change which have arisen in the course of fifty years. Other kinds of innovations have also come from the outside to affect the self-integrating community unit. These include social institutions such as a consolidated school that has blotted out the little red schoolhouse; revised educational programs; labor unions on the wharves, mill, and railroad; a modern police system; welfare agencies and medical insurance. There have been alterations too in voluntary association patterns, with the dropping out of such organizations as the Dining Club, the Whist Club, the Quadrille Club, the Brass Band, the Library Society, the Law and Order League, and the Sabbath Day Alliance. New associations are seen in the Kiwanis Club, Little League

Baseball, Parent-Teachers' Association, and the Motion Picture Council.

All such changes are accompanied by—are indeed expressions of—changes in sentiment. New sentiments have been developed, partly consciously, partly unconsciously, to cope with new situations; and old sentiments have been modified or abandoned. Many alterations have been indirect, due to the overlapping and linked character of sentiments; an alteration in one sentiment often calls for alterations in others logically and/or functionally interlocked with it, and these in turn for changes in still others, and so on.

Finally, the incoming of new sentiments in and of themselves is to be noted as of major importance. Over and above the alterations in the sentiments of the Harbor Town which can be considered as part of technological and institutional innovation, there is the repeated arrival of new ideas and the engendering of new feelings that have effects in their own right. Modern thoughts about how children should be treated and of racial equality are examples. Aided by the technological developments in communication, such ideas from the world at large bombard the town much more insistently than they could years ago. Radio, movies, television, and newspapers help, but so too does greater transportation mobility, through roads and automobiles, with the result that members of the Harbor Town have numerous and extensive contacts outside their community.

Over-all, then, it may be said that the fifty-year time span suggests that the systems of sentiment which guide the flow of the quasi-organism's daily activities and its response to new experience are in turn modified by such experiences. There is an adaptive and adjustive groping, characteristic of living things, to achieve a modified set of shared sentiments appropriate to the new situation, to the changes within the system, and to the continuation of its functioning. This behavior of the unit depends, of course, on the individual members picking up new sentiments and modifying the old, and hence rests on personalities—the functioning of persons. By this, I mean that it rests on the object striving and motivations of persons which lead them to adapt and adjust their sentiments in response to the changing conditions in which they find themselves. Germane to this is what has been said in the last chapter about the changing of specific objects as a means of keeping the basic patterns of striving intact in the face of altering circumstances.

The Sociocultural Environment

There is also resistance to change and attempts made to maintain the basic patterns of striving; and hence the occurrence of general change through time of systems of sentiment in a quasi-organism depends on the long-run experience of most members that altering objects works better than holding fast. The alternatives here, as well as the trend through time, are illustrated in the differing sentiments of Mr. Young and Tom with regard to oats. It is the balance of these two tendencies that gives the self-integrating community unit the quality of stability together with responsiveness to continued change. It is viscous rather than either fluid or rigid.

Change and resistance to change have bearing on the functional effectiveness of the self-integrating unit. On the one hand the behavior exhibited may constitute an adequate meeting of altered circumstances or an avoidance of disruptive consequences. On the other, it may amount to floundering and incoordination to the extent that the survival of the self-integrating unit as such is threatened.

V CONCLUDING REMARKS

This chapter may be drawn to an end by making two points. The first is that the features we have been reviewing may offer in some combination a basis for typing sociocultural environments with reference to fostering psychiatric disorder. By features I mean community units and their components: that is, families, neighborhoods, associations, friendship groups, occupational associations, institutions such as industry, religion and government, cultural systems, socioeconomic classes, sociocultural roles, communication, coordination, and system of sentiments.

The second point is that some of the ideas with regard to the nature of sociocultural phenomena can be presented as propositions. These may be designated as Series G.

SERIES G. PROPOSITIONS REGARDING THE NATURE OF SOCIETY
AND CULTURE

G1. Human society is composed of a network of interrelated sociocultural self-integrating units.

G2. Each self-integrating unit is an energy system and is in a constant state of performing functions upon which its existence depends.

G3. The functioning of the unit as a unit (G2) proceeds through patterns of interpersonal relationships based on the communication of shared symbols and coordinating sentiments.

CHAPTER NOTES

1. Russell puts the matter in congenial terms when he says that "propositions of the form 'A causes B', where A and B are classes of events . . . do not occur in any well-developed science." I have the impression that a great many man-hours are invested by social scientists in an effort to bend their problems so as to conform to just this paradigm, and that this is done in the belief that it will make their work more like that of the physical sciences, and hence "more scientific." Such an orientation offers considerable contrast to the approach through successive approximations which characterizes these pages.

Some words of Dobzhansky along these lines are also pertinent: ". . . students of man have again and again succumbed to the temptation to simplify things by ignoring some of the variables. The scientific monstrosities of biological racism and of diaper anthropology are among the consequences." One could add to this the early ideas of libido and the unconscious.

See: BERTRAND RUSSELL, A History of Western Philosophy (New York: Simon and Schuster, 1945), p. 664; THEODOSIUS DOBZHANSKY, "The Biological Concept of Heredity as Applied to Man," The Nature and Transmission of the Genetic and Cultural Characteristics of Human Populations (New York: Milbank Memorial Fund, 1957), p. 18.

2. A somewhat different point of view is represented by Angyal who contends that the individual organism is not a unit in its own right but an aspect of a larger process termed the "biosphere." The biosphere includes both the environment and the organism, and does away with a conceptual partition between. See ANDRAS ANGYAL, Foundations for A

Science of Personality (New York: Commonwealth Fund, 1941).

3. It will be easy for anthropologists and other behavorial scientists to attack this point on the ground that the psychiatrist never sees his subject as a whole either. This is, of course, true if one's standard is complete knowledge. It can, moreover, be said that since the clinician rarely sees the patient in his family and community context, his glimpses of personality are particularly deficient with regard to these major aspects, and he has to try to supply them by inferences from what he does see and hear. It may also be argued that the small tribe or community can be perceived in a manner which approaches that of the clinician.

While recognizing the merit of these counterpoints, I still feel there is a marked difference along the lines indicated between the psychiatrist and the student of culture and society, and that this difference has a significant effect on mode of thought. Perhaps the best justification I can advance for this view is to say that it is a strong impression gained from attempting to carry out both types of studies.

4. In this connection it is worth noting that both clinician and social scientist are in a deadly way exposed to dangers of convention, or Idols, which can intervene between nature and its appreciation by the observer. One of these is the convention of assuming that a theory of process conceived as underlying a particular phenomenon is, in fact, true. This usually begins as a convenient but tentative assumption, and then as it becomes generally known, it gets to be taken as generally true, and then eventually is mistaken for a fact. (The logic passes through the successive steps outlined by Ko-ko in explaining to the Mikado why he said that he had cut off Nanki-poo's head when in reality he had not.) As a result of such usage and acceptance, an instance of the phenomenon in question comes to be perceived as tantamount to a demonstration of the underlying process. Another of these Idols is in the convention of assuming that an index necessarily measures what you want it to measure, even though it has never actually been established and calibrated by any adequate procedure. Here again it is usually a matter, at first, of a tentative and convenient

assumption in a situation in which it is difficult or impossible to prove the validity of the index. General use, however, and familiarity often lead to the index being taken as a matter of course and its indications mistaken for facts.

5. A further discussion along these lines may be found in the last chapter of *Explorations in Social Psychiatry,* particularly pp. 393-394 and 396-405. (ALEXANDER H. LEIGHTON, JOHN A. CLAUSEN, and ROBERT N. WILSON, (Eds.), [New York: Basic Books, 1957].)

6. ALFRED NORTH WHITEHEAD, *The Concept of Nature* (Ann Arbor, Univ. Michigan Press, 1957), pp. 53-55.

7. The holistic ideas which pervade this frame of reference stem in general from an orientation in natural history and more specifically from Meyer and Smuts. *See:* ADOLF MEYER, *Psychobiology, A Science of Man* (compiled and edited by EUNICE E. WINTERS and ANNA MAE BOWERS), (Springfield, Ill.: Thomas, 1957), pp. 3-110; ADOLF MEYER, *The Collected Papers of Adolf Meyer* (EUNICE E. WINTERS, Ed.), (Baltimore: Johns Hopkins Press, 1951); JAN CHRISTIAN SMUTS, *Holism and Evolution* (New York: Macmillan, 1926).

A review and bibliography of psychologists and psychiatrists who have also used the idea of holism is provided by Hall and Lindzey. *See* CALVIN S. HALL and GARDNER LINDZEY, "Organismic Theory," *Theories of Personality* (New York: Wiley, 1957), Chap. VIII.

8. For a comment on the relationship of population size to cultural pattern, *see:* CLYDE KLUCKHOHN, "The Problem of Communication Between Cultures Seen as Integrated Wholes," in L. BRYSON (Ed.), *Approaches to National Unity, Symposium on Science, Philosophy and Religion* (New York: Harper, 1945); KENNETH BOULDING, "Toward a General Theory of Growth," in LUDWIG VON BERTALANFFY and ANATOL RAPOPORT (Eds.), *General Systems, Yearbook of the Society for the Advancement of General Systems Theory* (Ann Arbor: Braun-Brumfield, 1956), Vol. I, pp. 66-75.

Illustrative of this point is the following study in culture change: CHARLES C. HUGHES, *Sivuokakh, An Eskimo Village and the Modern World,* Thesis, Cornell University, 1957.

The Sociocultural Environment

219

9. *See* ROBERT REDFIELD (Ed.), *Biological Symposia* (Lancaster, Pa.: Cattell Press, 1942), Vol. 8, pp. 80-81.

10. It is of course recognized that an organismic view of human society has been rejected by numbers of authors. Indeed, among some social scientists it is a topic which can hardly with decency be mentioned. Some examples of those opposed are: GORDON W. ALLPORT, "The Historical Background of Modern Social Psychology," in GARDNER LINDZEY (Ed.), *Handbook of Social Psychology* (Cambridge: Addison-Wesley, 1954); HOWARD BECKER and HARRY ELMER BARNES, *Social Thought From Lore to Science* (Washington, D.C.: Harren Press, 1952); FAY B. KARPF, *American Social Psychology* (New York: McGraw-Hill, 1932).

For a view more in harmony with this frame of reference and one which has had considerable influence upon it, *see:* ROBERT REDFIELD (Ed.), "Levels of Integration in Biological and Social Systems," *Biological Symposia,* Vol. 8.

The recent writings of those interested in general systems should also be mentioned, especially those ideas which bear on the common denominators in their conceptualizations of many different kinds of living (and nonliving) phenomena. Ralph Gerard, Kenneth Boulding, and Alfred Emerson in particular give emphasis to the relevance of organic systems to sociocultural systems. *See* RALPH W. GERARD, "Higher Levels of Integration," in ROBERT REDFIELD (Ed.), "Levels of Integration in Biological and Social Systems," *Biological Symposia,* Vol. 8, pp. 67-87; RALPH W. GERARD, "A Biologist's View of Society," and KENNETH E. BOULDING, "Toward a General Theory of Growth," in VON BERTALANFFY and RAPOPORT, (Eds.), *General Systems, Yearbook of the Society for the Advancement of General Systems Theory,* Vol. 1, 1956, pp. 155-160, pp. 66-75; KENNETH E. BOULDING, *The Image* (especially chapters II and IV), (Ann Arbor: Univ. Michigan Press, 1956); ALFRED E. EMERSON, "Homeostasis and Comparison of Systems," in ROY R. GRINKER (Ed.), *Toward a Unified Theory of Human Behavior* (New York: Basic Books, 1956), pp. 147-163.

11. It can be said that the appropriate word for a comparative designation of the English- and French-speaking people of the Northeast is "subculture" rather than "culture." If

the Chinese and the Algonquins have separate cultures, then it is perhaps better to consider both French and English as subcultures within the larger mass of European culture. Such a technical manner for taking account of degrees of difference and similarity has been expressed by Steward; see JULIAN H. STEWARD, *Theory of Culture Change* (Urbana: Univ. Illinois Press, 1955), pp. 43-52.

The point for our purposes, however, is that pervasive patterned differences do exist between these two European derived Northeast groups involving fundamental sentiments and practices, and that in terms of feeling and interaction between persons, there is intragroup cohesiveness.

12. Components such as these and their arrangement in relation to each other are often called "structure" by sociologists and anthropologists. This usage of the term parallels that of psychiatrists and psychologists when they speak of the "structure" of personality in referring to the relationships of such components as id, ego and superego. In both instances the word means process. It stands for patterned events which tend to occur and recur with a certain amount of regularity. Hence, when one says that the structure of a community or a personality has such and such characteristics, he is, in effect, talking about an aspect of function.

It seems to me that "structure" as a term can be troublesome when one is trying to grasp and analyze the nature of sociocultural and psychological phenomena. This is probably not the case with those authors whose names are associated with the term, but in my experience it does confuse people new to the field, especially those from other disciplines trying to master the concepts and develop an understanding of both personality and sociocultural processes. Hence some impressions on the reasons for these difficulties may be worth recording.

The meaning attributed to "structure" by sociologists, anthropologists, psychologists, and psychiatrists is one that is limited, denotative, and reasonably clear. Trouble arises from the fact that connotative meanings are carried over from other contexts in which the word has markedly different significance. For example, the usage with reference to personality and society is dynamic, while in anatomy, in architecture, and in many everyday contexts the word refers to the static aspect of things. A structure is not something which keeps coming back in a regular flow of movement like a figure in a dance; it is something which just sits there like a chair.

Another and more important connotation is that of substance. The overwhelming force of the word in everyday usage is of an entity which can be seen and felt. It is—relative to other experiences in living—something directly available to the senses. This common meaning is also found in many sciences, particularly biology. When one speaks of the structure of the heart he is talking about visible-palpable substance, not the rhythmical contractions. The latter are an aspect of its functioning. Yet it is precisely the analogue in behavior of these contractions, this regular functional process, that is meant when one speaks of "structure" in a society. The brain offers another example. Its "structure" consists in the arrangements that can be seen with and without the aid of instruments such as the microscope—cerebellum, medulla oblongata, layers of the cortex, and so on. The recurrent electrical events called brain waves are not considered structure, but rather a manifestation of functioning. Again, however, they are the kind of phenomena which in discussions of society are called "structure." The closest analogue in a community of the anatomical use of "structure" is the arrangement of streets, houses, and other buildings.

A further point is this: in common terms, and also in biology, "structure" is for the most part a *description of* observed nature, whereas in discussions of personality and society it is usually an *inference from* observed nature. No one, for instance, has ever seen a class system in the same sense in which the layers of the body can be seen—skin, fascia, muscle, etc.

It seems to me likely that the word "structure" has been introduced largely as a metaphor, or diagrammatic term, into studies of personality and society, the aim being to emphasize regularities. It is exactly because it is a metaphor, however, that it brings with it so much unnecessary and unwanted baggage. It can lead one into error through static concepts, reification, and mistaking of inference for observation and description. It can also lead to misapprehensions with regard to different aspects of functioning. For, if some aspects are called "structure" and others "function," the connotations of "structure" may obscure rather than aid analysis.

From all of this one is led to wonder if it would not be wise to drop the term and speak rather of functioning, patterning, and systems, with various qualifications as to regularity and other characteristics according to context and purpose. It can be pointed out in justification for current usage in the social sciences that the word has been somewhat similarly stretched by other sciences, as when one speaks of the "structure" of a molecule and, even more, the "structure" of an atom. I would, of course, have to admit that this is true, but I would raise the question as to whether this employment of the term is not also metaphorical, and whether it is not here also misleading.

In a personal communication, Charles C. Hughes suggests that, although "structure" and "function" both refer to configurations of biosocial process, there is a temporal difference in their meanings. "Structure" refers to configurations which pre-exist other processes that are the focus of our attention—namely the "functions." He points to the following quotation from von Bertalanffy.

"The antithesis between *structure* and *function, morphology* and *physiology,* is based upon a static conception of the organism. In a machine there is a fixed arrangement that can be set in motion but can also be at rest. In a similar way the pre-established structure of, say, the heart is distinguished from its function, namely, rhythmical contraction. Actually, this separation between a pre-established structure and processes occurring in the structure does not apply to the living organism. For the organism is the expression of an everlasting, orderly process, though, on the other hand, this process is sustained by underlying structures and organized forms. What is described in morphology as organic forms and structures, is in reality a momentary cross-section through a spatio-temporal pattern.

"What are called structures are slow processes of long duration, functions are quick processes of short duration. If we say that a function such as the contraction of a muscle is performed by a structure, it means that a quick and short process wave is superimposed on a long-lasting and slowly running wave."

See LUDWIG VON BERTALANFFY, *Problems of Life, An Evaluation of Modern Biological Thought* (London: Watts, 1952).

Although on the whole and as a matter of broad orientation I subscribe to this view of the relationship of structure and function in organisms, I would nevertheless maintain that recurrent configurations in personality and society are more like heart beats and brain waves than like muscle and bone. For many purposes of analysis and investigation there remains a need for terms to distinguish configurations of apparent motion from configurations of apparent substance. I may be more sensitive to this than is necessary because in stressing the organismic view of communities, the comparison intended is strictly in terms of function, pattern and system, and not at all in terms of substance. At any rate, I do feel that to borrow "structure" and employ it to mean "function" is not one of the happier uses of the English language.

For a review of "function" as employed by sociologists and social anthropologists, *see* RAYMOND FIRTH, "Function" in WILLIAM L. THOMAS, JR., (Ed.), *Yearbook of Anthropology 1955* (New York: Wenner-Gren Foundation for Anthropological Research, 1955).

13. There is a further distinction cutting through both of these viewpoints with regard to societal functioning, namely, latent as compared to manifest function. Latent functions are those which are for the most part unrecognized by the people carrying them out and may be compared roughly to the unconscious trends that influence personality. Being unrecognized, it is possible that they are of considerable importance as factors influencing mental health and psychiatric disorder. For example, Eskimo suicide as a cultural pattern has been analyzed as consisting of both manifest and latent functions. *See* ALEXANDER H. LEIGHTON and CHARLES C. HUGHES, "Notes on Eskimo Patterns of Suicide," *Southwestern Journal of Anthropology*, Vol. 11, no. 4, 1955.

For a general discussion, *see* ROBERT MERTON, *Social Theory and Social Structure* (Glencoe, Ill.: Free Press, 1957), pp. 60-64.

It may be noted in passing that this use of "latent" is

different from that found in clinical psychiatry and medicine in general. In the latter it means not only hidden or covert, but inactive during a period of time with the potential of later emergence. Thus the plasmodium may lodge inactive in some part of the body and so be latent for many years before it reappears in an episode of malaria. Similarly, many of the sexual characteristics of the human are latent during childhood.

14. A further discussion of symbols occurs in the next chapter together with some references to the literature. See pp. 237-238, and Note 7 of that chapter.

Chapter VII

A Concept of
Sentiments[1]

T HE DEVELOPMENTAL TREND of this book calls now for a chapter which would set up a typology. We are in quest of a way to quarter the sociocultural environment so that epidemiological findings with regard to psychiatric disorder can be projected against categories with promise of revealing relationships that may have some bearing on etiology. The previous chapter was preparation for this step. Some additional preparation is, however, still necessary, and such is the concern of the pages to follow. The discussion of a typology will, therefore, be deferred until the next chapter.

The point for attention here is the concept of sentiments as a link between personality and communities. References to sentiments have appeared many times in preceding chapters. The concept has been employed in delineating the nature of personality, in discussing psychiatric disorder, in putting forward some propositions regarding the relationship of sociocultural factors and psychiatric disorder, and, finally, in depicting the functioning of sociocultural units. Since these uses have ranged rather widely and since the idea occupies a fairly central position in the frame of reference, it would seem well now to review and, where relevant, amplify. This revision and amplification will constitute a further instance of the expanding spiral mentioned at the beginning of Chapter I as part of the plan of the book.

Inasmuch as sentiments are conceived to be within and a part of personality, I shall begin with a discussion of this more inclusive concept. There will follow, then, sections on sentiments and personality, sentiments and mental health, sentiments and social groups, and sentiments as a bridging concept, one that is expected to serve in the analysis and grasp of problems bearing on relationships between patterns of group behavior and patterns of malfunctioning personalities.

I PERSONALITY

Let us first review the idea to which the word "personality" refers. In Chapter I it is described as the patterned functioning of a person considered as a whole, that is, a living, self-integrating unit, and the meaning of "pattern," "function," and "integration" are briefly discussed. A number of analytically separable subsystems, or aspects, are mentioned to illustrate the integration; these include cognition, affect, and basic urges, together with the dimension conscious-unconscious. Subsequent chapters show these aspects and dimension as prominent in the patterning of psychiatric disorder and in theories that have been adduced to explain such malfunctioning.

The conception of a whole with parts and components, or a system with subsystems and aspects, is considered of fundamental importance.

A Concept of Sentiments

This is because any explanation of any phenomenon produced by or occurring within the system must take into account the whole as being affected by the nature of its components, and the components as being affected by the nature of the whole.

Emphasis is also given to sequential relationships, with personality regarded as a continuous emergent from conception onward under the influence of both hereditary disposition and experience. The unit is viewed in terms of a life-arc with its characteristics at any given segment considered to be the product of the previous life-story and the interactions inherent in the cross-section of that moment. The capacity to anticipate and the expectations which bear on the future are of major importance, however, as components of the cross-section of the moment. The personality is not only under the influence of its past and the unfolding edge of its present but also under the influence of its perceptions with regard to the future. Hence, although (in the words of *The Tempest*) "The past is prologue," so too is the future.

In addition to being regarded as a continuous emergent, personality is regarded as an energy system. Energy is conceived in biological terms, and the person as an organism is thought to be in a state of dynamic equilibrium, of metabolic exchange with the environment. An attribute of the dynamic equilibrium is a tendency for the system to return, when disturbed, to its previous condition, as in the physiological concept of *homeostasis*.

The idea of dynamic equilibrium of the personality system does not, however, imply rigidity or inevitability of return to the *status quo ante*. There are several reasons for this, one being that circumstances rarely permit return to exactly the same pattern. Beyond such a consideration, however, is the occurrence of alternate resources and devices within the system through which a somewhat different arrangement of equilibrium may be achieved as an alternative rather than as a return to the previous state. Finally, there is the fact that endogenous shifts take place in the system itself, best exemplified by growth during the early years. It is presumed that changes of this sort continue during the whole of the life-arc so that the concept of spontaneity as well as the concept of adaptation has to be taken into account.

Those analytically separable aspects of personality which have been mentioned as cognition, affect, and basic urges, together with the conscious-unconscious dimension, may be referred to as "psychic processes." These form a part of the coordinating and managing aspects of the biological energy exchange. The psychic processes are not, however, to be considered purely reactive to alterations in the major energy system, as is the case, for instance, with the governor of a motor. On the contrary, they too are capable of endogenous (spontaneous) alterations in their own organization with initiation of effects which can pervade the whole organism.

In saying all this, it is important not to imply reification of one or another of the psychic processes as something apart from the rest of the personality. They are rather coordinative aspects, the transactions in which events are experienced, interpreted, acted upon, synthesized, and symbolized and the symbols stored for future reference. There is, however, one important point of distinction that has to do with the idea of psychic energy as compared to biological energy. As an aspect of personality (the functioning of a person) the psychic processes do involve the flow of energy. For each feeling and thought there is a physiological event. This energy is, however, small compared to that which moves the muscles. It is not a power which controls the rest of the system by virtue of its size, nor does one part of the psychic subsystem prevail over another because it is "greater" in terms of energy. Control by and within the psychic system is, in short, based not on amount of energy as such but on position and patterning. It is control in the sense in which a policeman on traffic duty at a busy intersection, with his relatively small amount of energy, nevertheless stops, starts, and directs the enormous energy in miles and miles of automobiles, busses and trucks.

Thus in the personality system, to the extent that the psychic processes involve energy at all, they involve the biological energy of physiological transactions. Their ability to control, whether in the form of cognitive reasoning, compelling affect, basic urge, or persistent unconscious motivation is due to their communicative and signaling place in the system. The construct of "psychic energy" as it is commonly used in clinical thinking is therefore not included in the concept of personality being advanced here. That there are insistent and enduring psychic patterns in all personalities is, of course, recognized, but it is not assumed that such patterns follow laws which approximate the conservation of energy. This point is made because it has important implications in considering the motivational aspects of personality and in the development of explanatory ideas.

A Concept of Sentiments

229

Personality is pictured as ever, while life lasts (so long as it is personality), in the act of striving. These strivings have their roots in the psychic processes and may be conceived as starting with certain given instincts, or inborn dispositions. The instincts are, however, as the person grows, differentiated through experience into basic urges, and these in turn into sentiments. This is not a process of stepping from one into the other so as to constitute three mutually exclusive segments of development. The instincts have expression in the basic urges and the urges in the sentiments. Hence, in the adult, all three are present, but in a way that may be represented diagramatically by saying that the sentiments occupy the surface of consciousness, while the other two are more underlying. By this I do not wish to imply that they are completely unconscious, but rather that they are in part somewhat less available and in part altogether unavailable to conscious recognition.

The striving characteristics of the psychic processes set the stage for satisfaction and dissatisfaction, for conflict between a personality and its environment, and between different subsystems within the system such as between various types of basic urges. Hence the necessity of coordination and integration *within* the psychic processes, a condition which is discernible as systems of sentiment. This is over and above the integration of the whole energy system *by* the psychic processes. The integration of personality is conceived to have at its core a process which has been labeled the essential psychical condition. This is regarded as a range of psychic activities, not a fixed point. Within the range there are constant variations in the direction toward conflict (or blocking of striving) and away from conflict (by numerous restorative devices such that the limits of the range are not infringed). It can be considered diagrammatically as a state of optimum tension which is always being either reduced, or exceeded and then restored. When the range is infringed, disagreeable feelings come through to consciousness and the personality is vulnerable to developing psychiatric disorder in some manner approximating that outlined in Chapter V.

This, of course, is only one of the gateways to such disorder, but it is the one most under the influence of perception and psychological experience, and hence open in a somewhat special way to sociocultural factors. Other sources of malfunction in the personality system may be grouped as hereditary defect and physiological experience.

This review of personality as it has been depicted through the preceding chapters is not exhaustive, nor have all the important implications been touched upon. It is, perhaps, nonetheless sufficient to give the reader a reminder regarding the general nature of the concept, and of how it may differ from other referents of the word "personality" with which he is familiar. As can be seen, the term as used here is more inclusive than such related constructs as basic personality, ego, self-system, or personality viewed as an individual's particular assemblage of patterns and interpersonal relationships.[2] It does not, moreover, designate psychic processes as distinct from the organic. These other constructs can be regarded as aspects or analytic divisions which can be usefully made for many purposes. The way the word "personality" is employed in these pages includes them but refers to a larger whole, the total functioning of the individual as a unit.

As pointed out in Chapter I, this is a working concept rather than one derived from a systematic consideration of theory (as might, for instance, be developed from learning theory). It is fundamentally an orientation for the study of a person when he presents a problem that has to be dealt with, as did Tom Young with his anxiety. There is no lack of interest in psychological theory, of course, but thinking begins from the question, "How can I study and so help men and women with problems like these?" rather than, "How can I build a coherent and systematic theory of individual behavior based on certain limited assumptions?"

The holism incorporated in this orientation arises from the nature of the question. If there is limitation to one or another level of abstraction, the problems with which psychiatric disorder confronts the clinician cannot be analyzed and comprehended without the error of reductionism. You can profitably stay within the specified limits of a particular kind of psychological phenomenon and psychological concept (say cognition) if you are concerned only with the development of knowledge in regard to that psychological process. If your problem, however, is psychiatric disorder, whether for therapy or for research, you must deal with all the major determinants and components no matter how they disregard traditional disciplinary lines and habits of abstract thinking. Genetics, biochemistry, physiology, psychology, sociology, and anthropology are names for areas of human knowledge and inquiry. They are not, however, names for mutually exclusive events in nature. They are all relevant to the events we call psychiatric disorder, and there is need for some concept in which they can meet. It is suggested here that this is the functioning of the person as a whole, for which the word "personality" is employed.[3]

This holistic working concept of personality has a long history in the discipline of psychiatry. Setting aside some of the terms I have used and some of the emphases such as that involving the distinction between biological and psychic energy, it has been in common use for at least half a century and remains widespread today. Sometimes it is more implicit than explicit, although there are in numbers of psychiatric texts attempts such as mine to sum it up from the viewpoint of this or that particular worker.[4]

This matter is emphasized because it is not always evident to those who approach the study of personality from other disciplines. For them, psychiatry is apt to be considered the same as psychoanalysis. It is important to observe, therefore, that psychiatry deals with all the kinds of disorders outlined in Chapter IV, whereas only some of these are appropriate for psychoanalytic treatment. Psychoanalysis is a specialization within psychiatry involving a technique that is suitable for selected kinds of cases. It also involves a body of theory, and this has, of course, much wider application than its technique of treatment. Indeed, few areas in the field of psychiatry have been without its influence and illumination. Nevertheless, the practical and conceptual necessity of dealing with many different kinds of disorders, from brain syndrome to sociopath, with many different levels of investigation and analysis from the biochemical to the interpersonal, and with many different types of treatment from vitamins to group psychotherapy, has led to the development of a working concept of personality that is capable of handling many levels of abstraction.[5]

II SENTIMENTS AND PERSONALITY

Several definitions of sentiment from several points of view have been given or implied in previous chapters. The word refers, of course, to an abstraction which is in turn part of the larger abstraction that has been designated by the term "personality." If we look at personality in the cross-section of the moment, then each sentiment may be conceived as a union of thought and feeling (cognition and affect), but one dependent upon basic urges and unconscious factors. This dependence varies toward more or less with different sentiments. One could represent this schematically by suggesting that sentiments constitute a kind of surface for personality, one through which there takes place perception, assessment, and expression. This includes most importantly the patterns of interpersonal relationships.

When sentiments are considered in terms of life-story, then they may be regarded as having emerged in the course of growth and experience, with progressive differentiation from instincts, from basic urges, and from each other.[6] This is the "genetic" or developmental viewpoint. It can be elaborated by suggesting that many of the unconscious factors that underlie any given sentiment in a given personality at a particular moment have their origin in the early functioning of instincts and basic urges and the circumstances attending this functioning. Other unconscious factors will involve sentiments which for reasons to be discussed later have become unconscious— that is, motives. In both cases, the unconscious factors which bear to a greater or lesser degree on any sentiment or cluster of sentiments are considered to have their origin in hereditary dispositions combined with life-story.

As with personality as a whole, so here again the perceptions and anticipations with regard to the future must be considered as having major influence on sentiment development and maintenance. The fact that these perceptions and anticipations with regard to the future are in part sentiments does not contravene this point. It merely illustrates what was noted a few lines above, namely, that sentiments become differentiated from each other. In other words, taking any given moment on the life-arc as a point of reference, some of those sentiments which already exist will exert an influence on the formation of later sentiments.

Both the cross-section and the life-story viewpoints have been discussed at a level that can be termed psychological, that is to say, they involve conscious mental processes and inferred unconscious processes analogous to the conscious processes. Despite the fact that sentiments are an abstraction, however, it is assumed that, like the larger concept, personality, of which they are a part, there is a referent at the physiological level. We may suppose, therefore, that for a given sentiment in a given personality there are a series of patterned physiological events in the organism.

I propose now to attempt some further explanation and description of the concept. Since a complete systematic development would not be feasible or appropriate within the intended scope of this book, what follows must be regarded as a few relevant explanatory notes. At the beginning some observations will be made with regard to the kind of concept the sentiment idea is, and then there will follow some discussion of the content.

The word "sentiment" (as used here) is applicable to a wide range of abstractions, many of which extend over, or "nest" in, each other. A similar relationship may be seen between word and concept in the case of society. "Society" can refer to aspects of the total population of the world (e.g., "human society") and to various subdivisions down to a small number of people with face-to-face relationships. Margins and level of abstractions depend on viewpoint and purpose. Thus, it is often possible to regard the same group of people as one society, as a number of separate societies, or as a cluster of societies bound together by economic, political, and other ties. The society of the Harbor Town, for instance, could be viewed as comprising not only the center of the community but both Hillcrest at its edge and Woodside (where Tom Young lived) farther out; or these could be considered separate societies; or they could be thought of as a cluster.

"Sentiment" has similar characteristics. The word can refer to the totality of certain kinds of thought-feeling in humanity or in particular subgroups of people or in a single, given personality. Within a personality it can designate subdivisions and clusters of thought-feeling about a central idea such as home, love, child, and success, and it can refer to highly specific items such as, "I would give my life for my country," or "I want my beer on Saturday nights."

This wide range of meaning and level of abstraction has the advantage of indicating a complex of related phenomena without assumption of detailed specification such as might prejudice observation. It is a concept that is in harmony with an approach to problems by means of successive approximations, since it permits beginning with very general meanings and then proceeding through observational and experimental interchanges with nature to more and more specific meanings. In using it one must, however, try to keep clear the level of approximation and context in which the concept is being employed. In the first five chapters of this book, sentiments have been seen as components of personalities. Within this range, the use was at first exceedingly general, but with the designation of the ten essential striving sentiments in Chapter V (page 148), a further step was made toward specification by stating categories of sentiments considered of major importance in the integration of personality and of major importance in mediating the effects of sociocultural environment. These ten do not, of course, constitute all the sentiments that go to make up a personality, but rather a central governing complex. There remain in any personality various particular sentiments and clusters of sentiments which are not part of such a complex. Furthermore, each of the ten major categories is reducible to many more specific sentiments, and it would also be possible to describe topically organized sentiment clusters that cut across one or more of the ten categories. The choice of all such various forms of conceptualization depends on problem and aim.

In the discussion above, the words "phenomena" and "nature" are employed. It is hoped the reader realizes that these are intended in a loose sense, for no matter how specific a study may be, sentiments are always an inference. No one has ever apprehended a sentiment in another personality directly with his senses; rather, he infers its existence from sensory data.

This stricture is of course true with regard to all appraisals of nature, and one could appeal to some philosophies to show what an enormous area of doubt surrounds every common-sense and scientific "fact," screened as it is through perceptions and molded by inference. There is no need, however, for our purposes to go to this extreme. For the practical requirements of the kind of research with which we are concerned it can be assumed that there is a range from inferences which are so close to phenomena as to be considered direct observation (for example, blood pressure) to those that are highly abstract (such as the essential psychical condition). The most discrete and least abstract sentiments—for instance, "He wants a promotion"—are here considered to be somewhat more inferential than blood pressure but far less inferential than the essential psychical condition or unconscious processes.

It is only in such a relative sense, then, that any sentiment is a "phenomenon" and "directly observable in nature." One can think of Tom Young's love for his wife or his dislike of hunting in such terms. On the other hand, the ten essential striving sentiments—physical security, sexual satisfaction, love, recognition, and so on--are derived from "observations" of such particular sentiments and hence are by comparison much more abstract. They occupy a position between these discrete sentiments and still higher-level abstractions such as the essential psychical condition.

With these notes made regarding some of the characteristics of the concept as a concept, we can turn now to a further discussion of what it represents.

Sentiments have a time dimension. This involves intermittent appearance in consciousness as a result of external stimulation or internal transitions of the psychic processes. The focal point of consciousness may be conceived as composed of a stream of thought-feeling in which certain patterns, the sentiments, recur. Hence, for a given sentiment there is, in this recurrent sense, duration on the life-arc, a certain degree of persistency and consistency. A union of thought and feeling which occurs once and is never repeated is not therefore regarded here as a sentiment. This makes it clear that sentiment is a general term not for all thought-feelings but only for those which have duration in a personality system.

Differences in duration between sentiments is another matter for consideration. Some sentiments may occupy only a small number of sequences on the life-arc, while others may extend through the greater part of its existence.

Related to this is the question of differences of duration in positions of vital significance to the personality system. The whole discussion of sentiments and personality has been in terms of the one having function in relation to the other. There are differences among sentiments, however, with regard to their controlling importance in the functioning of personality, and the ten essential striving sentiments have been marked out as categories with particular significance. We may suppose, therefore, that a sentiment, in addition to having origin and an end —that is, duration—may shift position relative to personality at different parts of the life-arc. Thus, even though a sentiment may endure over a great portion of the arc, its functional importance may alter from the crucial to the nonessential. A given sentiment could, for instance, be at one time a particular expression of one or more of the essential striving sentiments and at another be outside these categories. The reverse trend is of course also possible, and so too is alternation along the life-arc.

An illustration may help to clarify these points. When Tom Young was fifteen years old the good opinion of Bill Eaton, one of his few close friends, was of great importance to him. His specific sentiments in this regard could be grouped in such essential striving clusters as love, recognition, and belonging in a human group. Ten years later the sentiments concerned with maintaining Bill's good opinion still persisted, but were no longer in the essential striving clusters. Bill had moved away from Woodside eight years previously, and then Tom himself had entered the army and been sent overseas. Separation, together with new associates and new experiences, had attenuated the essential aspects of needing Bill's good opinion. The opinion remained nevertheless as something desirable when Tom happened to think of it, but this was not often. On the other hand, a new friend, René Vincent, first encountered on joining the army, had come to have the importance previously felt with regard to Bill. After another ten years, with the end of the war and the settling of Tom on his farm, René too had passed out of prominence in Tom's sentiment system. Bill on the other hand re-emerged as an object for certain essential sentiments, having returned to Woodside after the war and acquired a farm next to Tom.

A matter of major significance is the relationship between symbols and sentiments. Since a sentiment is a union of thought and feeling, a topic or idea is always involved and this topic is the basis of symbolic representation. Among adults, the commonest symbols are words, but a variety of other forms of representation are also employed in consciousness, both pictorial and diagrammatic. In fact, the mental representation of all the senses may be involved in the patterning of these images.

Not only do symbols stand for sentiments, however; they can also evoke sentiments not currently in consciousness. The most obvious example of this is with regard to the words we hear other people utter. Our response includes a flow of sentiments, with or without concomitants in action. Something very similar to this, however, can arise wholly within the personality. Giving thought to a topic or musing involves a succession of symbols which can evoke sentiments that were not, just before this, in consciousness. Such a flow is of course private and thus limited by the characteristics of the personality in question, and hence is not likely so open to new contributions as is an exchange with another person, but it nevertheless embodies the evocation of sentiments through symbols.

Symbols have other functions in personality besides those connected with evocation and representation of sentiments. It has been noted several times that, underlying sentiments, there are unconscious factors of varying degrees of influence. Some of these may be regarded as basic urges and others as more differentiated patterns which were once sentiments but which have through repression become unconscious motives. These unconscious factors that underlie the sentiments may also be represented and evoked by symbols. Examples of this have been given, as for instance the gun in Tom Young's case, the alcohol in Bernie Chiason's, and, with somewhat different quality, the oats in Mr. Young's. A symbol, therefore, may stand for and evoke both conscious sentiments and unconscious motives in the same personality at the same time. It seems likely, furthermore, that most, if not all, the symbols which stir very strong emotions stand on this multiple base.

Symbols are also important, of course, in interpersonal relations—that is, communication—but discussion of this will be reserved for Section IV on sentiments and groups.[7]

The sentiments of a personality, whether viewed in the cross-section of the moment or developmentally, are conceived as interconnected. This means that they are not so many separate stalks tied in a bundle, but have relationships of mutual interdependence, with some being more tightly clustered together than others. The nature of this connection and interdependence deserves some discussion.

Two different sentiments may be bound together through having in common certain underlying unconscious factors. Bernie Chiason's sentiments of desiring alcohol and disliking to go home could both have a common derivation from his unconscious hostility toward his mother, expressed on the one hand in revengeful self-destruction and on the other in rejection of his wife. Although this illustration is taken from a case of psychiatric disorder, the principle it demonstrates of unconscious linkage between sentiments can apply to well-integrated and adequately functioning personalities. For example, in such personalities sentiments regarding cleanliness and sentiments regarding money could have unconscious factors in common.

This point emphasizes again the statement made earlier that there are unconscious influences at work to a greater or lesser degree in all sentiments. Because this is at variance with the way in which many students regard unconscious processes, it is worth pausing a moment to consider the matter. To such people an item of behavior that is based primarily on unconscious tendencies is by that fact largely if not entirely pathological. This rests in part on a value premise with regard to rationality which prevails in our culture as a legacy from Greece, augmented by the Enlightenment, and which pictures the ideal (and so, healthy) man as one who is governed by reason. It also rests on the fact that the great bulk of studies into the unconscious have been carried out by intellectuals investigating people who manifest one or another pattern of psychiatric disorder. With this goes emphasis on defense mechanisms which protect the patient from realizing something painful. Since many of these painful items are tendencies or urges that are unacceptable according to conventional standards of rightness and decency, the analysis of unconscious factors generates an atmosphere of uncovering the abnormal. To counterbalance this, it is often said that these unconscious trends are found in everybody. This may then be further elaborated by saying either that the trends are therefore "normal" or else that everybody is "abnormal." This, however, rather than clarifying the situation and dispelling the aura of pathology, simply compounds uncertainty by introducing paradox. The fact remains that if one interprets a pattern of behavior, be it fondness for children, love of music, ability as a leader, religious devotion, or creativity as a painter, in terms of unconscious components, he produces a feeling in the minds of many persons that he is at best belittling that pattern, and very probably showing that it is at root unhealthy.

With all of this I should like to express disagreement. Taking the term "unconscious" as it has been defined in this book (pages 143-146), I consider such processes as functional components of all personalities. Words like "pathological" and "abnormal," complicated by the concept of latency, represent a viewpoint in terms of which the occurrence of certain configurations of this functioning are regarded as self-defeating to the personality or otherwise undesirable. On this basis, then, all sentiments can be looked upon without any implications of pathology as having underlying unconscious factors, and it may also be supposed that on occasion several sentiments are interconnected by one or more unconscious factors held in common.

It is striking, however, that when one attempts to illustrate this with examples drawn from life, there is a dearth of material available. The instances that come readily to mind are all derived from cases.

A Concept of Sentiments

239

This is a reflection of the imbalance already mentioned several times as characterizing psychiatry, namely, a focus on illness without a comparative study of personalities that show no evidence of disorder.

Sentiments focused on different objects can be linked not only by unconscious factors but also through sharing the same conscious, affective component. Feelings of tenderness may be the common denominator in many sentiments bearing on a variety of different objects, such as children, animals, and older people.

Interdependence can now be explained a bit. It means, in part, that, through unconscious and affective factors, change in one area of the system can have repercussions that amount to change in other areas. Alterations, for instance, in unconscious factors can affect many, apparently disparate but conscious sentiments. Much psychotherapy is, indeed, based on this supposition. By this I mean that the goal of such therapy is to alter unconscious process and by this means eliminate symptoms. The link with sentiments lies in the fact that many symptoms are constellations of sentiments.

A more controversial suggestion is that alterations in sentiments can effect changes in the unconscious processes such that other sentiments are affected and in turn altered. If Tom, for instance, were persuaded, say by his brother-in-law John, to alter his sentiments about staying at Woodside in order to be a good father, husband, and son, and to decide that his real obligation was to rejoin the army, this could have such repercussions through the whole dynamic network of his personality, including some of his unconscious processes, that his sentiments regarding heart failure would disappear—even though he went on having just as many extra-systoles. This illustration is again drawn from case material, but I would hold that the principle it illustrates applies with just as much likelihood to people who are by all ordinary standards well.

In addition to the unconscious factors and the conscious affective components, sentiments are also interconnected through their cognitive aspects; that is, the rational relationships of their various topics. This may range from compatibility (merely lack of contradiction) to tight logical interdependence. Many political ideologies provide examples of the latter. The nature of these interdependencies can again be made evident by considering the process of change. When new experience or new assessment demonstrates a fallacy in a sentiment, then all those linked to it by rational connections are apt to be affected.

The whole group may then be abandoned, or reworked so as to bring it, in a new form, back in line with the known facts and the demands of reason. This is one of the major ways in which experiences of the personality along the life-arc continuously exert influence on the sentiment system.

These observations suggest that not only can sentiments affect unconscious processes, but that reasoning itself can by altering sentiments reach indirectly through the psychic functions and have effects on unconscious processes. Most theories of psychodynamics emphasize the reverse direction in this relationship, and some people would assert that the rational processes are completely unable to affect fundamental unconscious transactions. Certainly this is the experience in clinical work where one deals specifically with patterns of behavior which are resistant to purely cognitive influences. As part of this frame of reference, however, I should like to put forward the idea that cognitive activity can, at least to some extent, modify unconscious process. If this were not so, it would be difficult to understand how Freud could ever achieve self-analysis. Although Freud's ability in this respect must obviously be regarded as exceptional, nevertheless it is not unreasonable to suppose that others can do something of the same sort, even though it be less fully realized and explicitly formulated.

Having noted the cognitive activities as one of the factors of major importance in the interconnecting and changing of sentiments, it is important to add that the degree of this influence is variable from sentiment to sentiment, or from one cluster of sentiments to another —just as is the case with unconscious factors and with conscious affect. In some, cognitive relationships constitute the main set of conditions upon which the existence and form of the sentiment depends. Such are the sentiments that readily change objects according to events. Other sentiments are more compellingly under the influence of affective and unconscious factors and so are modified less easily by rational considerations. This is not to say they are necessarily completely irrational in their patterning, but rather that they exhibit warping, biases, and blind spots in the relevant cognitive activities. It is as if the reasoning were being bent by the force of a wind the observer could not feel, much less see.

Hence it may be expected that the totality of sentiments in any given personality will never constitute a rationally congruent system. There will be areas within which all sentiments are in harmony with

A Concept of Sentiments

241

reasoning, but there will be spaces between that show little or no cognitive connection and which when examined closely reveal major contradictions. Most of us, for instance, have sentiments which are based on a belief in free will and at the same time we also harbor sentiments rooted in determinism, and we do this without any intellectual catwalk such as has been developed by philosophers and theologians to connect these apparent irreconcilables.

Such logical inconsistencies do not necessarily interfere with the functioning of personality. The latter is apt to happen only when particular circumstances bring these sentiment clusters into a conflict which disturbs the essential psychical condition. Few of us are sufficiently Cartesian to sit down and systematically examine the rational relationships between all the thought-feelings in terms of which we live.[8]

It may be noted finally that whether, from the point of view of an "objective observer," a given thought-feeling is true or not makes no difference to its being conceived as a sentiment. Mr. Young's belief in oats and Tom's belief in tractors are equally sentiments. So too are William Jennings Bryan's belief in Genesis and Clarence Darrow's belief in evolution.

Sentiment interdependence and sentiment change are important with regard to personality stability, adaptability, and spontaneity. Now it is functionally necessary for a sentiment to change, now it is necessary that it hold fast. In the general assemblage of sentiments that go to make up the complement of a given personality, it is important that some yield to events while others do not and that these trends and differences be accomplished in a coordinated manner that does not seriously disrupt the integrity of the functioning whole. Thus the question of why some sentiments are rigid or strong (that is, hard to change) while others are flexible is a matter of some concern in the analysis of personality. What has been written in previous paragraphs indicates that a number of major factors are involved in supplying this range of qualities to sentiments, and these factors may be grouped under rational, affective, and unconscious. The degree of flexibility-rigidity of a given sentiment and the circumstances in which it will veer toward one or the other depend on the particular blending of these factors.[9]

Let us consider now the question of sentiment organization. One of the summary definitions of personality given at the beginning of

Chapter I was: "the acting of a living self-integrating unit." Later on this word "acting" was replaced by "functioning," but I mention it here in order to begin with a discussion of the relationship of sentiments to acts.

Being aspects of the functioning of a personality, sentiments are themselves acts—acts of that particular kind which make up the flow of psychic events. Together with their symbolic representations, they participate in the processes whereby the organism can recall the past, analyze the sensory impressions of the current situation, anticipate the future, and synthesize all three in a constant state of preparation for adaptation and expressions of spontaneity. This includes the remarkable capacity to rehearse in the psychic processes alternative sequences that might take place in reality, and thus select, as it were, on the basis of experiences without having to undergo the experiences.

In addition to being acts, sentiments also play a part in the initiation and control of other acts. This is evident when one considers personality as a whole, rather than, as above, movement within one of the subsystems. Sentiments do not span the entire story of personality control, of course, since there are reflexes that may hold sway at least briefly over the actions of the entire unit. But sentiments are a main set of controls. This has already been expressed in noting the relationship of sentiments to the energy system in the previous section and in pointing to ten clusters of sentiments as governing and patterning the striving activities of the person.

Recognizing sentiment organization then as constituting certain governing aspects of a personality system, there is still open the question of control within the network of sentiments themselves. Here again the designation of the ten essential striving sentiments points to hierarchy, since these are a dominant ten in relation to other kinds of sentiments in any personality. Within the ten, one must postulate some alternation of dominance with circumstances, coordinated in terms of maintaining the essential psychical condition.[10]

These ideas may be illustrated by supposing a situation in which everything is proceeding satisfactorily in a given personality with regard to nine out of the ten essential striving sentiments. In such a case, actions relevant to the one sentiment cluster (e.g., sex) in connection with which there are difficulties could be expected to prevail at least for a time over actions relevant to other sentiment clusters. Things do not, of course, actually happen this simply, but in all the complexity of simultaneous and sequential events, alternating dominance according to circumstances and the maintenance of the essential psychical condition can be visualized as occurring. However, inasmuch as there are certain persistencies of circumstance along a life-arc, including not only environmental factors but also the effects of hereditary and acquired characteristics of the organism, there are life-long configurations of dominant sentiment. Thus one person appears mainly concerned with sex, another with recognition, another with giving and receiving love, and so on. More commonly there is a predominant constellation or set of sentiments which involves not one, but several, of the essential striving groups as prevailing most of the time over the rest.

In closing this section, a few words should be said with regard to the possible usefulness of the concept of sentiments in relation to the concept of personality. This may be considered under three headings: personality description, personality analysis, and general orientation with regard to process. Beginning with description, sentiments provide a way of taking hold of the vast and intricate patterning inherent in the idea of personality. Various personalities can be characterized in terms of sets of sentiments, and on the basis of this their acts may be predicted and explained.

Now this last suggestion with regard to explaining acts may seem a bit strange, since sentiments are inferred from acts such as speaking, gestures, facial expression, or some combination of these. The idea is not so circular as it might appear at first glance, however, for if act A leads to the inference of sentiment A', then sentiment A' may be used to explain acts B and C. It might be said, for instance, on the basis of remarks (verbal acts) made by Tom Young in the past, "One of Tom's prevailing sentiments is fondness for animals." On the basis of this in turn one could add the explanation, "And that is why he has given that lost kitten a home"; or the prediction, "Therefore he will give that lost kitten a home."

More than this, several sentiments, each derived by inference from different acts, may be the basis for inferring still another sentiment, not directly stated in the previous two. Thus one might say, "Because Tom Young is fond of animals and is also fond of the outdoors he would dislike living in a city." Such usage of sentiments is a commonplace of everyday mutual human appraisal, whether or not the word itself is employed or even known.

Moving on from the descriptive to the analytic use of sentiments, the concept provides a starting point for inquiry into why a certain person behaves in this or that particular way or has this or that particular feeling or thought. One can begin by assessing the sentiments obviously and immediately concerned, then those that are less obvious but still important because closely interdependent, and then the various other factors relevant in terms of both cross-section of the moment and life-story. Here is an approach, in short, whereby cognition, affect, basic urges, and the conscious-unconscious dimensions, both developmentally and in terms of current interactions, can be grasped in an orderly and coordinate manner.

The sketch of Tom Young's case gives some inklings regarding the analysis of human behavior when the problem is one of psychiatric disorder. The presenting problem involved Tom's forming the sentiment that he was in danger of dying from heart failure. His behavior, feelings, and thought could be analyzed and rendered intelligible by seeing this sentiment in the context of Tom's other sentiments, the reality situation as assessed by the doctor, the underlying basic urges, and the developmental life-story.

What I wish to suggest is that such analyses need not be limited to instances of behavior disorder, but can be applied to any subpattern of personality. This is not to assert a theoretical position to the effect that the processes of psychiatric disorder are the same as those of normal persons. This is an area in which it is very easy to assume too much or too little. My point here is limited to a methodological suggestion: that the construct "sentiments" provides a framework for making inquiry into the various kinds of factors which may play some part in a given behavioral event in a given personality, and for doing so without being overcommitted in advance to various theoretical assumptions derived from the study of psychiatric disorder.

To these descriptive and analytic usages, the third point may now be added, the one called earlier "general orientation with regard to process." What I really mean, I suppose, is that sentiments seem a good approximation to nature. In mind here is the balanced emphasis on the rational (cognitive) and the nonrational (affective, basic urges, unconscious factors). While it is unlikely that many people today take a Lockean position in trying to explain human understanding primarily in terms of rational, conscious mechanisms or take an opposing frankly mystical and intuitional view, we are, nevertheless, not out from under the shadow of these kinds of issues in prevalent attitudes toward human behavior. On the one hand there are those who see unconscious and nonlogical determinants as the only influences that matter, and, on the other, there are those who feel that we have gone too far in dethroning reason and would reestablish motivation in rational terms. There is consequently some tendency to seek explanation in one or the other of these alternatives and to carry each to monocausal, exclusive extremes. The concept of sentiments implies that neither can by itself represent what is going on in nature and cannot lead far in understanding personality. Man is both a thinking and a feeling animal, and he does both simultaneously in one integrated act as he recollects, experiences, and anticipates.

III SENTIMENTS AND MENTAL HEALTH

The relationship of sentiments to mental health (both seen in the context of personality) is described and discussed in Chapter V. To summarize briefly, it may be said that the quality and organization of the sentiment components of personality make considerable difference with regard to health or disorder.

Personality disorder can arise mainly outside the sentiment system as from heredity and physiological experience. In such cases the sentiments themselves are affected as part of the personality unit. Their characteristics, however, have an influence on the patterning of the disturbance and the balancing of difficulty and adaptation.

Personality disorder can also take origin primarily from the functioning of the sentiment system and such is the main point of our attention. This occurs due to psychological experiences in the course of sentiment formation in the early, developmental portion of the life-arc, and due to stressful sociocultural conditions at later parts of the arc operating after the main patterning of sentiments is already well developed. Cases of psychiatric disorder that are for the most part environmentally induced are thought to be compounded of both these types of difficulty. The second type may be an exogenous pressure on the personality at the time symptoms emerge and during the period of their existence.

Conditions of sentiment from these sources are regarded as paving the way toward psychiatric disorder through upset of the essential psychical condition. Ten categories of essential striving sentiments are suggested to indicate the kinds most commonly involved in the production of such an upset.

The essential psychical condition, no less than the sentiments, has a developmental history. If one moves his attention backward over the life-arc of a person into childhood and infancy, he may expect to find decrease in clearly-patterned sentiments and greater prominence of largely undifferentiated basic urges, and below these, instincts. Similarly, the essential psychical condition may be regarded as somewhat simpler and less differentiated in very early life, and dependent more directly upon these urges and instincts rather than upon sentiments.

Once the essential psychical condition has become disturbed, it is to be noted that patterns of sentiment are regarded as continuing to play an important part through exerting an influence on which of many alternative adaptations to this state of affairs is developed. Thus they affect whether the resultant patterning of personality is one that would be labeled healthy or disordered.

The bearing of sentiments on mental health from these several points of view is not entirely a matter of sentiment content—of objects and their apparent feasibility with reference to striving. Also germane are qualities discussed in the previous section, namely, degrees of coordination and flexibility. Some personalities constitute a functionally very close-linked web of sentiments while others are by comparison more loosely organized. Extremes of either type can be a disadvantage in living.

Having considered this overview, let us enlarge on one particular aspect, namely, the nature of the major difficulties which can occur in the functioning of sentiments. The central point here is interference with striving. What is meant by striving is indicated in the ten essential striving sentiments (physical security, sex, love, etc.). Interference is regarded not as a physical fact external to the personality, but as a matter of perception and anticipation. Since perception and anticipation are themselves under the influence of the sentiment system, then, as suggested on page 142, *interference may be defined as a state of conflict among sentiments.*

This idea can be further developed if we recall the aspects of sentiments noted in the last chapter:

1. Thought-feelings regarding what has been, is and can be—the reality aspect.

2. Thought-feelings regarding what ought to be—the value aspect.

A Concept of Sentiments

3. Thought-feelings regarding what is wanted—the desire aspect. As mentioned previously, these are not separate categories, but rather types of functioning, one or more of which may be performed by a given sentiment. All the essential striving sentiments have the last aspect, but they may also have the other two types as well. When they do, this is something of an ideal state for the personality as a whole. It means that all the objects in the striving system are perceived as in harmony with regard to desirability, rightness, and possibility of achievement.

A major kind of interference is one in which an essential and hence wishing sentiment is incompatible with reality and value aspects. This is not the only pattern of conflict, of course, but it is a significant one. Another significant type is conflict between wishing sentiments themselves, that is, between two or more incompatible desires. It is understood that underlying such conflict are the unconscious factors discussed earlier.

Personalities are always in a state of adjusting to incompatibilities; sentiments are forever being reworked through psychic activity to reduce minor interferences. The interferences which foster psychiatric disorder through upsetting the essential psychical condition, therefore, are major disjunctions which not only involve essential sentiments but are of such extent and duration as to severely tax the usual processes whereby the personality carries on its adjustments.

In Chapter V it is pointed out that interference with essential striving sentiments can often be removed by changing specific objects while retaining the functional characteristics of the over-all sentiment. This, indeed, may be considered the common mode of response, whether the factors producing the interference are exogenous or endogenous to the personality system. It is the main way in which the incompatibilities between sentiments are renovated and adjusted, and interferences with striving neutralized.

It may be noted now, however, that it is also possible for a sentiment to be converted into a motive or, in other words, repressed into the unconscious level of psychic activity. This is another way in which the personality system commonly deals with a major conflict between sentiments which are all important to its functioning. By repressing one part of a conflict, the remaining sentiments are left unopposed so far as consciousness is concerned. Although this process is generally considered pathological in the context of a psychiatric disorder, it is apparently common and it may well be proper to regard it as also part of "healthy" adjustment. That is to say, it may aid in the restoration of the essential psychical condition without bringing after it major long-range disadvantages.

In suggesting this I am again diverging markedly from those who feel that unconscious motivation is virtually the same thing as psychiatric disorder, and that the healthy person is one who is aware of most of his feelings and urges and so emotionally poised as to be able to deal with them rationally. This gives too much prominence to cognition and fails to appreciate the functional importance of other aspects of the psychic processes. Consciousness seems to be primarily concerned in dealing with new situations, whereas the sheer complexity of personality integrative functioning precludes the possibility of being aware of everything one does. We walk, but we do not think about the steps unless the ground is rough. So, too, we deal with our friends, colleagues, bosses, helpers, mates, and children without thinking out all the meanings of each act in advance. We focus when there is trouble, but a perpetual state of complete analysis and foreknowledge would be impossible for any human mind as it is now constituted. Aside from this matter of feasibility, unconscious processes are, I think, a protective device and as such have their uses. They can for instance serve to keep fruitless conflicts from disintegrating the personality. The fact that they can go wrong, in part and at times, does not necessarily mean that they are always, or even mainly, malfunctional. If capacity to go wrong were taken as a criterion for such appraisal, then virtually every known physiological function would have to be regarded as pathological since all of them from blood clotting to digestion can at times be malfunctional and in many instances lethal. It is not unconsciousness *per se* that is malfunctional, but rather the way it can and does sometimes operate so as to be damaging to the personality's capacity for adaptation and spontaneity.[11]

With these qualifications, then, one may note that unconscious urges and motives do at times exert influences against recovery of the essential psychical condition. Since these are unconscious, the person is ordinarily limited in his ability to deal with them in any rational manner, and hence repression in such a situation, instead of leading to relief, contributes to particularly intractable patterns of psychological illness.

Due to the fact that the classical concepts of psychic energy are not incorporated in this frame of reference, however, there is no reason to suppose that all sentiments banished from consciousness remain active as unconscious motives able to influence the essential psychical condition. Rather, the question for inquiry is raised as to why this sometimes appears to occur and on other occasions does not.

Against the background of this discussion of disorder, I should like now to suggest that sentiments offer a convenient approach to understanding mental health as contrasted to psychiatric disorder. This is of some importance in view of the difficulties inherent in formulating a concept of mental health. In this book it has been defined as the absence of known pathology. Such a definition is, of course, unsatisfactory for many purposes, since it provides no content for a conception of health. Its main virtue lies in that it persistently raises the question as to what health is.

To go beyond this, however, requires a framework, and a number have been suggested, usually involving some idea of maturity, balanced adjustment to the challenges of life, knowing and accepting oneself, reality testing, and so on.[12] The difficulty with this approach from a research point of view is that it predetermines too much. The nature of mental health is being asserted rather than discovered. If the assertions took the form of testable hypotheses, then one might not object. It is difficult, however, to see how many of these formulations can be tested, since they seem to be statements of value and preference. One could conceivably learn what factors lead to the development of the indicated personalities and, in time, even how to foster such development, but one might miss entirely other patterns of personality which could also be considered instances of mental health.

Looking at the matter from the other viewpoint, if the absence of apparent illness is the starting place for approaching a concept of mental health, one would have to expect that a group of outwardly not-ill people would be found on closer inspection to contain some with covert illness or incipient illness. The rest, however, could be expected to exhibit patterns of personality organization which constitute a variety of different healths. These might then be examined to discover their patterning of sentiments and the relationships of these sentiments to other aspects of personality. The organizational characteristics of the ten essential striving sentiments could be a means of giving focus to such an investigation, but one should realize that these ten have emerged largely from pathological studies, and hence he should be alert to the possibility of finding new key sentiments. With sentiment and sentiment functioning as the basis of inquiry and analysis, it should be possible to outline in both descriptive and dynamic terms a number of patterns of mental health.

IV SENTIMENTS AND SOCIOCULTURAL GROUPS

The circumstances and intent of the present section differ considerably from those of its two predecessors. With "Sentiments and Personality," and "Sentiments and Mental Health," it was a question of reviewing, pulling together, and then amplifying ideas which had already been laid out through the preceding chapters. To a large extent it was a task of rounding off what is to be said in this volume on these topics.

"Sentiments and Sociocultural Groups," on the other hand, has had only partial treatment (Chapter VI). Since we are still in the midst of discussing relevant aspects of sociocultural phenomena and concepts, some of the main points are still to come. Hence the review and amplification of this section is preparatory and stands out pending further discussion of sociocultural patterning and processes.

In the previous chapter it is said that the existence of a community —a self-integrating quasi-organism such as the Harbor Town—depends on sentiments and their representation in symbols. No matter how one defines the limits of a community, and no matter what the patterning one selects in order to describe or analyze—whether roles, class, associations, kinship, or culture—the collective behavior of any given moment is under the influence of sentiments already existing in the people and operating through the instrumentality of symbols. This point is illustrated by means of a fragmentary description of the town on a stormy night.

Communities as sociocultural units have not only patterning and organization but also continuity and relative stability in the configurations of their sentiments. This holds despite the turnover of individuals. At the same time, however, there are continuous adaptive changes in the systems of sentiment, some of which may be of great magnitude when viewed over a period of years.

These characteristics of sentiments in sociocultural groups are said

A Concept of Sentiments

to depend on the nature of personality. Thus, stability of group patterns arises from the fact that each person born in a community has to evolve and differentiate sentiments as part of his development, and in doing this he draws on the already existing sentiments of the group in which he finds himself. This is not a matter just of conformity, but of necessity in personality formation; there cannot otherwise be, for an individual who is a member of a group, growth into a functional integration of cognition, affect, basic urges, and unconscious factors.

The changing of group patterns of sentiment is also no less than stability based on the characteristics of personality. Recalling that this word "personality" stands for a process concept, let us observe that, aside from growth and decline, its essence is continuous adjustment to continuously altering circumstances. As part of this, specific sentiments are always being reworked within the broader framework of general clusters that are relatively constant. Through time there can be an accumulation of many specific changes and innovations of sentiment leading ultimately to alterations in the general clusters. This is most apt to occur in response to a persistent set of influences, often coming from outside the unit, such that alteration of sentiment is more functionally effective for the person than is resistance. The turnover in the sociocultural group provided by death and birth (allowing the growth of new personalities under the new circumstances) facilitates these long-range adaptive trends of community units.

If the sentiments of groups are thus rooted in the dynamics of personality, it follows that much of what has been said so far in the present chapter which amplifies the concept of sentiment in the context of personality also bears on the concept in groups. Shared sentiments are thus a type or category among the sentiments which go to make up any given personality, and the sentiments in this category have all the relationships and dependencies within the system that have been outlined in Section II.

In observing that many sentiments are shared, let us also note that every individual is unique in his own particular constellation of sentiments, just as every leaf in the forest is unique. This individuality comes mostly from combination of patterns, that is, the elements in the patterns are not unique, but the particular way they are combined varies a bit from one individual to another. Allowance must be made, however, for a few discrete sentiments, usually minor items, which are peculiar to each individual. Most complexes of sentiment, nevertheless, are not idiosyncratic, but are shared, to varying degrees, with other people, family group, village, class, or nation.

If one considers sentiment complexes rather than individual persons, if one is thinking of categories of sentiment rather than the sentiments that a particular person has, it is evident that sentiment complexes encompass groups of people. A given complex may be shared by a given group, and such occurrences render it possible to distinguish groups according to sentiment, just as it is possible to distinguish people by the geographic area in which they live or by their physical characteristics or by their tendency to share certain social institutions in common, such as monogamy or polygamy. Thus, Jews, Republicans, Zunis, Englishmen, can be distinguished by their sentiments. Although these groups share many sentiments with other groups, and some sentiments with virtually all mankind, there are large complexes of sentiments which are peculiar to each group and which mark it off from the rest. To return to the leaf analogy, although each leaf is unique and although all leaves have certain basic elements in common with each other, there are large clusterings of patterns which enable us to distinguish beech, white pine, and sugar maple.

The idea of sentiments shared between personalities extends the concept of interdependence and interconnectedness of sentiments beyond the purely intrapersonal considerations discussed in Section II. Of course "sharing" does not mean that two or more individuals have joint ownership of a single sentiment as they might have of a car. It means rather that they hold very similar sentiments which can be evoked by the same symbols and which when evoked can lead to joint or reciprocal action. Actually, all sentiments are fundamentally private. The feeling of sharing is a matter of mutual inference, and we may suppose that it is never completely accurate.

According to this view, any given personality is bound through communication and symbols in a web of sentiment relationships to other personalities, and this has implications regarding the process of interpersonal change which may now be added to what has been said about sentiments and personality. It will be recalled that the maintenance of a particular sentiment in a given personality is regarded as dependent on cognition, affect, basic urges, unconscious factors, and, through these, on interdependence with other sentiments. Now we must note that through the medium of symbols there is also linkage to the sentiment constellations of other personalities and hence to the system of the whole sociocultural unit. Alterations in the shared sentiments of a given personality, therefore, necessitate realignments that extend interpersonally as well as intrapersonally, and this has consequences for speed and facility of change.

Two points will, perhaps, illustrate the matter. First there is the question of sheer prevalence. A person who changes with regard to some sentiment that is widely shared, while the others of his community do not, is by that fact to some extent out of step with the sociocultural group. The degree and significance of this depends, of course, on the function of the particular sentiment both in his own personality system and in the group system. There is also the matter of the degree to which the alteration is overt or covert. In any event, although the change can be trivial in its consequences, it can also be very serious and bring into difficulty all his essential striving sentiments, because their functioning is dependent on his articulation with other people and his fitting more or less with their patterns of sentiment and behavior. To be outside the system of the community is to be exposed to severe multiple stresses.

Aside from prevalence as such there is also the possibility of a person coming into disharmony with the sentiment systems of people who are important to him. It is not only the widely shared sentiments that matter but also, and perhaps especially, those of a limited number of other persons on whom one is dependent for the functioning of his essential striving sentiments.

For these kinds of reasons, the alteration of sentiments by an individual so as to render himself out of phase with the trend of the shared sentiments of the group is an exceedingly difficult matter. On the other hand, his choice of object substitution is limited and guided along certain channels which may or may not provide sufficient scope to meet the needs of his personality system.

Turning now from the consequences that group sentiments have for personality back to our main topic, the functioning of sentiments in groups, the question may be raised as to how these can be conceptually organized. We have the community viewed as a self-integrating unit and the sentiments designated as a coordinating aspect or subsystem. Do we not need, at this point, some further breakdown of these group sentiments into analytic categories?

It would be possible to develop a typology of "essential shared sentiments" with reference to characteristics indispensable for group functioning. Such a list might contain items such as the following:

1. Family formation and perpetuation.
2. Indoctrination of new community members.
3. The maintenance of government, law, and order.
4. Patterns of leadership, followership, and association.
5. Organized methods of meeting emotional needs in life's crises and in day-to-day living—religion and recreation.
6. The maintenance of communication.
7. Protection against weather, disease, and disaster.
8. Systems of economic enterprise.
9. Maintaining the stability of the sentiment system itself.

One could go beyond such a list and suggest some kind of "essential social condition" which can be upset by failure in the functioning of shared sentiments and which leads then to various restorative activities by the system.[13] These activities could be classified in terms of those that are successful and those that are self-defeating, tending toward disintegration of the unit, or some kind of malfunctioning that could be visualized as "social ill health."

Despite some attractions in these possibilities, however, I prefer at this time not to pursue such a line of thought in any detail. There are several reasons for this, one being that it follows the model of personality so closely as to be open to suspicion. Another is that we are not concerned in this book with a frame of reference for the "ill health" or disorder of societies and the factors contributing thereto. Our focus is on the individual, his psychiatric disorder, and the interest in sociocultural units is limited to how different kinds and qualities of these can make a difference in the prevalence and characteristics of such disorder.

An additional reason for avoiding the model at this point is that it involves inventing a whole new set of constructs and terms with which to describe and analyze sociocultural phenomena. Such a labor hardly seems warranted in view of the many concepts already at hand. This is especially so since these ideas can for the most part be adapted so as to encompass sentiments. While it is true that this particular word is not always, or even often employed, a variety of other words which cover part if not all of the same areas of thought are almost always used and given a central place. Examples are "beliefs," "opinions," "attitudes," "perceptions," "themes," "patterns of culture," and "values." If these are considered as roughly the equivalents of sentiment, then it is evident that sociocultural groups are frequently described and analyzed in such terms, or can be characterized in such terms after having been differentiated in whole or in part according to other criteria. For example, cultural groups such as the French-speaking and the English-speaking of the Harbor Town, can be distinguished one from the other by their sentiments. So too can socioeconomic classes and families like the Chaunceys, the Youngs and the Chiasons. Although each of these groups shares many sentiments in common with other groups and each is divided within itself by many sentiments, there are, in accordance with the point made earlier, systems of sentiments which are more or less characteristic of each and which mark them off one from the other.

In addition to differences of sentiment content, communities and their components may also be compared in terms of degree of sentiment integration. A quasi-organism with poorly knit sentiments is apt to be also poorly knit and deficient in its functioning. On the other hand, rigid patterns of sentiment imply rigidity of unit function such as to render adaptation to changing circumstances difficult.

For these various reasons, the attempt here will be to use sentiments within the confines of existing concepts such as culture, class, role, and social integration. The thought is that for each of these ways of viewing phenomena, the concept of sentiments gives a framework for description, analysis, and explanation.

In making these observations it is realized that sentiments are not in and of themselves the whole story in the functioning of a community, just as they are not the whole story in the functioning of a personality. They are rather in both instances a convenient way of designating and grasping the intersection of a number of factors. In the case of sociocultural units it must be recognized that behavior is affected by a host of other conditions such as climate, the raw materials available for economic activity, and the practices of neighboring groups. Nevertheless, these environmental forces and potentialities which may stimulate and limit group behavior do so only as they are screened through the sentiment system and as they may contribute to its maintenance and alteration.

V SENTIMENTS AS A BRIDGING CONCEPT [14]

Having discussed sentiments in relation to personality, mental health, and the functioning of sociocultural groups, we arrive now at what is possibly the chief use of the idea. It is suggested that sentiment as a conceptual device constitutes a bridge for analysis and inquiry between sociocultural processes and personality processes. Furthermore, it is thought that this bridging is of a type particularly relevant to the problems of mental health and sociocultural environment.

The bridging stems from the functioning of sentiments both in sociocultural integration and in personality integration. It is not a question here of analogy, or of like processes having a similar name, but of the same process having both a group and an individual aspect.

To repeat an earlier observation, sentiments are never literally shared, but rather invoked by means of symbols which are shared. Symbols have therefore a double role, one in mentation and one in communication. Thus, to speak more precisely though less conveniently, it is the symbol-sentiment-interpersonal process that has both a group and an individual aspect. It is hoped that this will be understood whenever there is reference to shared sentiments.

For illustration, let us take the sentiment "By and large, virtue is rewarded." In the Harbor Town this is widely shared and is an important element in the complex of sentiments upon which sociocultural integration depends. If the sentiment were, by some magic, removed and replaced with "Virtue is never rewarded" there would be far-reaching consequences in other sentiments, in group patterning, and in group functioning.

Aside from its part in sociocultural integration, "By and large, virtue is rewarded" has a function also in the integration of the individual personality systems which compose the group. For most persons, it has a place in the sentiments having to do with the need for belonging to a moral order and has interconnections with other essential striving sentiments as well. For any one of these personalities, removal and replacement with "Virtue is never rewarded" would involve extensive repercussions in the whole system, and for some it would mean serious disintegration.

It is not, of course, being asserted that all sentiments are coequally important at both the group and individual level. All kinds of gradations at both levels are possible and many sorts of combinations of these various gradations can and do occur. The point it is desired to make is that the concept of sentiments raises these kinds of questions regarding individual and group relationships and provides a framework for their exploration.

Suppose, for instance, we want to achieve some understanding of why the sentiment "By and large, virtue is rewarded" exists in the Harbor Town, that is, its origin and present functions. A preliminary step would consist in some clarification and definition as to what shall be meant by these words and what kinds of phenomena shall be considered as indicators. Following this, historical sources and diffusion could be traced in order to answer such questions as: Where did the sentiment come from? And what are the origins of the various forms which it takes? These considerations would lead one into the history of religious and philosophical ideas of the West and how they came to be precipitated in the Harbor Town.

A further step would be inquiry into the functional significance of this sentiment so far as the present community is concerned. This would require mapping of the sociocultural patterns of the town in terms of some set of anthropological or sociological criteria and then seeing what part this "virtue" sentiment played in the total complex. With what other sentiments is it most closely interdependent? What activities of the community and its subsystems are most heavily dependent upon it? Such analysis could be sharpened by repeatedly asking the question: What difference in this or that context would the absence of the sentiment in question make?

Having secured a picture of the historical origins and current functioning of the sentiment, there are several directions in which one could go. One of these might be comparison of a number of different kinds of communities (say of different cultures) in order to see what range of functional configurations the sentiment has and, by this means, learn something about group process.

On the other hand, turning in a different direction one might want to know why individuals participate in sharing this sentiment which is so important for the group. What is it to the persons who manifest it? What are its psychological underpinnings? With such an interest, the sentiment could be examined in a sample of personalities in order to see how it has been acquired in the course of their development and how it is interdependent with other sentiments in these individual systems. This would require its scrutiny in the context of both life-story and the cross-section of the moment. No doubt a number of different types of relationship of the sentiment to the rest of the sentiment system of personality would emerge among these different persons and this could lead to conclusions regarding several different patterns of personality organization and functioning that contribute to the presence of the sentiment in the group. As personalities differ in their total configurations, so the factors contributing to the maintenance of a particular shared sentiment may vary from person to person. Indeed, several personalities can share the same sentiments due to factors that are in sharp contrast. Two men, for instance, could be ardent Democrats, one mainly because his father was a Democrat, and the other mainly because his father was a Republican.

Despite such differences, we may suppose nevertheless that certain combinations of factors or organizations of personality with reference to a particular sentiment are prevalent while others are rare. Hence, generalization regarding why the group supports a shared sentiment may be possible in terms of a limited number of different configurations of personality. All this can be considered at the level of conscious behavior but it is also possible to push the inquiry still deeper, seeking to understand the sentiment in relation to basic urges and unconscious processes.

The suggestion is, then, that a whole range of considerations from the history of ideas to unconscious processes can be seen in relation to each other, rather than as independent or competing systems of explanation. They can be brought to bear on understanding the existence of the "virtue" sentiment in the Harbor Town at mid-century.

In this illustration we began with a group sentiment and worked from it through a series of steps to the same sentiment in the context of personality. It would of course be equally possible to select a sentiment first noted as functionally important to an individual and trace its interconnections and interdependencies both in that particular personality and in the sociocultural group of which the person is a member. Thus, one could take this or that among the essential striving sentiments (derived for the most part from clinical studies of individuals) and, subjecting it to this treatment, examine its functional significance in sociocultural self-integrating units. This might shed some light on the ways and degrees in which functional patterns of personality are and are not consonant with the functional patterns of groups.

A Concept of Sentiments

This line of thought leads to formulating four types of sentiments as targets for investigation.

1. Sentiments which function effectively in the integration of the individual and of the group; that is, the total functioning of the sentiment for individual and group is adequate.
2. Sentiments which are effective for the individual, that is, in maintaining the personality as a functioning whole, but which are destructive to group life.
3. Sentiments constructive in group life but damaging to the integration of the individual.
4. Sentiments damaging to both.

The effects of duration come into this picture also and we must therefore consider sentiments as possibly functioning well now but with disastrous consequences later, for either the individual, the group, or both. We must also consider sentiments which, though giving difficulty now, will work out later to produce greater effectiveness in the individual, in the group, or both. In short, in contemplating the function of sentiments, the time dimension as well as the cross-section of the moment has to be taken into account.

One does not have to begin with a sentiment as the presenting problem in order to use this framework for analysis and investigation. Many events or trends can be resolved into major sentiment components and so tackled in such a manner. This is demonstrated to some extent in *The Governing of Men,* in which a strike at a Japanese Relocation Center is studied and explained largely in terms of the origin and functioning of conflicting sentiments.[15] Although the study does not go very far into the analysis of the functioning of the relevant sentiments in any particular personality, nevertheless the framework for so doing is there. In *Gregorio,* the presenting event is a cultural pattern, hand-trembling among the Navaho.[16] Here, in contrast to the Relocation Center strike, the effort is to examine the function of the pattern in a particular personality and not in a sociocultural group. In proceeding thus the problem becomes largely one of explaining Gregorio's sentiments with regard to the pattern in question. One can, however, put the analysis reflected in both books together within the same framework. If this were done with hand-trembling as the focus it would mean a comprehensive study that took into account both the functions of the pattern in Navaho society and its functions in Navaho personalities. Such a study would provide some advance in understanding both why and how the pattern exists in the group, and why and how individuals participate in it. In short, group functioning and psychological motivation could be brought into relationship with each other.[17]

These lines of thought suggest that it would be possible to apply such an approach to understanding Tom's anxiety crisis. The very first point of attention is his feeling that he was dying, which, since it has some duration, could be regarded as a sentiment. Interdependent with it were other sentiments having a longer history and having to do with his standards, his sense of measuring up, and his self-doubts. Examples of various contributory possibilities in terms of cognition, affect, basic urges, and unconscious factors, together with the developmental life-story and the cross-section of the moment have all been outlined in Chapter III. The group functioning aspects, however, have not been explored for their significance. The sentiment "I am dying" is not by itself widely enough shared so that it can be called a cultural pattern, even though at any given moment there may be in a society numbers of people suffering from acute anxiety and many may have a basic existential uneasiness. On the other hand, the interdependent sentiments regarding standards, the importance of measuring up, the definitions of goals, and the criteria for self-evaluation and self-disparagement are indeed widely shared and have many implications for the functioning of the community and for most personalities in the community.[18] Here, then, is both an avenue and target of inquiry: What is the sociocultural function of these sentiments which play a significant part in the genesis and maintenance of Tom's disorder, and, on the other hand, how do they articulate into those personalities who are apparently free of psychiatric disorder? Given the discovery that in the sociocultural environment there are sentiments which in some personalities are part of a malfunctional process, while in others these same sentiments are not, we can seek to understand what factors (including what different kinds of environments and what different kinds of personalities) contribute to this difference.

Tom Young's case is not unique among instances of psychiatric disorder in that the presenting problem, or central symptom pattern, is mainly a sentiment. This is true of most of the different types outlined in Chapter IV. With obsessive-compulsive disorders, for example, the presenting symptom is usually an extreme form of a sentiment such as the importance of cleanliness. Similarly, depressions, paranoid states, psychopathic conditions, and other disorders have the way the patient feels about something as a central issue. Unlike Tom's case, this feeling is often one that is shared, though to a lesser degree or somehow differently, by other persons who are not patients. The presenting front of many psychiatric conditions is therefore some kind of distortion of sentiment pattern. The similarities and differences between the distorted sentiments and the comparable sentiments in the community are open to investigation, both with regard to person functioning (personality) and community functioning.

More important, however, than the complex of sentiments that make up a presenting pattern, is the entanglement of shared sentiments underlying—but contributing to—this central issue. This repeats on the larger scale of most psychiatric disorders what was said in the case of Tom's anxiety neurosis. By identifying and tracing these sentiments to their place or lack of it in the functioning of the sociocultural unit, there is promise of considerable illumination regarding both the personality and societal processes at work. When we can identify sentiments or sentiment clusters which play a significant part in the malfunctioning of personalities as outlined in Section III of this chapter, and which at the same time are widely shared and hence important in group integration as outlined in Section VI, then we can be sure that our attention is on a crucial and researchable matter.

Having discussed sentiments at both group and personality levels, a word may be said with regard to the intermediate idea of role.[19] This is in itself a bridging concept between individual and societal patterns and the question must be raised as to how the notion of sentiments can articulate with it. I believe that role concepts are, in part at least, a particular way of ordering sentiments. A role can be regarded as made up of a constellation of sentiments that have a specific societal function as their focus. For example, the role of father means the cluster of main sentiments regarding what fathers can and should do, what they cannot and should not do, and how they should and should not be treated in a variety of situations.

From roles, let us return once more to the community level and touch on a general matter for which we are now prepared. Instead of picking a single item arbitrarily, like the "virtue" sentiment, one can ask the more general question: What sentiments play a major part in

the unit's functioning? When some constellations of these are identified, one can then, on a sampling basis, attempt to see what part
they play in the functioning of personalities, with particular attention
to disorder and health.

This again opens opportunities for comparative studies. If different
groups of people differ in their main patterns of shared sentiment,
then such groups must differ from one to the other with regard to their
effects on the personalities of constituent members. Some patterns of
shared sentiment, in short, may provide a more healthy environment
than do others. There is here a basis for understanding the behavior
of a community as a whole—its trends, how it may respond to the
events of this changing world, some of the reasons behind otherwise
anomalous behavior, the nature of its articulation with the still larger
society (contributive and disruptive tendencies), and other broad, yet
significant, questions. There is, as in the case of personality, the
foundation for limited prediction and limited explanation.

It should be observed in passing that the above includes the opportunity for taking into account latent as well as manifest functioning of
the sociocultural group.[20] Thus the concept of sentiments provides a
starting point for the examination of underlying factors at both the
individual and the group level.

It is not the purpose of this volume to present all the bridging implications which adhere to the concept of sentiments. Some of the
main areas spanned may, however, be summed up as follows:

1. Psychiatric disorder and mental health.
2. Surface behavior and intrapsychic aspects of personality.
3. Individual behavior and group behavior.
4. Sociocultural integration and personality integration.
5. Social pathology and psychopathology.
6. Social health and social pathology.

It will be noted that nothing so far has been said of the practical
questions of method, as for instance, how does one identify and measure sentiments in groups? And how does one secure and study a
sample of personalities? Development of such topics would be outside
the purposes of the frame of reference, but an approach to method
with regard to the instance chosen will be taken up in succeeding
chapters.

A Concept of Sentiments

VI CONCLUSION

The concept which is designated in these pages as "sentiment" has been given many names by different writers over a very long period of time. This far antedates the emergence of the social sciences and psychiatry and it has extensions wholly outside these fields. To give a comprehensive account of the concept would, therefore, not be feasible within the bounds of this volume. Yet some perspective is important as part of understanding the nature of the concept. It cannot be adequately grasped in purely psychological or sociocultural terms and it cannot be appreciated if seen only in a contemporary framework. The history of human thought as reflected in literature and philosophy presents opportunity for gathering some perspective. For this reason a brief review and discussion of some aspects of both its historical and contemporary use are offered in Appendix A.

Such longstanding, plentiful, and protean employment of an idea suggests its utility as an instrument for grasping and analyzing human behavior. A statement to this effect by Ortega y Gasset will be used to close this chapter, because it brings together the idea of striving, personality, characteristics of human society, and the trends of history, and also because of its power of expression. Employing the words "convictions" (*convicciones*) and "beliefs" (*creencias*) where we would use sentiments, he says:

The most trivial and at the same time the most important note in human life is that man has no choice but to be always doing something to keep himself in existence. Life is given to us; we do not give it to ourselves, rather we find ourselves in it, suddenly and without knowing how. But the life which is given us is not given us ready-made; we must make it for ourselves, each one his own. Life is a task. . . . Each individual before doing anything must decide for himself and at his own risk what he is going to do. But this decision is impossible unless one possesses certain convictions concerning the nature of things around one, the nature of other men, of oneself. Only in the light of such convictions can one prefer one act to another, can one, in short, live.

It follows that man must ever be grounded on some belief, and that the structure of his life will depend primordially on the beliefs on which he is grounded; and further that the most decisive changes in humanity are changes of belief, the intensifying or weakening of beliefs. The diagnosis of any human existence, whether of an individual, a people or an age, must begin by establishing the repertory of its convictions. For always in living one sets out from certain convictions. They are the ground beneath our feet, and it is for this reason we say that man is grounded on them. It is man's beliefs that truly constitute his state. I have spoken of them as a repertory to indicate that the plurality of beliefs on which an individual, a people, or an age is grounded never possesses a completely logical articulation, that is to say, does not form a system of ideas such as, for example, a philosophy constitutes or aims at constituting. The beliefs that coexist in any human life, sustaining, impelling, and directing it, are on occasion incongruous, contradictory, at the least confused. Be it noted that all these qualifications attach to beliefs insofar as they partake of ideas. But it is erroneous to define belief as an idea. Once an idea has been thought it has exhausted its role and its consistency. . . . A belief is not merely an idea that is thought, it is an idea in which one also believes. And believing is not an operation of the intellectual mechanism, but a function of the living being as such, the function of guiding his conduct, his performance of his task.

This observation once made, I can now withdraw my previous expression and say that beliefs, a mere incoherent repertory insofar as they are merely ideas, always constitute a system insofar as they are effective beliefs; in other words, that while lacking articulation from the logical or strictly intellectual point of view, they do nonetheless possess a vital articulation, they *function* as beliefs resting one on another, combining with one another to form a whole: in short, that they always present themselves as members of an organism, of a structure. This causes them among other things always to possess their own architecture and to function as a hierarchy. In every human life there are beliefs that are basic, fundamental, radical, and there are others derived from these, upheld by them, and secondary to them. If this observation is supremely trivial, the fault is not mine that with all its triviality it remains of the greatest importance. For should the beliefs by which one lives lack structure, since their number in each individual life is legion there must result a mere pullulation hostile to all idea of order and incomprehensible in consequence.

The fact that we should see them, on the contrary, as endowed with a structure and a hierarchy allows us to penetrate their hidden order and consequently to understand our own life and the life of others, that of today and that of other days.

Thus we may now say that the diagnosing of any human existence, whether of an individual, a people, or an age, must begin by an ordered inventory of its system of convictions, and to this end it must establish before all else which belief is fundamental, decisive, sustaining, and breathing life into all the others.[21]

CHAPTER NOTES

1. In addition to the general acknowledgements mentioned later, in Appendix C, it should be noted that this chapter has benefited from discussion of the concept of sentiment with Christoph Heinicke, David Mandelbaum, and Robert N. Wilson.

2. Most of these terms are sufficiently well known not to warrant detailed reference. An example, however, of the emphasis given one aspect of personality in contrast to the inclusiveness of "personality as a whole" is Kardiner's and Linton's description of "basic personality type."

"The *basic personality type* for any society is that personality configuration which is shared by the bulk of the society's members as a result of the early experiences which they have in common. It does not correspond to the total personality of the individual but rather to the projective systems or, in different phraseology, the value-attitude systems which are basic to the individual's personality configuration. Thus the same basic personality type may be reflected in many different forms of behavior and may enter into many different total personality configurations." See ABRAM KARDINER, *The Psychological Frontiers of Society*, Foreword by RALPH LINTON (New York: Columbia Univ. Press, 1945), p. viii.

Personality as a "pattern of interpersonal relationships" is an emphasis used by many social scientists. Among psychiatrists this is also found in Sullivan and Whitehorn. For example: "Personality is the organized system of sentiments or attitudes by which one establishes relationships with others and negotiates interpersonal transactions." See JOHN C. WHITEHORN, "Guide to Interviewing and Clinical Personality Study," *Archives of Neurology and Psychiatry*, Vol. 52, no. 3, 1944, p. 212.

3. A review of the anthropological concepts of personality is to be found in Note 10, Chapter III. For brief compara-

tive review of psychological and sociological formulations of personality, *see* GUY E. SWANSON, "Personality," to appear in the forthcoming United Nations Educational, Scientific, and Cultural Organization *Dictionary of the Social Sciences.*

A more extensive though by no means exhaustive review is in CALVIN S. HALL and GARDNER LINDZEY (Eds.), *Theories of Personality* (New York: Wiley, 1957). *See also:* CLYDE KLUCKHOHN and HENRY A. MURRAY, *Personality in Nature, Society, and Culture* (New York: Knopf, 1953); GORDON W. ALLPORT, *Personality, A Psychological Interpretation* (New York: Holt, 1937); GARDNER MURPHY, *Personality, A Biosocial Approach to Origins and Structure* (New York: Harper, 1947); DAVID C. MC CLELLAND, *Personality* (New York: Dryden, 1951); GEORGE A. KELLY, "Theory of Personality," *The Psychology of Personal Constructs* (New York: Norton, 1955), Vol. 1; J. L. MC CARY, (Ed.), *Psychology of Personality, Six Modern Approaches* (New York: Grove, 1956); KINGSLEY DAVIS, "The Individual and His Society," in *Human Society* (New York: Macmillan, 1948), Part II; ALEX INKELES, "Personality and Social Structure," in ROBERT K. MERTON, LEONARD BROOM, and LEONARD S. COTTRELL, JR. (Eds.), *Sociology Today: Problems and Prospects* (New York: Basic Books, 1959), pp. 249-276; EDGAR F. BORGATTA and HENRY J. MEYER (Eds.), "The Person as a Social Unit," in *Sociological Theory, Present-Day Sociology from the Past* (New York: Knopf, 1956), Part II.

One of the problems inherent in the convenient and necessary division of nature into topics, and of study into disciplines focused on topics, is what Cooley has called the "illusion of centrality."

"Very like this is what I may call the *illusion of centrality,* the fact that if you are familiar with any one factor of life it presents itself to you as a centre from which influence radiates in all directions, somewhat in the same way that the trees in an orchard will appear to radiate from any point where you happen to stand. Indeed it really is such a centre; the illusion arises from not seeing that every other factor is a centre also. The individual is a very real and active thing, but so is the group or general tendency; it is true that you can see life from the standpoint of imitation (several writers have centred upon this) but so you can from the standpoint of competition or organization.

A Concept of Sentiments

The economic process is as vital as anything can be, and there is nothing in life that does not change when it changes; but the same is true of the ideal processes; geography is important, but not more so than the technical institutions through which we react upon it; and so on." *See:* CHARLES H. COOLEY, *Social Process* (New York: Scribners, 1918), pp. 50-51.

The particular disciplines Cooley employs in his illustration are not perhaps those which today would occur to us most readily, but the tendency in each discipline and in subareas within disciplines is certainly there. For each of us, our own apple tree still appears to be the center of the orchard. Hence the need for bridging concepts to correct the illusion.

4. Henderson and Gillespie provide an example of the kind of definition to be found in psychiatric texts.

"Personality, as used in clinical psychiatry, is the integrated activity of all the reaction-tendencies of the daily life of the individual. It is, in other words, the person as he is known to his friends. This is the simple clinical connotation of the word. It has lately been the custom to use the term also in a much wider sense, regarding personality as the total integrated expression of the various 'levels' of which the individual is constructed—the lowest, or vegetative level (endocrine-sympathetic), the sensorimotor level (central nervous system) and the psychic level."

See DAVID HENDERSON and R. D. GILLESPIE, *Text-book of Psychiatry* (New York: Oxford Univ. Press, 1950), p. 126.

A well-known statement of personality from Karl Menninger also stresses the holistic viewpoint.

Personality ". . . means the individual as a whole, his height and weight and loves and hates and blood pressure and reflexes; his smiles and hopes and bowed legs and enlarged tonsils. It means all that anyone is and all that he is trying to become." (KARL MENNINGER, *The Human Mind* [New York: Knopf, 1937]).

See also: WENDELL MUNCIE, "Psychobiology, The Study of Normal Behavior," *Psychobiology and Psychiatry* (St. Louis: Mosby, 1948), Part I, pp. 17-136; OSKAR DIETHELM, "Study of Personality," *Treatment in Psychiatry* (Springfield, Ill.: Thomas, 1955), Chap. II, pp. 10-37; JULES H. MAS-

SERMAN, "Glossary," *Principles of Dynamic Psychiatry* (Philadelphia: Saunders, 1946), p. 290; ARTHUR P. NOYES, *Modern Clinical Psychiatry* (Philadelphia: Saunders, 1953), p. 18.

5. One of the major exponents of "personality as a whole" was Adolf Meyer. For many years, in his teaching at Johns Hopkins, he was accustomed to take as a central point in explaining his ideas of personality "the functions of the 'he' or 'she' or 'you' or 'I.' " By this he placed emphasis on the functioning of the person as contrasted with focus on either physiological or psychological parts (e.g., hormones, intelligence, or libido). He also emphasized the patterned nature of this totality by frequent use of the word "organization." Thus, for personality viewed in terms of the cross-section of the moment, he spoke of "subject organization," and for personality viewed in terms of the total life-story leading up to the moment, he spoke of "personality organization." *See:* ADOLF MEYER, *Psychobiology, A Science of Man* (compiled and edited by EUNICE E. WINTERS and ANNA MAE BOWERS) (Springfield, Ill.: Thomas, 1957), pp. 3-110; ADOLF MEYER, *The Collected Papers of Adolf Meyer* (EUNICE E. WINTERS, Ed.) (Baltimore: Johns Hopkins Press, 1951), Vol. III, "Medical Teaching," pp. 271-278, 429-443.

Meyer acknowledged the general influence of William James a great many times in his writings, and it seems probable that this included James' concept of the "Self" with the pronoun "I" at its center. *See* WILLIAM JAMES, *The Principles of Psychology* (New York: Holt, 1890), Vol. I, p. 291.

Although this kind of thinking has been characteristic of psychiatry, it would be inaccurate to suggest exclusive possession by this field. In recent years similar ideas have been expressed in other disciplines, such as psychology. Donald Adams utilizes the following point of departure which is very much like that of Meyer:

"By the term personality I shall mean an entity of the sort you are referring to when you use the first personal pronoun. When you say 'I' you mean something definite by it, and your hearer understands something definite. His referent for your use of the term will not be quite the same as yours, since you have experienced things about yourself that he has not and he has experienced things about you that you have not; but the two referents are nearly enough the same to make communication possible. That is the best we can hope for in this imperfect world, and it will do for a start." *See* DONALD K. ADAMS, *The Anatomy of Personality* (New York: Random House, 1954), p. 7.

Smith, Bruner, and White, to take another instance, have apparently developed their view independently of psychiatry, since they reject psychoanalytic theory as unsatisfactory for their purposes and make no mention of any other psychiatric orientation. Nevertheless, they arrive at a particularly well-expressed statement that is in harmony with the idea of personality employed here. I shall give this at length because it serves a double purpose in that it illuminates the concept of personality employed in this book and at the same time provides an example of relevant thinking from outside the field of psychiatry.

Considering personality as a construct inferred from a number of consistent regular forms (i.e., patterns) of behavior, six main characteristics are outlined:

"1. It is marked by *striving*. As an organization of behavior tendencies formed in the process of adaptive striving after goals, it includes the tendency to be selectively aware of objects related to certain goals, to pursue these goals, and to employ certain favored techniques in their pursuit. The aims of striving, most generally stated, are *construction* and *defense*. We seek gratification, learn to adapt to the circumstances in which gratification can take place. This is constructive striving. But we also strive to defend ourselves against what is disruptive and anxiety-arousing, to protect against what upsets gratification and adjustment.

"2. *Striving characterizes cognitive activity:* perceiving, remembering, thinking, etc. Not only does cognition function in the service of other needs, but it seems to be intrinsically motivated: an 'effort after meaning' or, as Tolman has called it, a 'placing need' which can be activated by a lack of structure in the individual's life space.

"3. Personality is an *organized* whole rather than an unrelated congeries of tendencies. The various aspects of personality are mutually interdependent and mutually adapted. Since not all behavior tendencies are of equal potency, we may expect to find a *hierarchical* organization in which some take precedence over others. Thus, a change in a basic need may bring about a change in a series of related, dependent attitudes. A change in one dominant attitude may change various others which are subservient to it.

"4. While the interdependency of personality functioning is sufficient to lead to a considerable degree of *unity, conflict* within the personality as well as between personality and environmental forces often occurs. Such conflicts pose problems for the maintenance and growth of the person. Some of the main lines of development of the personality are determined by the strategy adopted for dealing with them.

"5. The social and even the physical environment of the individual are not random series of events; rather, they are patterned by the culture of which he is a member. It is also clear that the opportunities for learning to respond to the environment are finitely delimited by the culture. In this respect, the individual, in Dollard's terms, is not only to be considered in his biological and psychological individuality, but also as a 'specimen in a cultural series.'

"6. Finally, a special place in the hierarchical organization of personality must be given to those inferred processes which underlie the experience of self. Whether we use the term Phenomenal Self, Ego, Self Image, or some other, it is quite apparent that a major contribution to consistency of behavior can be referred to the person's reactions to his experience of self."

See M. BREWSTER SMITH, JEROME S. BRUNER, and ROBERT W. WHITE, *Opinions and Personality* (New York: Wiley, 1956), pp. 32-33.

This quotation gives among other things some prominence to a hierarchical ordering of personality, and particular emphasis to the concept of self. Such points have been implied in the treatment of personality given thus far in the frame of reference, but they have not been explicitly stated. The matter of hierarchy is discussed in the present chapter on pp. 291-293. Some orientation with regard to the self concept may be found in ALEXANDER H. LEIGHTON, JOHN A. CLAUSEN, and ROBERT N. WILSON (Eds.), *Explorations in Social Psychiatry* (New York: Basic Books, 1957).

A Concept of Sentiments

6. It is assumed that the development and differentiation of sentiments involves learning. For the purposes of this frame of reference, however, it is not thought necessary to outline a position with regard to learning theory. The general orientation is in terms of Pavlov's formulations of conditioning. See I. P. PAVLOV, *Conditioned Reflexes* (G. V. ANREP, trans.) (London: Oxford Univ. Press, 1927).

7. The literature on symbolization is extensive. The ideas that have been set down here have been derived primarily from Adolf Meyer. *See:* ADOLF MEYER, *Psychobiology, A Science of Man,* pp. 3-110; ADOLF MEYER, *The Collected Papers of Adolf Meyer,* Vol. III, "Medical Teaching," pp. 271-276, 285, and 432-435. *See also:* EDWARD SAPIR, *Selected Writings of Edward Sapir in Language, Culture and Personality* (DAVID G. MANDELBAUM, Ed.) (Berkeley: Univ. California Press, 1951), especially, "Symbolism," pp. 564-568; ERNST CASSIRER, *An Essay on Man* (New Haven: Yale Univ. Press, 1944); SUSANNE K. LANGER, *Philosophy in a New Key* (Cambridge: Harvard Univ. Press, 1942); CHARLES MORRIS, *Signs, Language and Behavior* (New York: Prentice-Hall, 1946); W. LLOYD WARNER, "The Society, the Individual, and his Mental Disorder," *The American Journal of Psychiatry,* Vol. 94, no. 2, 1937, pp. 275-284; A. IRVING HALLOWELL, *Culture and Experience* (Philadelphia; Univ. Pennsylvania Press, 1955), pp. 2-13; SOLOMON E. ASCH, *Social Psychology* (New York: Prentice-Hall, 1952), pp. 43-71.

8. For a previous discussion of this point, *see* ALEXANDER H. LEIGHTON, *The Governing of Men* (Princeton: Princeton Univ. Press, 1946), pp. 289-290.

9. An earlier discussion of flexibility and rigidity in sentiments may be found in ALEXANDER H. LEIGHTON: *The Governing of Men,* pp. 291-292, 299, 314-320, and 385-386; and *Human Relations in a Changing World,* (New York: Dutton, 1949), pp. 78, 87-94.

10. Most of us have a tendency to think of a central point of control with regard to personality that is probably off the mark. This is very likely a natural carry-over from everyday experience. Thus, if we consider a car, we think of a driver controlling the car, and the driver's brain con-trolling the driver, and the cortex controlling the brain. The implicit model is of an executive controlling a system, a super-executive controlling the executive and so on. A difficulty is that the final authority—the ultimate seat of control—keeps always retreating before you as this line of analysis is pursued. Such can be obviated if it is assumed that in personality there is no ultimate point from which all governing basically emanates, but rather that control is a resultant of the functioning of a number of interdepend-ent parts or subsystems.

For some discussions of hierarchy and integration in personality, *see:* A. H. MASLOW, *Motivation and Personality* (New York: Harper, 1954).

11. For a different view regarding the relationship of un-conscious process to psychopathology, *see* LAWRENCE S. KUBIE, "Social Forces and the Neurotic Process," in LEIGH-TON, CLAUSEN, and WILSON (Eds.), *Explorations in Social Psychiatry.*

12. A number of authors have formulated ideas about what constitutes mental health. An excellent review of these is to be found in MARIE JAHODA, *Current Concepts of Positive Mental Health,* No. I, Joint Commission on Mental Ill-ness and Health, Monograph Series (New York: Basic Books, 1958).

The last chapter of this book written by Walter E. Bar-ton, M.D., is entitled "Viewpoint of a Clinician." It differs considerably from the rest of the volume and is on the whole more in harmony with the orientation of this frame of reference.

Two other references are: FREDERICK C. REDLICH, "The Concept of Health in Psychiatry" in LEIGHTON, CLAUSEN, and WILSON (Eds.), *Explorations in Social Psychiatry;* and M. BREWSTER SMITH, "Optima of Mental Health: A General Frame of Reference," *Psychiatry,* Vol. 13, 1950, pp. 503-510.

13. A number of social scientists have similarly outlined a list of necessary conditions for social functioning. Among them are WILLIAM MC DOUGALL, *The Group Mind* (Cam-bridge, England: University Press, 1920); D. F. ABERLE, A.

K. COHEN, A. K. DAVIS, M. J. LEVY, F. X. SUTTON, "The Functional Prerequisites of a Society," in *Ethics,* Vol. 9, January 1950, pp. 100-111.

14. In connection with sentiments as a bridging concept and the relationship between sentiments, symbols, personality, and culture, acknowledgement should be made of the influence of Edward Sapir. This has been in part directly through his writings and in part indirectly through the influence he exerted on Adolf Meyer and on Clyde Kluckhohn.

See EDWARD SAPIR, *Selected Writings of Edward Sapir in Language, Culture and Personality,* especially Part III, "The Interplay of Culture and Personality," pp. 507-597.

15. *See* ALEXANDER H. LEIGHTON, *The Governing of Men.* The term mainly used (and indexed) in this volume is "system of belief," but, as noted on p. 386 of the book, this is equivalent to those sentiments which are socially shared and relatively resistant to change.

16. *See*: ALEXANDER H. LEIGHTON and DOROTHEA C. LEIGHTON, *Gregorio, The Hand-Trembler, A Psychobiological Personality Study of a Navaho Indian* (Cambridge, Papers of the Peabody Museum of American Archaeology and Ethnology, Harvard University, 1949).

17. The number and kinds of problems that can be approached in this manner are virtually limitless. Some examples are: race prejudice, class systems, factors involved in war and peace, resistance to and acceptance of technological change, drug addiction, juvenile delinquency, gangsterism, radical political groups, conservatism, liberal patterns, community development, and the capacities of groups and individuals with respect to religion, art, and science. These remarks should not be interpreted as a grandiose claim that satisfactory solutions are at hand to humanity's problems. The point is rather that here is a way into these problems that has sufficient promise to be worthy of attention.

18. A clinical analysis somewhat along these lines regarding disparaging sentiments may be found in E. J. CLEVE-

LAND and W. D. LONGAKER, "Neurotic Patterns in the Family," in *Explorations in Social Psychiatry*.

19. *See* Chapter Notes 14 and 15 of Chapter III.

20. For reference to the concept of latent function as applied to groups, *see* Chapter Note 13, Chapter VI.

21. *See* JOSÉ ORTEGA Y GASSET, *Toward A Philosophy of History* (New York: Norton, 1941), pp. 165-168.

A Concept of Sentiments

275

Chapter VIII

Selection of Sociocultural Categories

THE PROBLEM NOW is to choose, against the background of all the preceding pages and from among a number of possibilities, a system of sociocultural categories that will be meaningful in terms of disposition toward psychiatric disorder and mental health. To achieve this, attention will be given in the present chapter first to some criteria, then to the community unit in the light of the criteria, next to the designation of a framework for categorizing and comparing communities, and, finally, to considering alternative approaches.

I SOME CRITERIA FOR CHOOSING A SYSTEM OF CATEGORIES

1. *The system of categories should refer to patterns at the sociocultural level of conceptualization.*

This view has been outlined previously in Chapter VI. It is based in part on considerations of economy of effort, since it opens up the way to utilizing concepts and methods already at hand in social science, and in part on expecting for theoretical reasons a relationship between group functioning and personality functioning.

There is here, however, a turning away from two other possibilities. One is to attempt building relatively independent concepts of sociocultural categories based on considerations of mental health and psychiatric disorder. The other is to approach the matter from an empirical viewpoint and, after obtaining a probability sample, examine those persons who do and who do not have psychiatric disorder in terms of all conceivable sociocultural influences in the hope of factoring out significant complexes of relationships. Neither of these approaches is to be wholly rejected, but, because of the enormous work entailed in both, there is merit in trying first to see if some more efficient strategy can be developed. This is in line with the view that much of science consists in trying to find hidden ways through high, thick walls.

2. *The system of categories should cover the entire life-arc of the persons who are the focus of the study.*

This follows from what has been said about life-story and cross-section in personality and the development and maintenance of psychiatric disorders (Chapters I, III, V, and VII). Categories which touch only on a segment of life refer to phenomena that can have only a partial effect, with the result that large areas of personality experience are thus omitted from consideration, areas which may include some events of major significance. More important still is the danger of missing altogether the effects of combinations of factors, the cumulations along the life-arc together with the cross-section of the moment.

According to the frame of reference so far presented, it is these combinations rather than particular environmental factors that are expected to have most influence with regard to psychiatric disorder. Since combinations include not only various noxious factors but also benign and health-promoting agents, the kind of influence a given sociocultural pattern possesses may be easily misconstrued if considered in isolation. This can happen if a particular pattern under study is damaging but is compensated by other sociocultural patterns which are not under study. For example, a man might be under severe psychological stress in his job situation, yet able to handle this due to assets in his family and community relationships and in the preparation given him by his previous life experiences.

As can be seen, this criterion is an expression of the preference for approach by successive approximations and pertains to a desire to discover polar categories of sociocultural patterns in terms of many and few psychiatric cases. It sets aside for the time being the more specific testing of theories regarding particular constellations of conditions at limited periods on the life-arc, as for instance maternal deprivation during infancy or general stress during adulthood.

3. *The system of categories must be relevant to expectations regarding the influence of sociocultural environment on the development of psychiatric disorder as outlined in Chapter V and provide the basis for the statement of at least some general hypotheses.*

By this I mean that there should be ground for gathering evidence for and against some kind of proposition, however broad. While this, as noted earlier, avoids a purely empirical approach, it is important to realize that our ambitions to establish hypotheses should be limited, given our level of knowledge, concepts, and instruments. The aim is somewhere between full-fledged empirical investigation and crucial testing with a highly specific research design. Both extremes are thought to be wasteful and very likely futile under present circumstances.

The circumstances regarded as noxious are summarized at the end of Chapter V and may be recapitulated here as follows:

a) High degree of apparent difficulty and risk with regard to physical security, sexual satisfaction, expression of hostility, expression of love, securing love, obtaining recognition, expression of spontaneity, orientation to society, membership in a human group, and a sense of belonging to a moral order.

b) Conditions which permit or foster the formation of those behavior patterns (intrapersonal and interpersonal) which lead to psychiatric disorder, rather than to more constructive forms of adaptation.

c) The absence of therapeutic and remedial resources, formal and informal, overt and covert.

4. *The categories should be capable of containing large enough numbers of people to permit statistical treatment.*

This is important not only in the first stage of locating gross relationships between prevalence of psychiatric disorder and sociocultural patterns but also later when it will be a question of progressive searching for more discrete relationships with control on many variables.

5. *The system of categories should be workable within the common limitations of time, money, and personnel.*

This point is self-evident enough to require no comment.

II THE COMMUNITY IN THE LIGHT OF THESE CRITERIA

The community, considered as a self-integrating unit or quasi-organism, is not in and of itself a system of categories. Before attempting to establish a typology of communities, however, it is appropriate to consider whether or not any system of categories based on communities could fulfill the criteria that have been outlined.

With regard to the first item, "The system of categories should refer to patterns at the sociocultural level of conceptualization," some objection could be raised on the ground that the quasi-organism orientation is not one that is current in social science thinking. If it does not hark back to Herbert Spencer, at least it does to Malinowski and Radcliffe-Brown and seems rooted in a type of functional theory which some would claim has failed to be very fruitful and in which there is no longer much interest.

It would be a digression to argue such points. The kind of functional theory that is meant, and its use, can best be indicated by the total report contained in these three volumes. For the time being all that need be pointed out is that Merton's and Parsons' theories of function, Williams' views of the workings of American society, some of the concepts of general systems and the more pragmatic ideas and methods of community study have, it seems to me, something

Selection of Sociocultural Categories

in common with what is intended here by sociocultural self-integrating unit and its processes. Thus many people who might reject the orientation of the quasi-organism could nevertheless feel at home with the idea of communities as one way of quartering the sociocultural fabric and agree that workable methods for community study have been developed.[1]

Turning to the second item, it is evident that the community unit is one in which a person can spend his entire existence. Not everybody does, of course, but in some communities most people do and it is consequently possible to think in terms of total coverage of the life-arc. This is in contrast to many other sociocultural patterns that could have been selected, such as the family or roles. Despite the tremendous importance of the family to personality, people do not live all of their lives in a family and the same applies even more strongly to most of the roles of which one can think. In fact, this criterion of life-span calls in question, so far as our purposes are concerned, most of the other sociocultural categories that might be used. A return to this topic will be made later in the last section of this chapter where some alternatives are considered.

So far as items 4 (statistical) and 5 (practical) are concerned, communities would appear to offer no outstanding obstacles. That there would be difficulties to overcome goes without saying, but these are in keeping with the general and pervasive problems inherent in any study of human society.

The question remaining, then, is the matter of being able to devise a system of categories for communities that would have theoretical relevance as required by item 3. This topic is large enough to command a section to itself.

III A FRAMEWORK FOR CATEGORIZING COMMUNITY UNITS

It will be recalled that the goal in view is to find some way to identify species of communities in which instances of psychiatric disorder congregate and others in which there is relative absence of such conditions. This is a first step toward the more long-range goal of progressive examination of the factors in such a relationship.

One possibility is to use culture as a basis for typing communities. It is fairly easy to see the relevance of culture and the potential importance of cultural contrasts for differences in personality and hence for differences in the prevalence of psychiatric disorder. On the other hand, it is not so easy to think of categories suitable for our purposes by which cultures might be classified; indeed, it is difficult to select even two cultures such that one can be regarded as necessarily more noxious than the other. Since these matters are of importance they will be discussed at some length.

As a place to begin, let it be recalled again that the community is here viewed as a quasi-organism with features of energy utilization, integration, and duration through time. Culture may be conceived as the patterning or style in which these phenomena proceed. Thus, all cultures must include primary activities such as food-securing, reproduction, and the preservation of health. It is likely that there are also certain primary psychological needs on the part of human beings which must be met, as for instance the urge for love, the urge for belonging in a group, and other items indicated in the essential striving sentiments.

There are many styles, however, in which the primary activities can be conducted—in other words, cultural differences. In part these may be attributed to conditions of physical environment. Thus Eskimos hunt seals and walruses whereas Navahos raise sheep. But in other respects the difference can be seen as the product of a succession of events with their effects in skills and sentiments transmitted cumulatively from one generation to the next. Navahos raise sheep, for example, whereas Pueblo Indians in the same areas give emphasis to crops.

Differences are also derived from the fact that any particular style for the procedure of primary activities brings with it need and opportunity for other procedures. The Eskimo carves ivory to make harpoon heads for his seal hunting, the Navaho and his family live a semi-nomadic existence in order to keep their sheep in grass, while the Pueblo farmer has techniques of irrigation. Each of these procedures in turn creates opportunities for or impels others with the result that complex interdependent systems of practices and sentiment can be delineated, each constituting a culture and one often markedly different from the other.

Selection of Sociocultural Categories

The illustrations have been made fairly elemental for the sake of exposition. The same characteristics can, however, be presumed to exist in relation to emotional and interpersonal needs. If, for example, sexual and family functions are performed through patterns of monogamy here, polygyny there, or polyandry in another society, each of the patterns brings with it widely different opportunities and needs ranging from the control of property to the control of jealousy.

When one speaks therefore of two or more cultures he is referring to two or more differently patterned fabrics of social behavior through which the same primary activities are performed and through which certain other activities characteristic of each particular style are also accomplished.[2]

With this definition in mind, it is possible to think of comparison regarding the effectiveness of functioning. Some cultures, for instance, have subsistence techniques that keep them well supplied while others fail to avoid undernutrition and at times famine. The fact that non-cultural circumstances also enter the picture should not obscure the difference culture can make. Reflection on North America as it was at the time of purely Indian cultures and as it is today can bring this out. The Indians had oil, coal, and steel in their land, but these resources were of no use to them. Similar contrasts in the peoples of different cultures may be made in regard to the capacity to achieve protection from disease as revealed in comparing morbidity rates and life expectancy.

These differences in the effectiveness of cultures with regard to rather stark matters of survival suggest that there may also be functional differences of a more subtle kind. Cultures could, for instance, differ in the sort of medium they provide for the satisfaction of essential striving sentiments. Just as some cultures do better than others in matters related to physical security, so they may also differ in matters related to love, sexual satisfaction, recognition, and all the other items that have been listed in the E series of propositions on pp. 158-159. In saying this, I am not ignoring the possibility that some shared sentiments of the culture may well so color perceptions as to minimize the traumatic effect of interference in what have been termed essential striving sentiments. In other words, deprivations are relative and depend to a large extent on how circumstances are perceived. My assumption is that, although such modifying influences exist, they have their limits. The needs reflected in the essential striving sentiments are assumed to be pan-human even though different cultures may vary in the degree to which they influence the sensitivity of their constituent members to interference.

In a similar manner one culture as compared to another might offer many inducements to symptom development and perpetuation, be rewarding to certain patterns of self-defeating behavior as suggested in the B series of propositions (pages 168 and 177).

To reverse the picture, one may also suppose a culture that would, as compared to another, offer rich opportunities for satisfying essential striving sentiments indicated in the E series and encourage nonpathological modes of adaptation as in the C series (pages 169-170, and 177).

These considerations must also be viewed in the perspective of personality development. An aspect of any given culture has to do with the formation of the personalities of children born into the group such that these personalities will fall on a range that makes it possible for them to fit into the system. Cultures could, however, differ from each other with regard to effectiveness in this matter. Some might do it well, whereas others might show considerable deficiency, with problems of adjustment and stress appearing in later life. In short, the sentiments laid down in childhood might not fit well the situations and demands of adulthood.

These rather broad perspectives open the way for thinking about more specific possibilities in cultural contrast. For example, while all cultures probably expose some people more than the rest to noxious influences, it may be possible to find cultures which differ from each other considerably as to the number in such disadvantaged categories.

Difference might also lie in the kind of stress applied to personality. Some only of the essential strivings may be seriously limited in this way of life, while a different set may meet with interference in that. The obstacles to satisfaction in sex and love in Western culture have often been pointed out, while food is almost never mentioned. Holmberg has indicated that among the Siriono sex does not seem to be this kind of problem, while food is, and the social control of hunger appears to involve conflicts of the type we associate with sex.[3]

The period of impact on the life-arc may also vary. Whether the noxious influence is most prevalent in childhood, youth, middle life, or old age may make profound differences in its effect. Relatively mild disturbance in childhood might, for example, be more damaging than far greater noxious influence at a later time.

Selection of Sociocultural Categories

283

Many more illustrative examples could be given indicating the richness and promise of cultural comparisons. The multiplicity of patterns involved and the numbers of potential relationships make it exceedingly difficult, however, to predict exactly how one culture would differ from another insofar as prevalence and type of psychiatric disorder are concerned. Looking at the French- and English-speaking groups of the Northeast, and setting aside the many qualifications and exceptions that would be needed were this more than an illustration, it is possible to describe the French way of life as highly organized and specific. There is dominance of the Church, clear-cut priestly authority, an unequivocal code of behavior, and a definite answer with regard to the meaning of life. The upbringing of the child is loving and consistent within this framework.

The way of life of the English speakers, on the other hand, can be pictured as variable. Although there are main anchor-points of conduct, each person is thrown much more on his own with regard to decisions, both sacred and secular, and is confronted with many alternatives. He sees a number of different kinds of standards of morals expressed by people of his own culture; there are competing religious authorities; and there are many answers to the question of the meaning of life. Children in neighboring families, while loved, may be treated quite differently, and also with marked inconsistency even within the same family.

Assuming a central element of truth in these generalizations, it would be possible to advance the view that the French way of life is more conducive to mental health because of the relative stability and support and the greater protection of the person from serious disturbance of the essential psychical condition all along the life-arc. Conversely, however, it could be held that the way of life of the English speakers gives more scope to spontaneity, has more niches in which a wide variety of personality types can make a satisfactory adjustment, gives a more realistic and self-sufficient pattern for relating to life's experiences, and is free of the frustrations, constraints, illusions, and inducements to dependency which could be expected to render personalities of the French speakers more susceptible both to upset essential psychical condition and to maladaptive responses.

This kind of problem in deciding which culture or subculture might be the more benign and which the more noxious is not limited to these two groups in the Northeast. It is difficult with cultures even when one has the entire world from which to select. In most, if not all, there are many aspects to suggest features that would tend to produce at least some kinds of psychiatric disorder and on the other hand features which would tend toward prevention.

Navaho life may be cited as an example of a blend of noxious and benign influences which have to be considered together in assessing the cultural disposition toward psychiatric disorder. On the one hand there are innumerable rules the violation of which creates a situation perceived by Navaho to be exceedingly dangerous. The number of such rules and situations is so great as to seem oppressive and nerve-wracking to an outsider and to have serious implications for personality development and symptom formation. On the other hand, one must consider that Navahos live in a physical and social world where they have had little control over an unpredictable environment—be it lightning storms, late spring frosts, white encroachment, or government practices. The taboos, proscriptions, and rituals therefore can provide some peace of mind by giving a sense of control, of having something to do which may lead to avoiding danger. Thus, using the same data one can argue for a situation bound to produce a disturbed essential psychical state in most Navahos, or conversely that they are psychologically a well-protected people.

Cultural analysis is, of course, a far more detailed and careful study than is reflected in these sketches. Nevertheless, when I have attempted to carry it further in the cultures with which I have had at least some firsthand experience (Northeast, Navaho, Japanese, and Eskimo) the picture has not been greatly altered. Culture differences appear fraught with significance for psychiatric disorder, but provide as yet little basis for making a selection as to most and least noxious.

In this state of affairs two alternatives are apparent. One is to make an assessment of the cultures of the world from the viewpoint presented in Chapter V and summarized on pages 177-178. Through such a step it might be possible to predict that the peoples of certain cultures would show a greater prevalence of psychiatric disorder than a corresponding group in other cultures. Once this were done, some evidence bearing on the underlying theories could be obtained by finding the numbers and kinds of instances of psychiatric disorder in populations of the relevant cultures.

The other alternative is to forego the effort at prediction and to compare, in order to see what comes of it, a limited number of cul-

Selection of Sociocultural Categories

tures with regard to both patterning of social behavior and prevalence of disorder. This is our choice in the Northeast. As already noted, we expect to find differences in the prevalence of psychiatric disorders in the French culture as compared to the English. Even more is the expectation that there are differences in types of disorder. At the same time I am unable to say on the basis of what I would consider sound theory which culture would have the population with the greater percentage of cases, or of this or that type of case.

Of course it is always possible to create hypotheses, and, by selecting suitable premises, predictions can be made. This is sometimes done with the idea that one has nothing to lose, or that this is the only procedure to which the term "scientific" can be applied. I believe, however, that building and testing poorly founded hypotheses can add to the complexity and burden of research operations without commensurate gain and that there is an actual loss from narrowing of attention. Thus, one can spend time and resources on the minute examination of areas which are in fact barren of useful findings. Such is prone to happen when research questions are not framed with sufficient relevance to the actual character of phenomena, and this in turn is an easy error when the degree of specificity attempted is out of keeping with the degree of knowledge.

Exploration, then, rather than hypothesis testing seemed most appropriate at the level of approximation at which we could hope to work so far as culture is concerned. The goal is set, therefore, of selecting and studying comparable community units, some French-speaking and some English. For each there is cultural analysis and analysis of the numbers and kinds of psychiatric disorders. But this still leaves us without a predictive set of categories, and hence the search must be carried further.

Running through the preceding discussion is the idea that cultures differ in their functional effectiveness so far as personality is concerned, but also the realization that we lack criteria whereby such cultures, as cultures, can be distinguished. The only clear indicator would seem to be the product, namely, high frequency of malfunctioning personalities.

Suppose, however, the idea of function is considered from a different point of view, that is, in relation to the community unit rather than in relation to personality. As already noted, it is possible that some cultures function better than others with regard to the survival of the unit. Some do much better in providing security and multiple resources by which to deal with the flux of impinging events. It seems likely that objective criteria might be developed whereby cultures could be placed in middle-range or polar categories in terms of such functional effectiveness.

If this were accomplished, would it have a bearing on functional effectiveness so far as personality is concerned? Is there reason to expect any connection with sociocultural conditions fostering psychiatric disorder? The probability is high that there is such a connection. Since the community is a self-integrating unit and culture is the style or patterning of the integrating process, it seems likely that a deficiency of unit functioning would have widespread ramifications through the system. If there are two cultures which differ from each other markedly in their functional effectiveness in matters of nutrition, reproduction, disease, and attack from outsiders, it seems probable that there will be effects on the sense of physical security, to say the very least. It could well go much beyond this, however, since infant mortality, a heavy burden of adult disease in the group, and the threat of community disruption from outsiders could, through the interdependencies of the system, have effects bearing on sexual satisfaction, love, obtaining recognition, expression of spontaneity, and orientation in society. Moreover, one could speculate that in such cultures there would likely be an absence of those patterns tending to prevent the development of psychiatric disorder in response to a disturbed essential psychical condition, and of therapeutic resources for dealing with disorders once they had appeared.

This brings us to a proposition that is roughly testable, namely, that if cultures are classified according to the functional effectiveness of the relevant community units, a relationship will be found between malfunctioning units and malfunctioning persons—namely, psychiatric disorder. This suggests adding the question of community functioning to the assessment of world cultures noted earlier. Were this made the main point, it would, despite the many complexities involved, constitute a far simpler task than that of analyzing cultures in terms of all the criteria developed in Chapter V. One would much sooner get to a proposition that could be weighed by means of evidence.

In taking some preliminary steps in this direction, I came on what appeared to me a striking fact. If one is concerned to locate community units which contrast with each other in the effectiveness of their functioning, then a better framework than cultural difference is avail-able. It is degree of cultural integrity.

Looking at the Indians of the Southwest as an instance, it was evident that considerable contrast could be found between community units functioning well and those that were functioning poorly. These differences, however, lay as much within cultures as between them. Among the Navaho, for example, one could find a range from groups that were doing fairly well to those in an extreme state of functional difficulty. In most instances these contrasts are marked on the one hand by the relative integrity of the cultural system and on the other by its fragmentation, disarticulation, and admixture with unassimilated elements of other cultures.

When consideration was given to comparing the culturally integrated and culturally disintegrated units from the point of view of noxious and benign influences on personality, much of the difficulty mentioned previously in connection with cultural comparisons disappeared. The evidence seemed overwhelming that the disintegrated groups contained a combination of situations much more damaging to personality than did the groups with a more or less intact cultural system. This difference seemed far more important than the question of whether they were Hopis, Navahos, Papagos, or Zunis.

Following upon this impression, data from a number of communities in different cultures were scanned. These included units in Peru, Thailand, Burma, India, and Japan as well as in the Northeast and among the Navaho.[4] The studies strengthened the view that rapid cultural change, social disintegration, and functional deficiency tend to go together.

My experiences with the Southwestern Indians, particularly the Navaho, began before the war, whereas the assessment of the other cultures was based on a Cornell project carried out after the war. Between these occasions I had the opportunity to study a number of exceedingly disrupted sociocultural groups, first in a Japanese war relocation center and later in Japan itself.[5] Here, in the interplay of drastic disintegrative forces and surging integrative countertrends, were many displays of what seemed to be exceedingly noxious circumstances. Out of the acute and severe it was possible to draw ideas with regard to process in less dramatic circumstances and to suppose that conditions of relative disintegration and malfunction might exist more or less chronically in some community units.

In the Northeast a preliminary review of selected areas indicated that marked contrast in functional effectiveness of community units could be found, and that evidence might be gathered with regard to the proposition that malfunctioning communities tend to foster malfunctioning personalities. Hence *social disintegration* was selected as the framework for rating the sociocultural unit with regard to conditions most likely to make a difference in psychiatric disorder. The meaning of this will be discussed in the next chapter and some of the points thus far treated in a brief fashion will be given further amplification.

This section may be concluded by presenting a series of propositions which sum up its central points and which constitute the final set. If all the propositions are taken together from A in Chapter V to H here, they will be found to constitute the core of the frame of reference. Moreover, inspection will show that they are not a list but an interrelated set of statements. For these reasons they are assembled together in Appendix B.

SERIES H. PROPOSITIONS RELATING SOCIOCULTURAL PATTERNS TO PSYCHIATRIC DISORDER

H1. Given that human society is composed of functioning self-integrating units based on patterns of interpersonal relationship which include communications, symbols, and sentiments (G series), it follows that the different functional parts of a particular unit such as associations, socioeconomic classes, and roles may have differential effects on personalities exposed to them and hence on mental health (B5, C5, D2, D3, E series, and F).

H2. Given that human society is composed of functioning self-integrating units based on patterns of interpersonal relationship which include communications, symbols, and sentiments (G series), it follows that different units with different patterns of organization (culture) may have differential effects on personalities exposed to them and hence on mental health (B5, C5, D2, D3, E series, and F).

H3. Given that human society is composed of functioning self-integrating units based on patterns of interpersonal relationship which include communications, symbols, and sentiments (G series), it follows that social disintegration will affect personalities in such a manner as to foster psychiatric disorder (B5, C5, D2, D3, E series, and F).

Thus the relevance of the various aspects and subdivisions of the sociocultural unit is recognized. In approaching the problem, however, our emphasis is on culture and social disintegration, with the latter offering an opportunity for a more specific statement. The reasons for setting aside, at least for the time being, some of the other possibilities will be discussed in the next section.

IV SOME ALTERNATIVES

It goes without saying that many other ways of conceptualizing sociocultural phenomena could have been selected. These may be viewed either in terms of parts within or aspects of the community unit, or they may be considered as widely extending in the sociocultural fabric disregarding or transcending community units. Thought was given to such overlapping categories as family, culture, socioeconomic class, urban and rural patterns, associations, institutions, religious groups, and roles. A full description of all the influences bearing on decision with regard to each would have greater length than its value warrants. Nevertheless, some main points can be made in order to indicate the thinking and in order to bring out more fully the reasons for choosing the community unit rather than some other.

It has been mentioned earlier that persons do not pass their whole lives with their families of procreation or of orientation. Even less do they spend their lives in most associations, institutions, religious groups, or roles. Hence the noxious effect of conditions related to one of these may be neutralized or masked by the benign effects of another.

To some extent this is also true of class, particularly as class exists in the Harbor Town and its environs and in other units of a similar character. For instance, while some women, like Mrs. Chauncey, might pass virtually all of their lives in the interactions and sentiment systems of the upper class, there would be few if any men who were not through their daily contacts in work and recreation steeped in the interactions and sentiments of several classes simultaneously. At the lower socioeconomic range the women as well as the men may mix in several levels.

Looking at the matter chronologically, there are also complications. Not only is there upward mobility, but there is another kind of shift that goes with age and occupational development. At school, children tend to live in a social world made up of all classes. In youth a person may work and associate for a time at a level below that of his parents. Upper-class girls, for instance, may work as clerks among middle- and lower-class girls and mix socially with them and then resume after marriage a condition of more limited contact with people of their own level. In a parallel manner, the sons of managers and professional men may, as part of their training and career development, work for years in a blue-collar status.

Added to this is the impression that in the Northeast as in many other parts of the world the socioeconomic system is in a state of transition. This means that the class (however defined) that many persons experienced at early stages of their life-arcs would be different from the class of adult periods. It would also mean that people of several age-levels, even though all nominally of the same class, would have actually had different kinds of class experience. This sort of shift has been indicated in discussion of the Chauncey family and it would seem fair to say that, although Helen and her mother had both been members of the same upper class, the phenomena covered by this term had been vastly different for one as compared to the other.

Additional factors complicating a typology based on socioeconomic class in this area are the emphasis on kinship found in small town and rural districts, the existence of French and English cultures, and the mixing of the two.

Thus, despite the fact that Warner's pioneering work was done in the Northeast, and despite the fact that communities like the Harbor Town have similar patterns to those he describes, our preliminary investigations raised doubts as to the appropriateness of class for our purposes.[6]

Having noted that such categories as family, associations, institutions, religious groups, roles, and socioeconomic class appear relatively unsuitable because they subsume only parts of the person's functioning and only parts of the life-story, it may be pointed out that these categories are also parts and aspects rather than units in the sociocultural fabric. They are thus much affected, as noted in Chapter VI, by

Selection of Sociocultural Categories

the characteristics of the whole and may not be comparable so far as mental health is concerned from one community to another. This argues strongly for an approach that seeks understanding of the part or aspect in the context of the whole, since otherwise, the effect on the personalities involved may be overlooked or misconstrued. Such a viewpoint stems directly from considering the community in terms of a quasi-organism.

The objection can be raised that communities, too, are portions of larger wholes and hence offer no escape from this difficulty. They have to be understood in the context of a still-larger society of which they are a part.

This must be accepted as true, but with the important qualification that communities as self-integrating units constitute functioning wholes with relation to basic life processes such as energy utilization and survival, and in relation to surrounding environmental influences. They are of a different order from the functioning of such parts as family, class, and associations. There can be detached, self-sufficient communities over periods of time far beyond the life span of individuals, but there cannot, in this sense, be detached classes, associations, roles, or even families.

Recognizing that dealing with any unit in nature out of its context raises serious questions, it has seemed to me that, since this is nevertheless necessary in order to analyze and investigate, the community unit is the best place to begin. It permits consideration of its parts in relation to its whole and this whole in relation to other wholes with which it articulates, or of which it is in turn a subsidiary unit.

An additional difficulty with utilizing some of the other concepts of sociocultural patterns is the problem of an appropriate system for categorizing them. Roles, for example, offer much that is attractive because they vary in the degree to which they expose the enactor to conditions bearing on failure or fulfillment of his essential striving sentiments and to opportunity for dealing with the consequences. This suggests the possibility of conceiving society as a role network and trying to forecast in which parts of the network the greatest prevalence of psychiatric disorder would be found. In practice, however, I have found it difficult to work out a system of role types that is based on their sociocultural characteristics and which at the same time offers promise of providing contrasting categories with regard to high and low prevalence of psychiatric disorder. Very often specific roles are exceedingly suggestive, as in the stressful position of the wife of a country doctor, a backwoods schoolteacher, or the plant foreman caught between management and labor, but there are so many thousands of roles potentially definable at this level that marshaling them into any set of categories is an exceedingly difficult task.

The role concept taken alone as a starting point for categorizing the sociocultural fabric for our purposes is rendered even more problematical by the realization that role combination is very likely more important to personality than any particular role or type of role. This faces one with the need to develop categories of role combinations in terms of compatibility and conflict. To put these into operation for the research aims envisioned here would require detailed observation and analysis of many thousands of specific roles. The immensity of this task encourages one to look for some more simple approach, at least in the beginning.

Nevertheless, the role concept remains important. It often proves exceedingly useful in analyzing the factors affecting a given personality in both the life-story and in the cross-section of the moment, especially with regard to psychiatric disorders. And it may well turn out to be useful in analyzing process within defined sociocultural units in terms of how roles do and do not contribute to psychiatric disorder and mental health.

Similar problems with regard to establishing appropriate categories also lie in attempts to set up typologies of families, associations, institutions, and religious groups. A system with minimal overlap and objective criteria, which takes into account context, and which has meaning both in mental health and sociocultural terms is difficult to find.

Two alternatives remain to be noted: culture and urban-rural differences. Since attention to culture has been given in the previous section, it is sufficient to say here that, when considered apart from the community unit, it is apt to be exceedingly heterogeneous and difficult to manage. Within one culture there are usually many kinds of communities embodying a range of conditions which cannot very well be ignored when one is concerned with psychiatric disorders. Over-all cultural comparisons are only meaningful when they refer to groups that are similar in their more or less noncultural dimensions such as size or degree of heterogeneity. One can think of comparing two African tribes of different cultures, but some breakdown into suitable units is necessary if he is going to compare an African tribe with France, or India with the United States. The same applies to the French and English speakers of the Northeast, since there is here within each culture a great variety of conditions.

The dichotomy, urban-rural, does some violence to the concept of a sociocultural fabric composed of self-integrating units. In speaking of the Harbor Town as such a unit, the "environs" were included, and this vague term was meant to indicate as much of the population of the adjoining countryside as was functionally part of the town. This usage visualizes each self-integrating unit with its indeterminate margins extending to other such units, be they large or small. There is no doubt, however, that major differences of pattern exist between the centers of the nodes, especially the larger towns, and the marginal areas between them. Hence it would be possible to select criteria by which to distinguish urban from rural and so establish a system of contrasting sociocultural categories that might have differential effects on psychiatric disorder.

Having done this, it is exceedingly difficult to predict in which category the greatest prevalence of ill health would occur. As with comparing two cultures, a good case can be made for either alternative. The town can be pictured as confused, competitive, uncertain, and unstable as compared to the calm rhythm of rural life. On the other hand, the country can be pictured as isolating, frustrating, and otherwise damaging to personality as compared to the opportunities for economic betterment, education, and more rounded social life in a town.

A further consideration interrelated with all those discussed in this section is the matter of feasibility. Some of the obstacles noted, as for instance with roles, might be surmountable in an ideal situation of limitless resources. In the region selected, however, and in the light of the concepts, methods, and financial support that could reasonably be expected, they appeared formidable.

The choice of the community unit as a starting point does not imply a feeling that these other concepts of sociocultural patterns should be discarded. Indeed, when considered within the context of the self-integrating unit, most of them lose the disadvantages that have been noted. Viewed in conjunction with each other and within a larger whole, they span the life-arc and encompass the cross-section of the moment. The objection that they are parts and aspects examined in isolation disappears.

CHAPTER NOTES

1. Illustrative of how the functional point of view has been used in analysis are the classical anthropological studies by Malinowski and Radcliffe-Brown and Williams' sociological study of American society. *See:* BRONISLAW MALINOWSKI, *Argonauts of the Western Pacific* (New York: Dutton, 1953); A. R. RADCLIFFE-BROWN, *The Andaman Islanders* (Glencoe, Ill.: Free Press, 1948); ROBIN M. WILLIAMS, JR., *American Society, A Sociological Interpretation* (New York: Knopf, 1951).

A more theoretical approach is the contemporary sociological view of the functional integration of society. *See:* TALCOTT PARSONS, *The Social System* (Glencoe, Ill.: Free Press, 1951); ROBERT MERTON, "Manifest and Latent Functions, Toward the Codification of Functional Analysis in Sociology," *Social Theory and Social Structure* (Glencoe, Ill.: Free Press, 1949), pp. 21-81; KINGSLEY DAVIS, *Human Society* (New York: Macmillan, 1948).

Elsewhere in this book reference has been made to the literature on general systems, especially with regard to the similarity of system principles in various disciplines. Numerous other contributions which represent the same viewpoint may be of interest. *See:* LUDWIG VON BERTALANFFY and ANATOL RAPOPORT (Eds.), *Yearbooks of the Society for General Systems Research* (Ann Arbor: Braun-Brumfield, 1956, 1957, and 1958).

Community studies have often been carried out on the basis of a similar viewpoint with regard to functional integration; however, only minimal leads to this growing literature can be given here. Much of anthropology has centered on analysis of individuals living in small communities. One historical review and critical assessment is CONRAD M. ARENSBERG, "The Community-Study Method," *The American Journal of Sociology*, Vol. 60, no. 2, 1954, pp. 109-124.

See also: ROBERT REDFIELD, *The Little Community, Viewpoints for the Study of a Human Whole* (Chicago: Univ.

Selection of Sociocultural Categories

Chicago Press, 1955); GEORGE P. MURDOCK, "The Community," *Social Structure* (New York: Macmillan, 1949), pp. 79-90; RAYMOND FIRTH, "Structure and Organization in a Small Community," *The Elements of Social Organization* (London: Watts, 1952), pp. 41-79.

The reader who wishes to explore further the nature and range of such studies, especially from the sociological and rural sociological points of view, may find helpful the bibliographies in: IRWIN T. SANDERS, *The Community, An Introduction to a Social System* (New York: Ronald, 1958); WALFRED A. ANDERSON, *Bibliography of Researches in Rural Sociology* (Ithaca, New York State College of Agriculture, Rural Sociology Publication 52, August 1957).

Of special interest in relation to the point that communities can be viewed as quasi-organisms is the work of Amos Hawley in human ecology. He states:

"The community has often been likened to an individual organism. So intimate and so necessary are the interrelations of its parts, it has been pointed out, that any influence felt at one point is almost immediately transmitted throughout. Further, not only is the community a more or less self-sufficient entity, having inherent in it the principle of its own life process; it has also a growth or natural history with well-defined stages of youth, maturity, and senescence. It is therefore a whole which is something different from the sum of its parts, possessing powers and potentialities not present in any of its components. If not an organism, it is at least a super-organism.

"A full review of the history of the organic conception of the community is unnecessary here. Other authors have adequately performed this task. However, it may be pointed out in passing that the idea was first exploited by social scientists. Although Herbert Spencer was not the originator of the theory, his cogent application of it in his systematic description of human society was primarily responsible for its gaining wide currency in the latter part of the nineteenth century. Later the idea fell into disrepute as the result of abuse at the hands of writers such as Lilienfeld and Novicow, together with a general reaction against the close dependence of social upon biological science. The ensuing criticism was vigorous and often unwise; it accomplished little more than a repudiation of the terminology that had accumulated in the exposition of the thought. The idea itself persisted and gathered force. At a somewhat later time students of plant and animal life took up the organic conception of collective life and found in it a fruitful generalizing tool." (AMOS H. HAWLEY, *Human Ecology, A Theory of Community Structure* [New York: Ronald, 1950], pp. 50-51.)

2. In this frame of reference, culture is equal in importance to personality. Both are conceived as processes which at different levels of abstraction can be viewed as having similar attributes.

Because of the parallel emphasis intended it would be desirable on some accounts to review culture in about the same way that personality has been considered. On the other hand, there are several reasons for feeling that this is not necessary. In 1952 Kroeber and Kluckhohn prepared a monograph on culture in which there are clear-cut explanations of the various ways in which the concept has been used and where a variety of alternative definitions are presented. They comment on 164 different but overlapping views of culture, and they show that these discrete conceptualizations lend themselves to groupings, each of which has a central focus. The six main groups are: descriptive definitions, historical, normative, psychological, structural, and genetic. With their volume available, it is possible to see any one view of culture, such as that presented here, in a perspective relative to others. For example, it is possible to place this one on a range along with those which emphasize the content of culture; those which stress history and tradition; those which propose that culture is the rule or way of life of a people; those which focus on psychological adjustment, problem-solving, learning, and habit as points of departure; those which define culture as the patterning or organization of behavior; those which attend to the question of "how culture has come to be"; those which see culture, *sui generis,* as an order apart from human behavior; and so on.

Although numbers of definitions of culture are in circulation in the fields of anthropology and sociology, it is not thought that they represent nearly as large a range of divergent points of view as those found in psychology and psychiatry with regard to personality. In comparison to personality, culture as a concept has not been elaborated and ramified in like degree, nor has it been the focus of a similar heterogeneity of theory. This is not to say, of course, that the idea of culture is simple and universally understood. Nor does it mean that everyone who uses the term means the same things by it. Popular writings about culture have made certain aspects of the concept widely known. When the term is used by persons outside those fields in which technical definitions have been worked out, it often means something quite unrecognizable as "culture" in the sense intended by social scientists.

What I mean by culture emerges from the way it is employed in the book as a whole and need not be reduced to one succinct definition here. It can be stated, however, that there is general agreement with the summary which Kroeber and Kluckhohn give when they say:

"Without pretending to 'define,' however, we think it proper to say at the end of this summary discussion of definitions that we believe each of our principal groups of definitions points to something legitimate and important. In other words, we think culture is a product; is historical; includes ideas, patterns, and values; is selective; is learned; is based upon symbols; and is an abstraction from behavior and the products of behavior." *See:* A. L. KROEBER and CLYDE KLUCKHOHN, *Culture, A Critical Review of Concepts and Definitions*, Peabody Museum Papers, Vol. XLVII, no. 1 (Cambridge: Peabody Museum of Archaeology and Ethnology, 1952), p. 157.

For more specific references which take a similar position to what has been said about primary and secondary needs, *see:* BRONISLAW MALINOWSKI, *A Scientific Theory of Culture and Other Essays* (Chapel Hill: Univ. North Carolina Press, 1944); JOHN GILLIN, *The Ways of Men* (New York: Appleton-Century-Crofts, 1948); KINGSLEY DAVIS, *Human Society* (New York: Macmillan, 1948).

3. *See* ALLAN R. HOLMBERG, *Nomads of the Long Bow, The Siriono of Eastern Bolivia*, Publication 10, Smithsonian Institution (Washington, D.C.: U.S. Govt. Printing Off., 1950).

4. *See:* ALEXANDER H. LEIGHTON and ROBERT J. SMITH, "A Comparative Study of Social and Cultural Change," *Pro-*

ceedings of the American Philosophical Society, Vol. 99, no. 2, 1955; ALEXANDER H. LEIGHTON, "Mental Illness and Acculturation," in IAGO GALDSTON (Ed.) *Medicine and Anthropology* (New York: Internat. Univ. Press, 1959).

5. *See* ALEXANDER H. LEIGHTON: *The Governing of Men* (Princeton: Princeton Univ. Press, 1946) and *Human Relations in a Changing World* (New York: Dutton, 1949).

6. At the beginning of the Stirling County Study, I was familiar with the concept of class as a framework for social science analysis primarily through the writings of Warner and Lynd. *See* W. LLOYD WARNER and PAUL S. LUNT: *The Social Life of a Modern Community* (New Haven: Yale Univ. Press, 1941) and *The Status System of a Modern Community* (New Haven: Yale Univ. Press, 1942); ROBERT and HELEN M. LYND, *Middletown* (New York: Harcourt, Brace, 1929).

During the course of working out the frame of reference and research, other influences were Williams and Whyte. *See:* ROBIN M. WILLIAMS, JR., *American Society, A Sociological Interpretation* (New York: Knopf, 1951); WILLIAM F. WHYTE, *Street Corner Society* (Chicago: Univ. Chicago Press, 1943).

For the reader who wishes a current evaluation and application of the class system as a means of sectioning for analysis, *see* JOSEPH A. KAHL, *The American Class Structure* (New York: Rinehart, 1957).

Variants of the concept of class have also been employed specifically in studies of mental illness. For example, *see:* AUGUST B. HOLLINGSHEAD and FREDERICK C. REDLICH, *Social Class and Mental Illness, A Community Study* (New York: Wiley, 1958); THOMAS A. C. RENNIE, LEO SROLE, THOMAS LANGNER, and MARVIN OPLER, Volume I of the forthcoming *The Midtown Series* (New York: McGraw-Hill).

PART THREE

A Plan for
Research

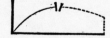

PART THREE

A Plan for Research

Chapter IX

Social Disintegration as a Basis for Comparing Communities[1]

WITH THIS CHAPTER, Part Three of the present volume begins, and it would seem appropriate for the sake of orientation to restate briefly the main purposes of the book. They may be considered as threefold:

1. To suggest a conceptual bridge whereby certain aspects of per-

sonality viewed as process, and certain aspects of society and culture viewed as process may be seen as related to one another.

2. To review and suggest ways in which sociocultural factors may affect personality to produce psychiatric disorder.

3. To formulate some problems and show openings for research operations.

A number of steps have been taken toward these ends. In Part One an indication was given of what shall be meant here by psychiatric disorders and of the factors concerned in the development and persistence of such conditions of personality. In Part Two effort was directed toward outlining ways in which sociocultural factors can affect personality so as to foster or mitigate the development of psychiatric disorders, toward outlining some characteristics of the sociocultural environment, toward reviewing sentiments as a bridging concept between sociocultural process and personality, and toward quartering the sociocultural environment into categories appropriate for study with regard to benign, neutral or noxious influences on mental health. It remains now in this last part of the volume to attempt a more specific formulation of problems and to lay the groundwork for some research operations.

The first question for consideration is epidemiological: finding out how psychiatric disorders are distributed in the selected sociocultural categories. It is thought that this could yield evidence for or against some of the propositions presented earlier regarding the influence of sociocultural factors. Beyond this, however, the identification of sociocultural categories containing high and low prevalence of psychiatric disorder is expected to open the way for a progressive and closer examination of causal relationships. More definitive questions as to the most noxious influence in the environment and the most susceptible points on the life-arc could be investigated, together with considerations of genetic and physiological influences and the problem of the degree to which the sociocultural conditions are the product rather than the source of the psychiatric disorder. Thus, epidemiological knowledge is viewed as a desirable foundation for these subsequent investigations.

The second question is clinical: finding out what sociocultural factors detectable in the lives of patients are critical in the development of psychiatric disorder. This implies a comparative study with people who are not patients and who appear to be free of symptoms. It is believed that the clinical and the epidemiological approaches should converge, complementing and supplementing each other.

In turning toward research operations, it may be noted that the field of attention is being narrowed. Choices have to be made, and, as is common with choices, the alternatives set aside carry with them large complexes of related possibilities. Each act of selection progressively limits the range available for the next selection.

Many factors inevitably enter into the judgments exercised in these acts. Some are the rational outcome of the frame of reference itself, but others have to do with opportunities and limitations of time, personnel, techniques, available subject matter, and similar items. Still others stem from faulty reasoning and from the sentiments of the investigators, factors of which we are not altogether aware or in full control. It is obvious therefore that an attempt at a really thorough explanation of all decisions intervening between the frame of reference and the actual research operations would be incomplete and yet so voluminous as to be impractical. In face of this, explication will be restricted to pointing out some main connections.

The successive judgments constitute the selection and invention of theories and hypotheses more or less within the orientation of the frame of reference. Results from research will therefore inevitably modify the theories and this may send one back again through the system of choices to pick up some of the alternatives that have been set aside, or to discover some that are new. Out of such revision comes a fresh series of choices, theories, and hypotheses and opportunity for another wave of research. Thus, a useful frame of reference is one which brackets both research design and the analysis of results, including the formulation and reformulation of theories. In the course of all this, obviously, the frame itself is also subject to change—the map has to be progressively refined and improved.

Implicit in these considerations is the fact that the present frame of reference has many more potentialities for investigation, analysis, and theory construction than will be indicated in the pages that follow. Although in the course of making certain choices some of the undeveloped alternatives will be pointed out, many others will be passed without comment. They remain nevertheless available for later consideration either on the basis of research results or as points of departure for altogether different lines of investigation.

Social Disintegration and Community Comparisons

In saying this no claim is made that the frame of reference is itself all-inclusive. It is necessarily a preliminary selection and, however broad, only one of many possible arrangements.

The present chapter is concerned with explaining a sociocultural dimension thought to be of maximal relevance to mental health and at the same time one by means of which communities can be compared. It is based on the concept of the community as a functioning, self-integrating unit with susceptibility to degrees of disintegration and functional deficiency. Since the groundwork has been laid in the previous chapters, the task now is a more amplified account of the dimension, its relationship to psychiatric disorders, some ways in which different degrees can be identified, and finally, some necessary cautions.

I A DEFINITION OF SOCIAL DISINTEGRATION

In order to bring out what is meant in these volumes by social disintegration, let us consider two constructs representing human groups at opposite extremes. Let one be an idealized model of a perfectly functioning community unit and the other a collection of human beings existing side by side in the same geographic area, but unpatterned in their relations to each other. For convenience, the first shall be designated the Model and the second the Collection.

Since the Model is by definition a perfectly functioning unit of energy exchange, or quasi-organism, it constitutes a system of interdependent parts able to maintain itself despite changes in the surrounding sociocultural and physical environment. It is also able to guide and regulate the personalities of which it is composed so that their various individual actions are constructive or neutral with regard to the system, and never disrupting. Since I am not positing perfection so far as heredity is concerned, this means various devices and compensations in the sociocultural system for taking care of range in individual capacities, limitations, and tendencies toward deviance. Similarly the system must contain patterns for dealing with some impairment or destruction of personalities through disease and accidents.

The perfection of function posited for the Model is, then, limited to its performance as a unit. Specifically, it does not by definition include a favorable medium for all the constituent personalities. There can be expendables and victims of the system. One can picture a tyranny, for example, or a slave state which permits physical suffering and early death among some of its members, that would nevertheless be strong in resources for its own preservation. There would have to be limits, however, to the proportion thus harmfully affected, otherwise functional failure of the unit would begin to occur and it would then fall short of the criteria of the Model.

The numbers and kinds of individuals that could be damaged in a particular unit without its ceasing to be a Model would depend on the patterning (culture) of the system. In some, such as the community units in the Northeast which are based on sentiments of voluntary participation and the consent of the governed, the network of interdependencies is such as to permit very few expendables. A model of this type would tend toward providing opportunity to most persons in the group for meeting their biological needs.

We may also suppose that it might provide a favorable medium with regard to psychological needs. This is not, as already noted, a criterion of the Model, but it does seem a state of affairs which would be concomitant. If the Model is a system, it must have parts and aspects, and these parts and aspects consist in such patterning of interpersonal relationships as family, government, economics, religion, education, and defenses of health, mediated through communications, shared symbols, and coordinate sentiments. Encompassed here are the procedures for the primary activities of unit preservation and those additional activities which are based on the particular style in which the former are accomplished. These patterns require the participation of functioning personalities, and functioning personalities presuppose a minimal satisfaction of psychological as well as biological needs.

It may be concluded, therefore, that, tyrannies and other special cases aside, the Model does tend to provide a benign environment for a large portion of its constituent personalities. Even in the case of tyrannies and other patterns potentially destructive to personality, it may be doubted that a system which consistently and persistently interfered with the functioning of a great many persons in the group could exist indefinitely at a level of unit perfection.

Although we may not know the full picture with regard to personality needs, those reflected in the ten essential striving sentiments point to certain areas of emphasis. When these and the Model are examined together, it seems plausible that most people during most of their lives would experience physical security (E1), sexual satisfaction (E2), giving and receiving love (E4 and E5), recognition (E6), orientation regarding place in society (E8), membership in a human group (E9), a sense of belonging to a moral order (E10), and opportunity to interact with different kinds of personalities (F1). The manner and degree in which people are provided with these opportunities could vary from one cultural system to another, but it appears exceedingly probable that a Model (a perfectly functioning unit) would, within the framework of any culture, offer some basis for object striving through defining relevant objects and hence for a sense of meeting these needs. There would be, in short, a shared system of sentiments that was functional for personalities as well as for group processes. Severe deprivation in such matters would result in disruptive acts in one or another part or aspect of the system, while satisfaction along controlled lines would provide powerful incentives for behavior contributing to the maintenance of the self-integrating unit.

It is less clear that the expression of hostility (E3) and of spontaneity (E7) are necessarily given much scope in the Model. There is little to indicate that interference with either is immediately disruptive to the system, whatever may be the indirect repercussions. One may suppose that the Model might or might not, depending on culture, offer a hospitable medium for these strivings.

Having dealt so far with factors having to do with the maintenance of the essential psychical condition, we may turn now to the question of what could happen if this condition were to become disturbed for one or more persons. It seems obvious that the Model, by virtue of its functional effectiveness as a unit, would do little to foster the formation of behavioral patterns which interfere with the system. This would apply regarding trends toward excessive use of alcohol, disruptive sexual behavior, living in a world of fantasy, paranoid states, hypochondriasis, hysterical paralyses, and amnesias. It is not necessary to insist that these tendencies would never occur, but rather that their development would be against and in spite of many patterns of action and systems of sentiment in the Model.

Reformulating this in terms of the various types of psychiatric disorder discussed in Chapter IV, it seems probable that there would be alternatives available to, and blocks put in the way of forming, such symptom constellations as sociopathic conditions, personality disorder, psychoses and many types of psychoneuroses. There would also be some indirect effect toward reducing those brain syndromes which are under the influence of adverse physical conditions, poor hygiene, and poor diet. With mental retardation, all one could expect would be a mitigating effect due to training for participation in the system at the level of the individual's capacity.

In the case of psychophysiological disorders the consequences are not so evident. There would be reduced disposition, of course, due to low frequency of disturbance of the essential psychical condition and to low prevalence of adverse physical agents. On the other hand, to the extent that these disturbances were perceived and treated entirely in physical terms, there might be little to inhibit their development and persistence.

There remains the possibility that despite the generally benign trend, certain types of psychiatric disorder could be fostered in the Model. Looking at personality developmentally, it can be recalled that events very early on the life-arc may have effects which only appear as overt disturbance in adult life. It seems possible that a Model could encompass a set of family patterns which, while contributive to the unit at the time, would have effects on the child that would emerge as detrimental only much later. Due to the time span between the event and the effects, it might be that neither by conscious recognition nor by cultural evolution through trial and error would this covert and inadvertent pathogenesis be eliminated. From the point of view of symptom formation, it also seems likely that the Model could foster some kinds of patterns, as for instance compulsiveness, which might be contributive to the unit where detailed and exacting tasks were required. Psychoneurotic interpersonal relations involving dominance and passivity might not particularly interfere with the ongoing system. In some respects, indeed, they might strengthen its integration.

Turning finally to resources that could be brought to bear on cases of psychiatric disorder after they had developed, since many of these are by their nature disrupting to the system, it can be assumed that the Model would have some way of dealing with such. In part this might consist in formal and informal therapy, the latter being provided by various types of leaders, counselors, general practitioners, and pastors in the group. In part it might consist in isolation from the system, in custodial care for the duration of the disturbance, or in exclusion from the unit altogether. Relatively few incapacitated or seriously limited people would, therefore, be found drifting about in the community.

To sum up, it appears that a Model would be limited in the degree to which it contained situations predisposing to psychiatric disorder, would have marked tendencies to inhibit many kinds of symptom formation, would have therapeutic resources, and would have devices for excluding from the system those disruptive types of psychiatric disorder which did not respond to treatment. The Model would not, however, be necessarily free of psychiatric cases, and might actually foster certain kinds of disorder. Several kinds of Models may be visualized, each perfect as a unit but having different frequencies of psychiatric illness according to the culture, or patterning of the system. As will be shown now, however, a Model at its worst would present a marked contrast to the Collection so far as noxious conditions for personality are concerned.

In the Collection there is by definition no sociocultural integration. Instead there are numbers of individuals occupying the same geographical area having nonpatterned encounters with each other. Such unity as exists is based on sharing physical space, on frequency of interaction (even if unpatterned), and on the absence of current membership in any of the communities that may lie adjacent to the Collection. The boundaries, in short, are largely boundaries of exclusion.

In terms of the unit, the Collection is posited as nonfunctional. While as individuals the people may be able to wrest a living from their environment and thus achieve participation in a process of energy exchange and biological survival, the Collection itself has no patterns of procuring food, shelter, and protection against disease. What persons do in these regards are separate acts without mutual linkage. There can be procreation, but with the care of children completely individualistic both maternal and infant mortality rates would be high.

Since the Collection by definition lacks patterns for these primary activities, those other patterns based upon the particular style in terms of which the primary activities proceed are also absent. There is, in short, no culture so far as the Collection is concerned. The individuals who compose it may have personalities that contain language, practices, and sentiments derived from cultures in which they originated, but in the construct as envisioned, these are too heterogeneous to constitute shared patterns. There are no *systems* of communication, no mutually understood symbols, and no coordinating sentiments.

One may feel perhaps some difficulty in imagining these candidates for work in the Tower of Babel as capable of surviving even a day. Yet if the individuals who compose the Collection are functioning persons, if we beg the question of their origin, and if the physical environment is conceived as exceedingly rich in easily obtainable food and other natural resources, perhaps the construct can be visualized at least in terms of a temporary existence.

The main point it is desired to make is probably self-evident—namely, that in a Collection there are circumstances conducive to psychiatric disorder. Children born in a Collection would not have a sociocultural environment in which they could develop basic urges, unconscious processes, cognition, and affect into coherent sets of sentiments, and hence there would be defect in personality formation. This would begin with the very early relations of mother and child and be extended and confirmed through all later interpersonal actions. Due to lack of patterns of human relations, object striving would be chaotic, unstable, and largely unsuccessful, with corresponding deficiency reflected in the relevant sentiments, creating prolonged and severe disturbance of the essential psychical condition. Physical security (E1), sexual satisfaction (E2), giving and receiving love (E4 and E5), recognition (E6), orientation regarding place in society (E8), membership in a human group (E9), belonging to a moral order (E10), and opportunity for interacting with other kinds of personalities (F1) would be difficult or impossible in a Collection—that is, a human group that is not a social system.

The one postulated need that might find frequent channels of expression is hostility (E3). The strong would be literally able to get away with murder.

The position of spontaneity (E7) is equivocal. In some respects the situation would be conducive to this trend in personality since there would be no conventional barriers to any form of originality of expression. On the other hand, there would not be a cultural heritage to provide inducements and guide lines for the definition of objects. There might be opportunity enough for the expression of spontaneous physical activity, but little for progressive and developmental spontaneity of thought.

Social Disintegration and Community Comparisons

Given disturbance of the essential psychical condition, it seems evident that the situation in the Collection would encourage reactions which masked discomfort rather than reorganized personality or situation so as to restore the essential psychical condition. This would stem from the almost total inability of any one individual to alter the deprivations exerting stress upon him. Short-range relief, however self-defeating ultimately, would be promoted by the unavailability of any other kind. Without a social system, long-range plans would be for the most part futile. Hence one could expect obliteration of discomfort with alcohol and sex, and with the more psychological refuges such as autistic fantasies, paranoid states, hypochondriasis, hysterical paralyses, amnesias, and obsessive-compulsive preoccupations. There would be nothing to interfere with the development of sociopathic conditions, personality disorders, psychoses, psychoneuroses, and psychophysiological disorders. The only limitation would be such degree of impairment as interfered with the individual's survival. Brain syndromes of some kinds might also be fostered due to life-long stressful experience and exposure to difficult physical conditions, poor hygiene and poor diet. Mental retardation would be at its most impaired level since there would be no opportunities for training. Therapeutic resources, since these necessarily involve sociocultural patterns, would, of course, be nonexistent.

It is patent that neither the Model nor the Collection can occur in nature. They have been posited in order to represent what might be called absolute social integration and absolute social disintegration. Now, while the extremes depicted in the two constructs do not exist, community units occur which approach the Model and others occur which approach the Collection in general character. It is suggested that such communities can be compared and contrasted to each other in this dimension.

Social disintegration as used here is therefore a relational expression, even if not always accompanied by words like "more" and "less." Since there can be no such thing as a completely integrated or disintegrated community, actual communities can be described in these terms only as they approach one or the other of the imagined absolutes, or as they contrast with each other. Thus if there are three groups, A, B and C, such that A approaches the Model in its general character, C approaches the Collection, and B is in the middle, one can say that C is disintegrated relative to B, and that B is disintegrated relative to A. To economize on words, one can say that A is integrated, B is mixed, and C is disintegrated.[2]

When one looks at the Northeast it is not too difficult to find communities for placement in such categories. If the Harbor Town itself is taken as occupying the middle range (B), then Slashtown, the backwoods collection of some twenty-five shacks where Rose Chiason lived and had her babies, can be regarded as disintegrated (C). Here one can see a gravel road as the only straight and tidy thing in a landscape of spindly trees, alder clumps, shallow soil, and granite outcroppings. The houses tend to be at a distance from each other, reflecting the social isolation, furtiveness and suspicion of the people they contain. A general air of dilapidation or of unfinished building also parallels in concrete terms the broken family life and the low and unstable economic base. The red flare of geranium in a rusty can at a window, or a one-armed teddy bear alone in the mud of a yard, serves to highlight the general absence of decoration and play, of the materials for the creation and development of human capacity for enjoyment and sharing. It is a place where both leadership and followership are weak, where channels of communications are deficient, and where the sentiment patterns are confused and, except for hostility, lacking in affective strength. From the overcrowded dwellings, little paths lead into the swamps and the woods.

In contrast to all this is a fishing village of Cap Aux Anges, one that is much more closely knit than the Harbor Town and so can be regarded as integrated (A). It lies boldly about a cove, looking part of the landscape rather than, as Slashtown, like an artifact thrown away and forgotten in the weeds. The comparatively large houses bright in paint, the several roads and the network of paths which run from dwelling to dwelling, reflect the solid family units and the busy interactivity and interdependence of the people. There are gardens and white picket fences, a two-story school with a flagpole in front, numbers of stores, a Masonic Lodge, a recreation hall where amateur shows are occasionally presented, a ball field, and, in the center of all, a white church with square tower and sturdy spire. The boats in the cove and the fish plants on the shore indicate the main subsistence base while the fields and the woods provide certain supplemental resources. The whole is a social system with relatively clear and functioning sentiments, with well-marked patterns of leadership and followership, and with highly effective means of communication.

Social Disintegration and Community Comparisons

Social integration and disintegration are not only relational terms; they also have implications of proportion and process. In any given community at any particular time it is to be supposed that both integration and disintegration are taking place. This necessarily follows since there are no absolutes. When one says therefore that a community is disintegrated, he can mean that it occupies a position on the range such that the disintegrational features are in ascendency over the integrational. Unequivocal if transient instances of this have been seen in boom towns and in communities swept by war.

With regard to process, disintegration not only means a relative absence of patterns which, if present, would improve functional effectiveness but also refers to ongoing deterioration in the system. Such deterioration on a small or large scale is inherent in response and adaptation to exogenous and endogenous changes. Where there is restoration of equilibrium, there must also be loss, and dynamic equilibrium is predicated on the concept of deterioration and rebuilding. Social integration may be considered the positive aspect of the process whereby the system maintains and adjusts itself, while social disintegration may be regarded as the negative aspect, with interruption and disarticulation in various parts of the system. Hence neither integration nor disintegration is here used to represent a static condition but rather an over-all balance of trends and countertrends with regard to particular communities at a particular period of time.

When, therefore, I say that Slashtown is disintegrated, I mean that both integration and disintegration are occurring but that the net effect is currently a system with loose and jumbled patterning and many functional deficiencies. Conversely, when I say that the fishing village is integrated, I mean that while both integration and disintegration are in process, on the whole the patterning of the system has much about it that is tight, coherent, and articulated and that the functioning of the unit is efficient in some respects and sufficient in all.

From this it can be seen that the idea of integration combines both patterning and function. Integration is not necessarily proportional to complexity of patterning, or to interdependencies or concensus by participants. Functioning of the community unit is really the central point, but this requires interdependence and patterning. On the other hand, there can be complex interdependent patterns which are nonfunctional or malfunctional with reference to the community unit.

The ritualism of some of the Southwestern Indian Pueblos in the context of their actual situations in the larger society is possibly an illustration of this. Hypertrophy of patterning which interferes with the functioning of the unit is not considered social integration, as the term is used here.

Conversely, disintegration is a moving away from the functional effectiveness of the unit. It is not just a relative lack of patterning in the system, since the more simply patterned of two communities might be the more efficient as a unit. It is rather a lack of the qualities and characteristics of the quasi-organism. Disintegration means being disorganismic.[3]

II SOME INDICES OF SOCIAL DISINTEGRATION

The attempt in the preceding section to give a description of what is meant in these volumes by social disintegration leaves a number of questions unanswered and many points still in need of clarification. One way to approach a further development of the concept is to visualize making use of it. Inasmuch as the integration–disintegration balance of a community cannot be directly apprehended, use means the selection of indicators, and this act constitutes a further definition.

Such a relationship between indicator and definition of referent is common in clinical psychiatry and social science. Typically the investigators have a general something in mind, but, as they work at choosing ways and means for indicating the presence of that something and recording variations in its characteristics, the decisions become part of the concept. This sort of procedure is perhaps best seen in the development of intelligence tests. It has been said that "intelligence is what the intelligence tests measure." Although this is facetious, to an important extent it is true. The tests have become a part of what we mean by intelligence.

Not all indicators in various fields of knowledge are so closely tied to the definition of their referents. When litmus paper is employed to indicate degree of acidity, the red color of the paper is not part of the definition of acid. If I use a galvanometer to measure nerve impulses in a peripheral nerve, I am not stating in effect, "I shall call that to which the galvanometer responds a nerve impulse." On the contrary I am relying on the evidence of previous research which says

Social Disintegration and Community Comparisons

that the nerve impulse (something transmitted along a nerve which can make a muscle contract) is in fact accompanied by electrical changes which can be picked up by a galvanometer. The same sort of thing is true if I am looking for sugar in the blood or using a patch test for tuberculosis. These indicators do not define the phenomena to which they refer and their validity can be assessed by independent means.

As already suggested, the case is different with most psychiatric and sociocultural indicators. For instance, if one were trying to distinguish a "paranoid case" he might choose such indicators as suspiciousness, hostility, and beliefs which other people in the same culture do not hold to be true. But these indicators are at the same time part of the descriptive definition of a paranoid case. Similarly, if one is seeking to identify "upper class" he may note area of residence, education, and income, each of which is not only an indicator but part of the definition. So close is the tie, in fact, that it makes little sense to argue whether these are good or bad indicators of paranoid condition or of class. One can only argue about the clarity and usefulness of a definition that has these components. To repeat, this is not the situation if a question is raised as to whether the Wassermann test is a good or bad indicator of the presence of syphilis.

These points of distinction have been introduced for several reasons. One is to make evident the kind of indicators that will be used in connection with social disintegration and to point out why their specification constitutes a further working out of the definition.

A second point is to suggest the desirability of avoiding confusion between the nature of these kinds of indicators and those of the litmus paper type. There is danger in doing this, since both are called indicators or indices and it is very easy to transfer the meaning of a name in one context to another context in which this meaning does not apply. The indicators we shall use are not validated, they are not pure readings with regard to a unidimensional characteristic, and their meaning has to be constantly reassessed as results are obtained from using them. They are parts of a pattern on the basis of which the rest of the pattern is being estimated. To treat them as one might treat litmus paper or galvanometer measurements of nerve impulses would be to run the risk of building constructs that have very little relationship to phenomena in nature. This is not an unlikely possibility, since the statistical opportunities with unidimensional readings are so inviting as to tempt one to forget the nature of these indicators and to use them as if they were purely unidimensional, validated, and not in part a definition of their referent.

A third point is that the nature of these indicators makes it necessary to use several of them. Being only a part of the definition, they have to be multiple in order to make identification possible. A comparison may be made with the problem of identifying the species of a bird one has seen. He must rely on such multiple indicator–definitions as size, color pattern, and characteristics of bill and feet. These indicators do not have to cover all the details of species differentiation, but they have to cover enough to reveal a total pattern and to give a sense of assurance that the rest would also be found if the bird were caught and the examination were pushed further. A length of seven inches, a blue back, and a red breast are not the whole of the pattern that makes up the characteristics of the species "Eastern bluebird" yet they are sufficient for identification.

A fourth point has to do with the nature of interdependence between indicators. Since we think we are dealing with several, though not all, visible aspects of a complex, it can be expected that these indicators will have a marked tendency to hang together. If one or two indicators point strongly to social disintegration, we would expect the others to do so too. If they do not, that is, if all the indicators vary independently of each other, then the definition of social disintegration is obviously in need of repair or abandonment.

On the other hand, some indicators may hang together more consistently than others. Finding out which these are would further clarify the definition. Hence we can expect that trial in actual observations in the field will make some important refinements and additions in our progress through successive approximations toward a better grasp of the phenomenon and its more precise representation in a concept. Through sufficient studies it may be possible to reduce the number of indicators to two or three shown under specifiable circumstances to yield results that are almost as good as using many. We cannot, however, start with such assumptions without running the risk of using an indicator that is not markedly interdependent with the rest of the complex. In such a case there would be no means of checking our assumption against actual relations. We would be saying, "Let so and so stand for social disintegration" without knowing what this means, and without clarifying through experience our ideas about the nature of the phenomenon which we think we perceive.

In what follows I shall as usual be using the Northeast as the point of reference. This means that the definition developed is particular for the given French and English cultures. It should be noted, however, that the underlying concept is put forward as representing a potential or actual phenomenon in all human societies. It is thought that by particular studies in a variety of different cultures and contexts and by their comparative analysis the underlying universal can be brought more clearly to light and its nature defined.

The indices of social disintegration are arranged for operational convenience in two sets of seven. The first of these may be stated as follows:

DISINTEGRATION INDICES—SET A

Community units that are markedly disintegrated will have:

1. *High frequency of broken homes.*

The point of reference here is the malfunctioning family. The "broken" state may be seen in the physical absence of mother or father without adequate surrogate, in frequent changes of patterns, or in relations between members which are chronically distant, hostile, and unstable.

2. *Few and weak associations.*

This means little or no grouping of people, either formally or informally. Thus there would be few clusterings about such interests and activities as religion, work, or recreation. The associations that did exist would be lacking in ability to act or to hold their membership together.

3. *Few and weak leaders.*

They will be small in number and those who exist will be weak with regard to power and influence.

4. *Few patterns of recreation.*

This means the absence of sports, hobbies, and avocations. The modes of enjoying oneself will tend to be individualistic and short-term, such as drinking and sexual promiscuity.

5. *High frequency of hostility.*

There will be numerous hostile acts and words directed at other members of the community and at outsiders.

6. *High frequency of crime and delinquency.*

> This state of affairs may not be reflected on the police blotter, but there will be violation of laws where one can get away with it and such acts as assault, robbery, rape, incest, cruelty to animals and children.

7. *Weak and fragmented network of communication.*

> As in the case of the broken families, this deficiency in communications can be regarded as both physical and psychological. On the one hand there will be features such as isolation, poor roads, and no telephones, and on the other there will be an absence of those patterns of interaction between people necessary as a basis for communication.

When one looks at this set, the question naturally arises, why these? Why these rather than some others?

It is difficult to give a complete answer and it is certainly not possible to maintain that they are necessarily the best choice. They are the product of thinking in the terms outlined in this and the preceding chapter and then taking a preliminary look at what seems to be the manifestation of disintegration in the Northeast.

When it comes to the use of these indicators, it is at once evident that they cannot be applied in any simple manner. Each requires fairly complex observations and the weighing of qualitative as well as quantifiable factors. Nevertheless they seem to be operable in the sense that they promise to distinguish such places as Slashtown, the Harbor Town and the fishing village at Cap Aux Anges and to define separate categories in which they could be placed.

To do this, however, would require intensive field observations over a fairly long period of time. It is not the purpose of this volume to enter into field methods, but I may perhaps carry the matter to that doorway by observing that the anthropological type of community study appears to be the method of choice for a first trial.

A serious problem still confronts us, however, namely, preliminary selection of communities for such intensive study. The research aim that has been developed calls for communities which contrast markedly with regard to social integration. This means some kind of selection from communities in the Northeast. Since it is obviously impossible to carry out this type of study on a large sample, much less

Social Disintegration and Community Comparisons

the universe, some way must be found for choosing a few communities such that contrast in social disintegration will be highly probable, if not assured. Some additional indicators are needed in terms of which many communities may be scanned, and for this purpose the second set has been devised. These are less closely tied to definition and are hence less certain as indicators, but they are more easily and quickly applied.

DISINTEGRATION INDICES—SET B

Communities are apt to be disintegrated if they have one or more of the following:

1. *A recent history of disaster.*

> In approaching the search for indicators that would imply a thorough fracturing of social integration, I was under the influence of experience in World War II in analyzing the morale of human groups which had suffered major disaster. This war provided numbers of examples of how extreme social disintegration could be, and thus helped crystallize the idea. It seemed natural to build on this and to attempt to translate it into terms that would be relevant in peacetime conditions. There was recognition, of course, that no simple counterpart of war-torn groups could be found in civilian communities and that the carrying over of inferences from one situation to the other had to proceed with caution.

> The nearest approach to a war kind of disaster one could expect in the Northeast is the burning out of communities. Although fortunately rare, it does happen from time to time in this region of forest fires and frame buildings and one could expect at least transient disintegration in the groups so affected.

> At a more subtle level is the possibility that some communities might have a sufficiently high frequency of accidents on an individual basis to constitute a disruption to the social system. It is conceivable that this could be the state of affairs in certain fishing villages or lumbering communities.

2. *Widespread ill health.*

This carried further the idea noted above with regard to the prevalence of accidents. It seems reasonable to expect that if a great many people in a community are suffering from physical impairment, this will interfere with family patterns, associations, leadership, economic activities, communications —in short the total system.

3. *Extensive poverty.*

Still thinking in terms of disrupted societies studied during the war, poverty was selected as an indicator because it appeared to have some disintegrating tendencies comparable to those of forced migrations and bombed-out cities. Even when poverty develops slowly, or exists as a chronic state permitting some adjustments, it seems likely that if severe it would adversely affect the functioning of the social system. Field observation among the Navaho and other Indians of the Southwest served to strengthen this conclusion. The Navaho, for example, provide an instance of a people with a culture that enables them to maintain an efficient social system at a very low subsistence level. Yet even here, dropping below a certain threshold produces difficulties which threaten the system's functioning. Kinship obligations, patterns of marriage and child-rearing, and the knitting together of the group through religious ceremonials can all be eroded by severe and prolonged want.

Preliminary investigations in the Northeast confirmed the applicability of these views to this region. It seemed likely that poverty not only was disruptive in this culture but was so at a much higher level of resources than among the Navaho.

4. *Cultural confusion.*

This refers to a situation in which two or more cultures exist in a community without ordered relationship to each other. Outstanding examples of this have been seen in the Southwest where the Indians are in a state of transition, or acculturation, from their own way of life to that of the Anglo world. This often amounts to communities having two largely incompatible systems of sentiments simultaneously, one partially forgotten, the other imperfectly learned. As a result there is confusion and fragmentation of both the sentiments and the patterns of social interaction based on them.

In the Northeast the obvious possibility for this sort of thing lies in the interactions of English- and French-speaking peoples. One could not expect such contrast here as between Indian and European cultures, and hence there might not be such a high potential for disruption of community. Nevertheless, it was thought that this was a question of degree and that we should look for groups showing evidence of cultural confusion. In the context of the Northeast, it was anticipated that these would be mainly French showing English acculturation, and only rarely the reverse.

5. Widespread secularization.

The word "secularization" as used here means the absence of religious sentiments.[4] A trend in this direction seems to be occurring in many parts of the modern world and to be accompanied by the breaking up of social norms other than those that are strictly religious. Preliminary exploration of the Northeast fortified this impression.

6. Extensive migration.

The rationale for the use of emigration as an index is that, like death, disease and disaster, it takes individuals out of the social system. If this happens at a rate faster than replacements can be conditioned and fitted, or if it results in a differential loss of certain age and sex categories, the results may be disruptive to the community and produce malfunctioning. Immigration can have a similar effect due to flooding a group with new members who have to find places in the system, and in so doing, disrupt it at various points.[5]

7. Rapid and widespread social change.

Social change is already implicit in some of the previous indices such as cultural confusion and secularization. To this may be added a more explicit idea with reference to technological innovations and the introduction of sociocultural patterns as such.

The idea for this item, as with some of the previous indices, had its origin in studies of nonliterate societies, but was reinforced by preliminary investigation of the Northeast.[6] Shifts in fishing methods had in the past changed the complexion of towns and villages and there was every reason to expect that the coming of the beam trawler and other devices might have even more far-reaching effects. The whole practice of woodcutting had altered in recent years due to roadmaking machinery and chain saws, with profound results for life in rural areas. The advent of central schools was doing much to break up the social system of the hamlet and to add its weight to other trends favoring town orientation.

None of these changes, however, are necessarily and always disruptive, since they are part of adjustment and growth, or of maintaining a dynamic equilibrium. It is when they occur rapidly, one right after the other and at many points in the social system, that the effect is malfunctional. In such a situation change follows change before adjustments are achieved; different parts of the group are in various stages and hence out of step with each other, and disarticulation and disruption tend to become cumulative.[7]

A characteristic of Set B is that these seven indicators constitute situations which, if they exist long enough and with sufficient severity, may cause social disintegration. This, together with the hope that they might be applicable to large populations, was the rationale for their selection. The thinking went something like this: Suppose one wanted to locate as easily and quickly as possible communities with a high frequency of typhoid fever and other gastrointestinal diseases, how might he go about it? One way would be to look for bad drainage and sewage contamination. It would be possible to drive through some regions and pick out communities of high probability without even getting out of a car. It seems reasonable to suppose that when the thing you wish to identify is difficult to see, but some of the factors which lead to its appearance are comparatively obvious, a preliminary selection can be made through a survey of the latter.

It must be emphasized, however, that the causal or antecedent character of Set B is relative. All the items used in the two Sets can act as both antecedents and consequents in relation to the total disinte-

Social Disintegration and Community Comparisons

gration complex. That is, what is a consequent in one period of the community's existence may be an antecedent to later events. To take poverty as an example, if it is due to circumstances wholly external to the community it can be considered in no sense consequent on social disintegration. If on the other hand it is in part due to sentiments and acts in the community which are an expression of already existing disintegration, it is then to some extent a consequent. More than this, as such a consequent it may serve nevertheless as an antecedent for still later and other aspects of disintegration. The case is similar with broken homes and the absence of leaders. In short, all fourteen indicators represent complex, interdependent relationships affecting each other through time as both antecedents and consequents.[8] These points are mentioned because it is thought that they are important in understanding the possibilities and limitations in the analysis of results obtained by these indices.

In applying the indices to the problem of selecting communities which present a marked contrast with regard to social disintegration, it was thought that one might begin with Set B and examine a region through the use of both anthropological and survey techniques. The first would rely on a variety of key informants and documentary data, while the latter would consist in a scheduled questionnaire given to a probability sample of the population. The anthropological methods would make contributions toward the content of the questionnaire and the design of the sample, while the two methods taken together could serve to supplement each other and, in the case of some kinds of data, act as a mutual cross-check.

On such a basis, those communities would be considered most disintegrated in which all seven indicators agreed in pointing strongly to that condition. If such uniformity were not actually found, then the proportion of indicators registering disintegration as well as degree of each would have to be considered. Conversely the selection of integrated communities would be based on a plurality of indicators pointing toward the opposite end of the range.

As might be anticipated, not all the indices in Set B proved feasible. This will be discussed in the account of trying them out to be given in Volume II, but we can anticipate by noting here that only three survived in this instance. These are Poverty, Cultural Confusion, and Secularization. Disaster did not turn out to be of sufficient frequency to be useful, and Health raised problems of separating psychiatric disorders from other kinds of illness in morbidity estimates. Rapid Social Change and Migration involved both field and analytic problems which, while potentially solvable, seemed so time-consuming that selection of communities for intensive study was made without waiting.

Once sociocultural units had been chosen as very likely presenting marked contrasts with regard to social disintegration, the Set A indices could be brought into play through intensive community studies. By this means several steps might be accomplished. The initial selection would be confirmed or modified and further selection within this group carried out in order to secure the desired contrast.

Beyond degree of disintegration, however, the intensive studies could also yield descriptive and qualitative information regarding kind and patterning of disintegration. One would hope to get a picture of the sociocultural unit as a whole, the integrating as well as the disintegrating trends and the relations between them. This would require a description of each community as a system and its functioning. In particular there would be need to give an account of the network of shared sentiments which serve to orient, coordinate, and guide its actions. For this purpose some method would have to be devised for selecting the most relevant sentiments out of almost infinite possibilities, and also for choosing an appropriate level of abstraction. An attempt might also be made to define salient roles.

The community studies could in addition increase the chances of understanding the relationship of sociocultural environment to personality and so bring us to a reasonably good position for interpreting the findings with regard to numbers and kinds of psychiatric disorder. One would not only have figures which might or might not confirm the disintegration hypothesis (H3), but he would also have a beginning for trying to understand how these came about. Should the expectations based on the disintegration hypothesis be fulfilled, there would be some ground for selecting among many alternative but more specific explanations as to how and why social disintegration should have this effect. By this means new hypotheses could be framed at more precise levels of approximation than those that have been given here.

The interest in exploring cultural factors noted in the previous chapter can also be accommodated in this approach. Thus, communities could be selected as French and English as well as in terms of high and low social integration. The research goal might then be partially represented in a fourfold table, as in Figure 6.

	French	English
Integrated	A	B
Disintegrated	C	D

FIGURE 6: *Fourfold table for relating community characteristics and prevalence of psychiatric disorder.*

This assumes, of course, that the communities are reasonably well matched with regard to size, type of economy and other factors not included in the characteristics shown on the table. According to the disintegration hypothesis (H3), A will have fewer psychiatric cases than C, and B will have fewer than D. For exploration are the possibilities that there will be differences in kind as well as prevalence between A and C, and B and D, and also that there will be culturally determined differences in prevalence or kind, or both, between A and B, and C and D.

III THE INDICES OF SOCIAL DISINTEGRATION IN RELATION TO INDIVIDUALS

This section will discuss the use of the indices for a purpose different from that so far presented. To recapitulate as a starting point, the fourteen indices have been developed as a means of selecting and describing *communities* which contrast to each other markedly in the matter of social integration. This is based on the proposition (H3) that social disintegration is conducive to psychiatric disorder. Attempting to explain this in a few words, one could say that severe social disintegration of a community produces both psychological stress and lack of resources for dealing with that stress; out of the resultant psychological strain, psychiatric disorder emerges. The view, grossly simplified and submerging the aspect of personality development, can be put in the form of a diagram:

	Psychological stress,	
Community social disintegration →	lack of resources for dealing with stress. →	Psychiatric disorder

If one looks at the indices it is evident that the majority could be used to indicate stress in the life-story and cross-section of the moment of *individuals*. These indices may not be the best collection possible to mark various kinds of sociocultural pressure on a personality, but they may nevertheless be usable. For convenience in considering this point, they may be restated here in terms applicable to an individual:

Set A	Set B
1. Comes from a broken home	1. Recent history of disaster
2. Membership in no, or few and weak, associations	2. Ill health
3. No, or few and weak, leaders available	3. Poverty
4. Few constructive patterns of recreation	4. Cultural confusion
5. Much experience with hostility	5. Secularization
6. Exposure to crime and delinquency	6. Migration
7. Poor system of communications available	7. Rapid social change

It seems highly probable that a person who had a history of long and intense exposure to the majority of these adverse influences would be more apt to have psychiatric disorder than one whose experience had been more favorable. In reaching such a conclusion, a distinction should be made between unhappiness and psychiatric disorder. It is obvious that a concatenation of these conditions would lead to unhappiness, but unhappiness does not necessarily constitute or produce psychiatric disorder. The thought with regard to the indices is more specifically in terms of disturbance to the essential psychical condition with destructive (B series) rather than constructive (C series) sequences.

To illustrate, a broken home might constitute a risk during personality development with regard to physical security (E1), giving

Social Disintegration and Community Comparisons

and receiving love (E4 and 5), recognition (E6), orientation in society (E8), and membership in a human group. Poverty might bring risk with regard to physical security (E1), sexual satisfaction (E2), giving and receiving love (E4 and 5), recognition (E6), spontaneity (E7), membership in a human group (E9), belonging to a moral order (E10), and opportunity to interact with a variety of personalities (F1). Hence both kinds of experiences might be considered as tending toward disturbance of the essential psychical condition. Should this occur, then again both broken home and poverty pose obstacles in one form or another in the way of a constructive type of restoration and could well favor some kinds of symptom formation (in accordance with B5).

A similar demonstration could be made for each of the remaining indices in both sets, but it seems hardly necessary to do this at the present level of discussion. The point is rather to suggest that if data of this sort were gathered on the members of a probability sample and some device for rating degree of exposure to stress were worked out, then here is an additional way of exploring the relationship between psychiatric disorder and sociocultural factors.

This raises a question: why not use this approach in the first place? Why bother with the cumbersome problems of assessing total community units and some of the risks that are inherent in such concepts and methods? It could be argued that in assessing individual experience with noxious sociocultural influences one is much closer to relating the experience to the person, and that the opportunity of finding the directly significant relationships is much greater. Methods of survey analysis and correlation could be applied with tests of significance. It would be complicated, of course, due to the need for dealing with multiple factors, but there is promise that this might be handled by advanced statistical methods.

These are good arguments for using the individual approach as well as the group approach, but not for displacing the latter. Two main reasons may be cited.

The first comes directly from the idea of the community unit as a quasi-organism. The unit is conceived as a system which is so highly interdependent through processes of energy exchange, networks of communication, and shared sentiments that malfunctional foci have ramifying effects that extend widely if not entirely throughout the whole. Hence it is assumed that a disintegrated community has influences on the personality of its members which are over and above those directly referable to the indices. The total collection of such second-ary effects might be designated as a noxious "climate." [9] Conversely, it is assumed that integrated communities have multiple resources for personality not directly tapped by the indicators used, whether con-sidered in terms of group or of individual, and these may be thought of as benign "climate."

Putting the matter more concretely, it is considered probable that individuals who have had a certain experience with noxious aspects of the indicators will as a group show a higher frequency of psychiatric disorder when members of a disintegrated community than they will when members of an integrated community. It is thought that this kind of relationship would be missed if one considered only individual experience with sociocultural factors, since we have neither the knowl-edge nor the instruments with which to foresee and take into account all the multiple influences inherent in community climate. On the other hand, if it turns out possible to identify types of noxious and benign communities, it may then be feasible to study these intensively in order to further identify the more salient of the otherwise hidden factors.

The second point is closely related to the first. If one used only in-dividual assessment of the kinds of sociocultural influences repre-sented in the fourteen indices, there would remain a considerable problem of finding the relationship of these influences to the larger sociocultural patterns of which they are a part. For instance, one might find that psychiatric disorder was highly associated with broken homes, but one would still not know how such psychiatric disorder is related to the functioning of society. For this, it would be necessary to understand the distribution and relations of broken homes in the social system and to know the characteristics in these relations which distinguish those broken homes which produce psychiatric disorder from those which do not. In other words there has to be a study of the sociocultural fabric at some point, subsequent to if not con-comitant with or in advance of investigating the individual relation-ships. Since one would expect association of psychiatric disorder with several of the indices, not just one, and since it is possible that particu-lar combinations of these factors may be more important than just plurality, the problem is actually far more complicated than it would be with a single item like broken homes.

As a result of these considerations, it seemed advisable to conduct

Social Disintegration and Community Comparisons

both the study based on the community units as wholes (with emphasis on social disintegration and cultural differences) and the assessment of the experience of individuals with the noxious influences represented by the indices. In this manner there would be a chance for one type of analysis to illuminate the other and possibly also an opportunity to see whether the orientation in terms of quasi-organism and community unit is as important as it is represented to be in this frame of reference. There may, for instance, be some constellations of stress factors which are highly associated with psychiatric disorder regardless of the kind of community in which they occur. If such exist, they would obviously be well worth identifying. Conversely, it might be possible to show that certain constellations of stress factors are much more prone to being associated with psychiatric disorder when they occur in people who live as part of a disintegrated community than when they occur in people who live in a relatively integrated community. If this were so, it would point to the importance of the characteristics of the system as a whole.

It is well to note that there is opportunity for some confusion because of the dual use of these indices. *As applied to communities,* they are for rating social disintegration and have nothing directly to do with psychological stress as such. The disintegration is presumed to have this effect and to have it in many ways that go beyond the phenomena directly represented by the indices. On the other hand, *when applied to the experience of individuals,* the indices are employed directly, regardless of community, for rating psychological stress. In order to preserve clarity as much as possible, they will be called "indices of social disintegration" when referring to communities, and "stress factors" when referring to individuals.

The comparison and discussion of these two types of analysis will be presented in Volume III. It should be borne in mind, however, that the investigation of the relationship of social disintegration and culture in community units to psychiatric disorder is the main purpose, and the criteria were developed with reference to this. The analysis of individual experience in relation to psychiatric disorder is an extension.

IV SOME CAUTIONS

In selecting the social disintegration hypothesis (H3) as a focus for research inquiry, a number of attending desiderata and limitations need to be kept in mind. Some of these have already been discussed, but others remain to be mentioned.

One point has to do with the emphasis in the frame of reference on successive approximations. This means beginning as a matter of necessity with very general concepts and methods of rough estimation. Under such circumstances it is important not to let testing the proposition become synonymous with the research, for to do so is to run the risk of losing touch with the phenomena and of attempting to work at levels of precision for which there are as yet neither the knowledge nor the resources. Overemphasis at this time on crucial tests can narrow awareness and lead to an illusory rigor based on disregarding essentials. The requirements of the level of approximation at which this work begins call for a great deal of exploration and observation with an open-minded ambition to hunt and find. There has to be emphasis on collecting facts within the orientation suggested by the frame of reference and on steeping oneself in data to see what one can make of it. It is desirable to increase in every way possible the chances of serendipity and to give the inquiring mind rich fare.

The position is, therefore, between pure theory construction somewhat removed from specific data on the one hand, and highly specific hypothesis testing on the other. It places much value on multiple, accurate observations and effective methods of recording. Three concomitant activities may be visualized as making up the effort. These consist in utilizing:

1. Hypotheses (e.g., social disintegration leads to psychiatric disorder);

2. Half-hypotheses, or exploration (e.g., cultures make a difference in the number and kinds of psychiatric disorder);

3. Serendipity.

A second point is the need to take into account the fact that any correlations which emerge may be due to concepts and methods rather than to causal relations in the phenomena. This problem was mentioned in the first section of Chapter VI on "The Sociocultural Environment" with reference to indices of individual and of group behavior. It is apposite now to the indices of social disintegration.

Social Disintegration and Community Comparisons

These are registrations of the activities of individuals interpreted in such a way as to yield an impression of degree of malfunction in a community. If some or many of these indices are actually manifestations of malfunction in personalities as well, then it may be that psychiatric disorder and social disintegration are different aspects of the same thing, rather than causal in their relationships. Clarification of such conceptual matters, however, may be regarded as a necessary aspect of the research and one which cannot be done through conceptual analysis alone. It requires experience and data.

A closely related point is the possibility that the relationship of psychiatric disorder and social disintegration is the reverse of proposition H3, namely that psychiatric disorder produces social disintegration. It is exceedingly unlikely that any research tactics which result in showing an association between social disintegration and psychiatric disorder will at the same time be able to demonstrate that disintegration is in the main the antecedent. It is my view that to attempt this is to bite off too much, although a certain amount of indirect evidence may be collected. The first order of business is to demonstrate the association. If this can be done, then the field of attention can be narrowed to research regarding the components of the process. The desirable steps are thought to be somewhat parallel to those inherent in making a diagnosis as outlined in Chapter I in connection with Tom Young's case. It is most important to keep the alternatives in mind as one goes about gathering and analyzing evidence and to attempt the formulation and reformulation of some scale of probabilities as a result of contacts with the data. In conformance with this line of thought, it is appropriate to restate here the alternatives and probabilities as they are presently visualized with regard to the disintegration proposition (H3).

It is thought most probable that the accelerating changes in cultural and societal patterns which characterize much of human group life today do result in considerable social disintegration. This in turn has an impact on the members of the societies so affected with the result that many people develop psychiatric disorder who would not otherwise do so. There is, in short, a group condition which, if it persists, can produce psychiatric disorder. Other factors to be mentioned presently can enhance this effect, but it can and does occur on a sociocultural and psychological basis alone.

It is thought equally likely that some, though not necessarily all, forms of psychiatric disorder can foster social disintegration and that some extreme types are capable of being the central cause. Hence there is a circular effect to be expected in the relationship between social disintegration and psychiatric disorder. Once both are established, they become interdependent and tend to perpetuate and increase each other. Hence any actual community which shows an association of social disintegration and psychiatric disorder will give evidence of causal relationships in both directions. The longer the duration of disintegration, the more complete this interdependence is apt to be.

It is considered possible, though somewhat less probable, that psychiatric disorder can be a pure antecedent and main cause of social disintegration. This could come about through the potency of physiological and hereditary factors and through sociocultural processes which precipitated malfunctional personalities into groups of their own kind.

Physiological and hereditary factors have been touched upon in Chapters III and IV and then set aside in the interests of developing the framework of sociocultural factors. If an association is found, however, between social disintegration (or any other sociocultural pattern) and psychiatric disorder, then heredity and physiological influences must be taken into account in any further research. Without this no accurate and significant illumination of causal relationships is possible.

The point is sufficiently important to warrant some further discussion, and we may begin with physiological factors. It could be, for instance, that social disintegration contributes to psychiatric disorder primarily through physiological damage to personality. A disintegrated pattern of living can mean greater frequency of birth traumata, numerous chronic and subclinical infections, head injuries, and poor diet. The noxious effects of these conditions may be delayed in appearance and of a low-grade, diffuse character, making the perception of relationship between origin and result far from easy.

Dietary deficiency can serve as an illustrative example. As is well known, lack of vitamins, particularly the B complex, can produce malfunction in the central nervous system and hence affect cognition and the ability to mobilize one's energy resources. In one form of deficiency, pellagra, there is dementia which is often indistinguishable, so far as behavior goes, from some kinds of schizophrenia. If such physiological factors can produce extreme forms of deranged behavior, they may also produce borderline states. Hence it is possible and even plausible that such symptoms as lethargy, general nervousness, depressed mood, anger, impulsiveness, and numbers of others might at times have their roots in low-grade, chronic, and not easily detectable vitamin deficiency. Many apparent instances of psychoneuroses, personality disorder, psychophysiological disorder, and sociopathic behavior could exist on such a basis.

In general, psychiatrists and clinical psychologists are leery of such explanations of personality malfunction. There are several reasons for this. Foremost is the fact that treatments based on such assumptions do little good. Another is finding that many patients seek to avoid coming to grips with their psychological problems by insisting that the root of the matter is organic. As in the case of Tom Young, one has to go beyond an organic explanation in order to get at the salient factors, and the patient has to realize this in order to be able to cooperate in the therapy. Psychiatrists also find on occasion some tendency on the part of their fellow physicians to reject blindly psychological diagnosis in favor of organic diagnosis.

After taking these matters into account, however, it remains clear that instances do occur in which physiological traumata of one sort or another produce symptoms and symptom complexes which are indistinguishable from some kinds of psychiatric disorder. What is unknown is the frequency with which this occurs, and such a frequency has to be discovered or controlled if one is going to conclude that the social environment produces its main effects by means of psychological experience.

The illustrative example just given for purpose of discussion points to social disintegration as capable of producing vitamin deficiency and other noxious physiological influences which in turn can produce psychiatric disorder. It may also be suggested that patterns of diet or endemic subclinical and even clinical diseases could produce psychiatric disorder which in turn could lead to social disorganization.

Turning now to heredity, it is obvious that, once sperm and egg unite, genetic factors are fixed. Hence the only way the sociocultural environment can affect the assortment of genes is through influence on mating. If sociocultural patterns tend to bring some kinds of male and female personalities together and if the genetic component is important in the determination of these personality types, then it may be possible for sociocultural patterns to have an effect on frequency and kind of malfunctional personality through selective breeding.

As noted in Chapter III, a glance at the patterning of Northeast society gives some plausibility to this idea. For instance, if it is supposed that most kinds of psychiatric disorder incapacitate people to some degree in maintaining a place at many points in the social system, then it seems likely that malfunctioning personalities would be gradually precipitated together in more or less walled-off parts of the system or outside the system altogether. This could then lead to an increased frequency of mating of these with each other and hence to a continuing or increased frequency of genetically determined personality disorders in such groups. Since these personalities would be incapable of adequate participation in a social system, their own group would necessarily manifest social disintegration. The sequence here might be visualized as the sociocultural throwing together of genetically defective personalities, the breeding of such personalities to yield a group with a high frequency of psychiatric disorder, and the psychiatric disorder producing social disintegration.

That this would happen in any such simple way is, I think, of low probability. This evaluation is not due to doubt with regard to the significance of genetic factors in psychiatric disorder. On the contrary, it is thought that various characteristics of affect, cognition, basic urges, and unconscious processes have capacities, limitations, and malfunctions that rest primarily on genetic factors. The low rating of probability is due to thinking that environmental factors greatly influence many of the genetic dispositions for better or for worse in the course of personality development. It is also due to some doubt about sufficient duration and consistency of the selective breeding necessary to establish and maintain groups of severely malfunctioning personalities. In other words, while the sequence outlined above is considered possible and also as occurring to some extent, it is thought to be overshadowed by other determinants which lie in the interaction of sociocultural environment and psychological experience. Nevertheless it must be considered important because it is a component big or little, in the process of establishment and maintenance of disintegrated communities.

Of the two sets of factors discussed in the preceding pages, it is probable that the genetic can be regarded as more significant and important than the physiological. This is because one can look forward to the eventual refinement of medical techniques to the point where appropriate tests can be run for the presence of physiological disturbances of the types outlined.

The problem of ascertaining the relationship between hereditary and environmental factors is more baffling. In this connection it is of interest to note that if the social disintegration association can be shown as generally occurring, then one avenue is opened for gathering some critical information. The first thought that occurs is, perhaps, that the family lines of a sample of people in integrated and disintegrated communities might be examined to see whether the coming together of persons with much psychiatric disorder in their ancestry tended to create disintegrated communities. Such an approach is fraught with very great problems of gathering accurate and relevant data. It might nevertheless be worth doing, especially if no other avenue were available.

There is, however, a more direct approach which involves taking advantage of a type of event that is not uncommon in nature. This is where a part of a homogeneous population is subject to social disintegration through purely exogenous factors, while the remainder is left unaffected. By homogeneous is meant a genetic composition such that the part of the population affected by the change would be essentially the same as the part left unaffected, and in addition that there should be at the start uniformity in culture and in the general picture of health.

It would, of course, be difficult to prove the genetic homogeneity, but it might be reasonable in many circumstances to assume that it did exist and that the changes creating social disintegration were unassociated with any inherent weakness on the part of the population that became disintegrated as compared to that which did not. If, under such circumstances, it is found that the disintegrated part of the population has a significantly higher prevalence of psychiatric disorder than the integrated part, then considerable evidence in support of purely sociocultural factors and psychological processes would be obtainable. This would constitute a base from which to move to the next level of approximation and to make more precise inquiry regarding the relationship of sociocultural processes and psychological processes and so determine which factors of the sociocultural environment are the most critical and salient.[10]

CHAPTER NOTES

1. With regard to this chapter, Gerald Berreman, Charles Hughes, Jane Hughes, and Toshio Yatsushiro gave help in searching the literature and providing analytical commentary on the concepts of integration and disintegration.

2. Because the idea represented by the words *integration* and *disintegration* occupies a central position in this frame of reference, and because these particular terms have replaced "organization" and "disorganization" used in earlier writings emanating from the Stirling County Study, some discussion of both concept and words is in order at this point.

In previous chapter notes, several other ideas of importance have been discussed. These consist in sentiment, personality, culture, holism, and function. For each an attempt has been made to indicate other literature in social and clinical science where the same ideas have been employed or where the same term has been used but with variant meanings. Sentiment has been treated separately in Appendix A because of its significance as a bridging concept and because it has not been as widely used as the others. The discussion which follows dealing with *integration* and *disintegration* will be more in accord with that carried out in connection with personality, for example. Like the others, this topic is exceedingly complex and has accumulated a large relevant literature, some of it going back many years. Within the confines of this book it is possible to touch upon it only briefly and indicatively.

Turning first to my shift away from "organization" and "disorganization," examples of previous employment of these words may be seen in ALEXANDER H. LEIGHTON: "Psychiatric Disorder and Social Environment," *Psychiatry*, Vol. 18, no. 4, 1955, and "Social Disorganization," in *The Governing of Men* (Princeton: Princeton Univ. Press, 1945), pp. 140-153.

The change to *integration* and *disintegration* has been made primarily because the terms seem to fit more easily and naturally into the development of this book, starting as it does from the notion of personality as the functioning of the self-integrating unit and moving on to consideration of the community as another level of integration. Additional reasons for the change have to do with the hope of avoiding some of the disadvantages in the terms "organization" and "disorganization" which have become apparent in attempting to use them. The situation is complicated, however, because some of the distinctions between the terms are subtle while others are obvious. In some instances "integration" and "organization" are used interchangeably or as only slightly different aspects of the same underlying concept. There are, on the other hand, genuinely different usages from what is intended in these pages. The range of similar and dissimilar employment extends, moreover, beyond the limits of the social sciences and includes ideas that have bearing on various ways of viewing process and function found in embryology, physiology, ecology, and other branches of biology. In order to minimize confusion italics are used to designate *integration* and *disintegration* when they have specific reference to the meaning explained in this book.

Some years ago, I began to employ "disorganization" as a term to mark what I thought was going on among certain groups of Navahos, and among Japanese and Japanese-Americans recently moved to a relocation center. When I turned to "organization," however, there were altered meanings which made it not altogether the counterpart I sought for "disorganization." I found myself a little like Bertie Wooster when he became aware that saying Jeeves was "gruntled" was not exactly the opposite of saying he was "disgruntled." Yet the need remained to find terms which would express two opposing aspects of one process.

In popular usage "organization" has come to stand for associations in which authority, hierarchy, and regimentation, often with a strong implication of coercion and outside force, are the primary modes of coordination. One speaks of "military organization," "bureaucratic organization," "the organization man," and "union organization."

In technical literature, on the other hand, "organization" has been conceived in a number of different ways. For example, anthropologists have designated kinship as "social organization." Lowie says that "The study of social organization deals primarily with the significant grouping of individuals," and he discusses such alignments as kinship, co-residence, voluntary associations, and social strata. Similarly Tax defines social organization in terms of biological generation as the universal focus for the integration of a social unit. *See:* ROBERT H. LOWIE, *Social Organization* (New York: Rinehart, 1953), p. 3; SOL TAX, "Some Problems of Social Organization," in FRED EGGAN (Ed.), *Social Anthropology of North American Tribes* (Chicago: Univ. Chicago Press, 1955).

In this volume, family and kinship obligations are considered part of the fundamental pattern of *integration* of the quasi-organism and crucially involved in the maintenance of the community unit as the means of reproduction. At the same time, *integration* has broader meaning and refers to functions which extend beyond the perimeters of kinship.

The British anthropologist, Raymond Firth, has a somewhat different view of social organization. For him, it means "people getting things done by planned action." He contrasts it with social structure and says: "In the aspect of social structure is to be found the continuity principle of society; in the aspect of organization is to be found the variation, or change principle—by allowing evaluation of situation and entry of individual choice." Insofar as Firth defines organization as the dynamic aspect of the system, *integration,* as I think of it, is similar. Continuity, in which he finds a separate expression of structure, I conceive as also an aspect of *integration.* Firth's suggestion that organization is the planned and conscious election of certain alternatives is one of the connotative meanings of "organization" which it is hoped can be surmounted. *See* RAYMOND FIRTH, *Elements of Social Organization* (London: Watts, 1951), pp. 36 and 40.

In sociology, *"dis*organization" has at times been a focal concept much like "social organization" in anthropology. The terms employed in the two disciplines are not, however, counterparts but involve essentially different points of reference. In addition to the kinship meaning, anthropologists have often used "organization" in the evolutionary sense implying increased differentiation of parts, specialization, and the achievement of new levels. In sociology, *"dis*organization" has meant disturbance in the functioning of the social group. In terms of evolutionary complexity and

Social Disintegration and Community Comparisons

339

specialization of functions, modern society is more highly organized than a primitive tribe. Yet when "organization" is conceived in terms of stability and the unifying force of custom, the primitive group is thought to be more highly organized. For the most part, "acculturation" or "cultural disorientation" have been employed by anthropologists to mark functional disruptions in nonliterate societies. The term "disorganization" has been applied primarily to urban society in which norms are ambiguous or where former rules and regulations no longer hold. It means the loss of a prior state of organization or the absence of adequate functioning at the evolutionary level of organization assumed by dealing with modern societies. It may be thought that the illustration of the Collection and the Model incorporates the same confusion between evolution and function. It should be reiterated, therefore, that they are conceptual devices and do not represent any natural phenomena, nor are any particular stages of evolutionary development in mind. What I mean by *disintegration* is that once the pattern for a quasi-organism has been established, whether it be the pattern characterizing a group of Eskimo hunters, a French Canadian fishing village, or a metropolitan block, disruptions may occur which send the group in a downward spiral of maladaptations.

Apart from the general differences in the sociological and anthropological usages of "organization" and "disorganization," there are further distinctions to be made regarding their use in sociology alone.

In re-evaluating the concept, Faris points out that there was a time when "disorganization" was used to "designate any undesirable condition of modern life." The "social problem" or "social pathology" approach focused on discrete aspects such as crime, delinquency, illiteracy, divorces, prostitution, and unemployment. Following a time when this use of the term was widespread, there came a period of reversal and criticism. Nonetheless, the orientation toward process, if not problem, which characterized the early writers in this field has much in common with what is suggested here as *integration* and *disintegration*. They conceive of "organization" and "disorganization" as continuous processes of a social organism, the one acting to maintain socially coordinated relationships, the other to disturb them. For example, in *Social Organization and Disorganization,* Queen, Bodenhafer, and Harper say: "It must be apparent from what has gone before that disorganization is simply the opposite of organization. If the latter consists of those processes through which groups are built up, strengthened, enabled to meet crises, and to control their own members, social disorganization consists of those processes through which groups are weakened, defeated, demoralized, and broken up." See STUART A. QUEEN, WALTER B. BODENHAFER, and ERNEST B. HARPER, *Social Organization and Disorganization* (New York: Crowell, 1935), p. 53. *See also:* ROBERT FARIS, *Social Disorganization* (2nd ed., New York: Ronald, 1955), p. 35; M. A. ELLIOTT and F. E. MERRILL, *Social Disorganization* (New York: Harper, 1941).

In criticism of the term "disorganization" as denoting the prevalence of social problems, Cuber points out that it began to mean a state of affairs in which "customary and approved ways of behavior no longer prevail." Because of the difficulty in separating the breakdown of traditional roles from the appearance of new roles, he recommended that "social change" be employed as a more adequate orientation to what had previously been called "social disorganization." He reserved the concept of "disorganization" for disturbances of overwhelming magnitude but short duration. Thus a group becomes disorganized during periods of riots or earthquakes, but such a situation is not permanent and the social unit will likely return to its former state. My view of *disintegration* suggests that the gradual processes of social change may be as malfunctional to the quasi-organism as short and devastating periods of chaos. *See* JOHN F. CUBER, *Sociology, A Synopsis of Principles* (2nd ed.; New York: Appleton-Century-Crofts, 1951), p. 520.

In addition to the equation of "disorganization" and "social problem," sociologists have been concerned with theoretical and analytic features of "organization" and the similar ideas denoted by such terms as "cohesion" and "unity." At this more abstract level, it has been pointed out that two types of organization need to be analyzed in studying a social system: consensus and functional interdependence. "Consensus" refers to that trend toward similarity, or at least agreement, in basic sentiment patterns, orientations, values, or meanings. "Functional interdependence" is the

Social Disintegration and Community Comparisons

complementarity of interactions and of exchange of goods and services—in Durkheim's terms, the "division of labor." Williams distinguishes between "cultural structure" as the values, norms, and beliefs of a group, and "social organization" as the specific social interactions of individuals within a group. Cuber speaks of "symbiotic interdependence" and "common value orientation." The consistency of values Cuber calls "integration," and, like Williams, he employs the term "organization" for the symbiotic interdependence of the constituent members of a social unit.

See: ROBIN M. WILLIAMS, JR., *American Society, A Sociological Interpretation* (New York: Alfred A. Knopf, 1951); JOHN F. CUBER, *Sociology, A Synopsis of Principles.*

The several facets of *integration* and *disintegration* outlined in this book are of somewhat different order than can be comprehended in the division between consensus and functional interdependence. The fourteen indicators of *disintegration*, for example, are not easily separated into these two aspects. They combine value consensus (or, in our terms, shared sentiments) and functional interdependence. And they pervade all phases of the whole quasi-organism. The word, *disintegration,* is meant to describe a multiphasic process, attributes of which are destroyed by too close analysis into aspects or subdivisions. Similar to my contention that consensus and interdependence cannot accurately be viewed as separate functions is a statement by Amos Hawley: ". . . the collective life of man, as of all other organisms, revolves simultaneously about two axes, one of which is symbiotic, the other commensalistic. The former pertains to the interdependence of unlike forms, i.e., units of dissimilar functions; the latter to the co-action of like forms, i.e., units of similar functions. The two types of relationship are found in all organized populations. Each represents a peculiar and complementary integrative force and together, therefore, they constitute the basis of community cohesion." *See* AMOS H. HAWLEY, *Human Ecology* (New York: Ronald, 1950), p. 209.

For further explanation of the various sociological and anthropological views of "organization" and "disorganization," where also a number of bibliographies are to be found, *see:* W. S. LANDECKER, "Types of Integration and Their Measurement" in PAUL E. LAZARSFELD and MORRIS

ROSENBERG (Eds.), *The Language of Social Research* (Glencoe, Ill.: Free Press, 1955); ALBERT K. COHEN, "The Study of Social Disorganization and Deviant Behavior," in ROBERT K. MERTON, LEONARD BROOM, and LEONARD S. COTTRELL, JR. (Eds.), *Sociology Today* (New York: Basic Books, 1959), pp. 461-484; W. I. THOMAS, "Social Disorganization and Reconstruction," in EDMUND H. VOLKART (Ed.), *Social Behavior and Personality* (New York: Social Science Research Council, 1951), pp. 232-237; FLORIAN ZNANIECKI, "Social Organization and Institutions," in GEORGES GURVITCH and WILBERT W. MOORE (Eds.), *Twentieth Century Sociology* (New York: Philosophical Library, 1945), pp. 172-217.

Implicit in much of this literature is the thesis that social disorganization is related to personal disorganization. And deviant behavior has often been taken as an index of personal disorganization. The May 1937 issue of *The American Journal of Sociology,* a symposium to which both sociologists and psychiatrists contributed, was devoted to the analysis of this relationship. Although many of the articles stem from orientations which are different from what is here outlined as a way of viewing the relationship between sociocultural environment and psychiatric disorder, one which has much in consonance is HERBERT BLUMER, "Social Disorganization and Individual Disorganization," *The American Journal of Sociology,* Vol. 42, no. 6, 1937, pp. 871-877. *See also:* HERBERT A. BLOCH, *Disorganization: Personal and Social* (New York: Alfred A. Knopf, 1952); LAWRENCE G. BROWN, *Social Pathology, Personal and Social Disorganization* (New York: Crofts, 1945).

"Organization" and "disorganization" are not the only terms which approximate what I have in mind by *integration* and *disintegration.* There is common ground, for instance, with function and malfunction or dysfunction, with anomie and eunomia, genuine and spurious, and the ordinary use of morale and demoralization. *See,* for example, TALCOTT PARSONS, *The Social System* (Glencoe, Ill.: Free Press, 1951); ROBERT K. MERTON, "Social Structure and Anomie," and "Manifest and Latent Functions," in *Social Theory and Social Structure* (Glencoe, Ill.: Free Press, 1957), pp. 21-81, and 125-149; GEORGE SIMPSON, *Emile Durkheim on the Division of Labor in Society* (New York: Macmillan, 1933), especially "The Anomic Division of Labor," pp. 353-

Social Disintegration and Community Comparisons

373; LEO SROLE, "Social Integration and Certain Corollaries: An Exploratory Study," *American Sociological Review*, Vol. 21, no. 6, 1956; EDWARD SAPIR, "Culture, Genuine and Spurious," in *Selected Writings of Edward Sapir in Language, Culture, and Personality*, DAVID G. MANDELBAUM, (Ed.) (Berkeley: Univ. California Press, 1951).

Thus in shifting to *integration* and *disintegration*, it must be recognized that no words will be entirely satisfactory and that in shedding the difficulties of "organization" and "disorganization" one may only be moving into a different range of problems. It is possible to spot connotations and implications relating to "integration" that could be a source of trouble. In biological literature, the word is often used with reference to organic evolution. Hence, like "organization," "integration" has two contrasting meanings. It has been used to describe the state or condition of a dynamic system: but it also has the meaning of level or progression from one type of integration to another. *See* ROBERT REDFIELD (Ed.), "Levels of Integration in Biological and Social Systems," *Biological Symposia*, Vol. 8 (Lancaster: Cattell Press, 1942).

Nevertheless there is the fact mentioned earlier that *integration* and *disintegration* fit into the general development of this volume. Another important criterion for their selection is the indication they give that something is going on *within the system*. Even in nontechnical language, "integration" means more than a reflexive or passive response to outside events. The disadvantage which stems from their previous employment in social science literature is again the problem of specific and limited meanings. Ruth Benedict, for example, emphasized the integration of culture about a single theme or motif. Julian Steward uses it primarily in the evolutionary sense. And as mentioned in the discussion of similar concepts in sociology, integration has been employed by some to indicate value unity and consistency without reference to the indices of *disintegration* (such as poverty, broken homes, and lack of leadership) which have been described in this book. Williams, for example, defines "integration" as the "sharing of common prescriptions and proscriptions for conduct, belief, valuation."

See RUTH BENEDICT, *Patterns of Culture* (New York,

Houghton-Mifflin, 1934); JULIAN H. STEWARD, *Theory of Culture Change* (Urbana: Univ. Illinois, 1955); ROBIN M. WILLIAMS, JR., *American Society, A Sociological Interpretation*, p. 517. *See also* ROBERT C. ANGELL, "The Social Integration of Selected American Cities," *American Journal of Sociology*, Vol. 47, no. 4, 1942, pp. 575-592.

In conclusion, *integration* and *disintegration* were selected for inherent qualities of meaning. Drawing, moreover, on the background of their use and the usage of similar terms in other social sciences, it was thought possible to redefine them in the context of this frame of reference so that a broader meaning would be conveyed than any of the specific references which the above notes and bibliography indicate have been attached to the terms. Just as "sentiments" cover what is elsewhere described as "attitudes," "opinions," and "values," *integration* and *disintegration* mean what has been designated as "functional" and "malfunctional," "organized" and "disorganized," "unified" and "interdependent," but without the restricted emphases these often have to one or another facet of a total process.

3. Malfunction, or a state of being disorganismic, is of course a human concept with a slant, not a pure designation of process in nature. More than this, however, it is a term which takes meaning only on the basis of certain assumptions and values which may be explicit or implicit. When I say this community is malfunctional as compared to that, I must have in mind a set of reference points applicable to both. One such set might be ability to survive under present circumstances. Others might be ability to grow, or ability to change. These are not necessarily the same in all circumstances, for the community best geared to survive under one set of conditions might be least well able to adjust to change. Or, two communities—one functional and the other malfunctional with reference to each other and existing under a common set of circumstances—might, while retaining their patterns, have their relative positions reversed in a different set of common circumstances.

The fluidity of the concepts of function and malfunction is not confined to problems of groups. It is to be found equally when it is a question of the function and malfunction of an individual. In their textbook on physiology, Winton and Bayliss say:

"Perhaps the most characteristic feature of health is that a man can move about as quickly and for as long as he likes. An active man moves freely, but his well-being is not measured directly by the extent or speed of his movements, but rather by the slightness of the changes produced in him by the severest exercise which he takes in the normal course of his life. Certainly, if an ordinary clerk, and an athlete ran together for half a mile to catch a train; the former might arrive exhausted, panting and sweating, and remain in a relatively distressed condition for some time, whereas the latter might suffer a little inconvenience and that soon over. The clerk, however, is not necessarily less healthy than his fellow, and the difference between their physical resources is a problem of physiology which will be considered later. An invalid, on the other hand, might suffer as much distress after walking but a short distance, and such a further degree of reduction of his physical reserve would clearly be due to his illness.

"Health and disease are primarily sociological concepts; they generally mean that a man can or cannot carry on his normal occupation."

In other words, "malfunction" is a value concept. *See* F. R. WINTON and L. E. BAYLISS, *Human Physiology* (4th ed.; Boston: Little, Brown, 1955), p. 1.

The same outlook applies to community units. There is always the question of "malfunctional with reference to what set of specifications?" The same applies to "disintegration" and "disorganization." My point here is to note the existence of the problem and the limit it sets on generalization. One has to begin somewhere, and there is no need to be any more paralyzed by these matters than medicine has been. Our point of departure for investigation is represented by the A and B indices presented in section II of this chapter.

These words from a book that is purely physiological in its orientation is a demonstration of the fact that biologists have had to cope for a long time with many of the same types of problems which beset the social scientist. In previous chapter notes mention has been made of both social scientists and biologists who have tried to express ideas regarding their conception of the nature of human behavior and the nature of a relevant scientific process. See Chap. III, Note 6, Chap. VI, Notes 10 and 12, and Chap. VIII, Note 1.

Numbers of biologists have also written in the same vein in regard to their own subject matter, without particular reference to human problems. These reflections on life and the science of life are, nevertheless, often exceedingly apposite to our preoccupations. *See,* for instance: MORTON BECKNER, *The Biological Way of Thought* (New York: Columbia Univ. Press, 1959); E. S. RUSSELL, *The Directiveness of Organic Activities* (Cambridge: Cambridge Univ. Press, 1945); J. S. HALDANE, *The Philosophy of a Biologist* (Oxford: Clarendon, 1935); J. H. WOODGER, *Biological Principles* (New York: Harcourt Brace, 1929).

4. The suggestion for this index came from Robin M. Williams, Jr.

In our use, "secularization" does not have reference to rational as contrasted to folk cultures, except insofar as the former may be associated with the absence of religious sentiment. The meaning is, therefore, narrower than that employed by Redfield and Becker.

See: ROBERT REDFIELD, *The Folk Culture of Yucatan* (Chicago: Univ. Chicago Press, 1941); HOWARD BECKER, *Through Values to Social Interpretation* (Durham, N. C.: Duke Univ. Press, 1950); HOWARD BECKER, *Man in Reciprocity, Introductory Lectures on Culture, Society and Personality* (New York: Praeger, 1956).

5. The migration index was not selected during the preliminary studies, but was added later when the field work proper had begun. It came from Robert N. Rapoport, who directed the surveys and community studies, and was a result of his first few months in the field.

6. *See:* ALLISTER M. MACMILLAN and ALEXANDER H. LEIGHTON, "People of the Hinterland, Community Interrelations in a Maritime Province of Canada," EDWARD H. SPICER (Ed.), *Human Problems in Technological Change* (New York: Russell Sage Foundation, 1952); STEPHEN A. RICHARDSON, "Technological Change: Some Effects on Three Canadian

Fishing Villages," *Human Organization,* Vol. 11, no. 3, 1952.

7. *See* ALEXANDER H. LEIGHTON and ROBERT J. SMITH, "A Comparative Study of Social and Cultural Change," *Proceedings of the American Philosophical Society,* Vol. 99, no. 2, April 1955.

8. For a similar use of antecedent and consequent indicators *see* ALEXANDER H. LEIGHTON, *Human Relations in a Changing World* (New York: Dutton, 1949), pp. 85-87.

9. For a comparable use of the term "climate," *see* ROBIN M. WILLIAMS, JR., "Place of Ecological Analysis in Comparative Study," in E. A. SUCHMAN (Ed.), *The Comparative Method in Social Research,* Cross Cultural Methods Project, Cornell University (in process), pp. 45-53.

10. At the end of this chapter, which is concerned with the assessment of social environment in relation to psychiatric disorder, it is appropriate to note that in 1937 W. Lloyd Warner published an article, "The Society, The Individual, and His Mental Disorder" *(The American Journal of Psychiatry,* Vol. 94, no. 2, pp. 275-284), which is at a number of points exceedingly relevant to the ideas set forth in this frame of reference. It was a pioneering statement and deserves to be quoted at some length.

"Society does three very necessary and useful things. In the first place, no matter how complex the society, a hunting and gathering one at the stone-age level, or a steel and electrical one such as our own, it uses its technology as a means of adjusting itself to its natural environment. The technical behavior of a people relates it to the natural environment so that nature is no longer hostile and the food-gathering behavior is no longer purely that of animals. The technology socially organizes this behavior for man.

"There is a second type of human adaptation which relates men together as social individuals. It formalizes relationships and limits the individual variation of each of these relationships. This kind of adaptation ties human individuals into a general kind of behavior, so that in any given situation they will act in a similar manner. Our social organization not only relates us to each other but helps us to organize our technology to provide a division of labor to handle the various tools by which we change nature to give us our living. Our social organization is also a social mechanism by which we divide the goods we get from nature. If there is a class system such as we possess, the division of labor and of goods is of an unequal kind. On the other hand, if there is a purely democratic society, as are some of the primitive ones, there may be an equal division of goods and of labor among the individuals of the group.

"Finally, there is another kind of adaptation which consists of the system, or systems, of beliefs or ideologies and sanctions; in other words, a symbolic level which serves to integrate the other two types of adaptation and integrate the group into a whole. Every society has a symbolic system or symbolic systems, and the symbolic systems of the several societies differ according to the kind of social organization and general behavior found in each group. There is a close relationship between the symbolic system and the organization of the society in which that system is found.

"These three adaptive systems not only relate the individual to the total situation in which he must live, but they also exercise control over his actions in the group. The social organization controls his behavior so that he is bound by a set of relations to other individuals in his group (pp. 276-277).

"Some of the situations in our society which are unbalanced and possibly disintegrate, and which may contribute to our mental disorders will be summarized:

"We have a shifting technology. Our rapidly changing technical system is constantly making people re-form themselves into new groupings and adopt new thinking after they have learned how to live in a certain situation which was dictated in part by the former arrangement of the technology. One only has to observe economic changes which have been taking place in New England with the textile, shoe and other industries leaving, or examine changes in the South where these industries are settling. There is a constant demand on the individuals living in the two areas to make readjustments. Many are not able to do it; others find it extremely difficult. The subtle and varied changes create too great a strain on the psychic life of these

Social Disintegration and Community Comparisons

individuals. We see in their behavior a disintegrating system to which they strive in vain to adjust themselves. Change continues in our social system, for as our technology shifts and our industrial revolution rapidly increases, the social organization must shift with it.

"Our society no longer provides a well-ordered system for us to use. The web, one might say, is frayed and broken and the individual himself must pick and choose, that is, think his way through it. Such thought is related to some of the more characteristic types of mental ailments which we recognize in this society at the present time. As part of our society has been reforming with attendant breaks in the social organization, we have had a decided change in our symbolic systems. The old absolute symbols in which we had complete faith, which dominated us, and which controlled us as absolute ideas beyond which we could not think, have been disintegrating. As a consequence, there has been no place where an individual could say privately or publicly, 'This is absolute and certain,' without thinking again that after all there are other absolutes, since the people around him may have additional absolute systems which in part will contradict his own. An example of such a conflict of absolutes is the conventional fight between science and the church. The break-up of the one church into many varieties of Protestantism is another. The existence of separate small ideologies or creeds in small groups thoughout the country is another. The city of Los Angeles is famous for them. There are thousands of people who come there from everywhere who bring scores of social traditions with them to a place whose social order was disturbed by the early inundations of populations and the social traditions which these people brought. Most of the inhabitants have no regular order which fits the need of the whole group. The farmers who lived a rural existence in Iowa and prayed to their God for rain to water their crops, and as such once had a workable social system, now find themselves in an urban environment where their old social system and prayers for rain are the antithesis of what their new situation demands. As a consequence we find thousands of little cults, none of which seems to be satisfactorily helping the individual solve his problems in relating himself to the world around him. One need not go as far as Los Angeles to find similar situations. One needs but look around him.

"Another interesting phenomenon, very closely connected with this shift in our technology and with the disorder in our symbolic systems is the appearance of a great variety of ethnic traditions which make up the present life of our larger cities and small towns and rural areas. Here again are conflicting social organizations and conflicting symbols, which theoretically might ultimately result in complete breakdown of the society. For the individual the interaction of the several ethnic traditions forms a region of conflict in which he must think and not feel his way. He cannot depend upon his social logics (an ordered thinking and way of action provided by his society) to solve his problems for him. He must select and choose, and to do so at all times may be too heavy a burden on his psychic life. In our society we place a high premium on intelligent choice and action, but despite this we cannot be consciously selective in most of our acts, since to be mentally healthy, our society must provide an ordered way of thinking and acting for us.

"Another social situation which has contributed greatly to some of the difficulties that are found in the mental life of many modern individuals is social mobility, that is to say, the going up and the coming down the social ladder in our class hierarchy. Many people move up rapidly, arrive at a certain place, and their upward progress is then stopped by pressure from above them: the individual's frustration often develops into neurosis. Other individuals have never been able to adjust themselves to any particular place in the shifting class world around them, and, as a consequence, they have difficulty in living effectively with other individuals. Personal insecurity because of class mobility is characteristic of American life and has provided at least the beginnings of many mental ailments" (pp. 281-283).

Chapter X

Case Finding and Case Study

IN PART ONE of this book a descriptive definition was offered as to what is meant by psychiatric disorder. Subsequent pages, being concerned with sociocultural factors, by-passed the problems of identifying and studying such disorders. It is necessary now to return to a psychiatric base and deal in these matters.

Two questions were pointed out in the beginning of Part Three (pages 304-305), one epidemiological and the other clinical. The epidemiological study implies some wholesale manner of estimating the total number of cases—whether already medically recognized or not—in a given population, and this in turn implies some adaptation of the principles of diagnosis. Hence in what follows discussion will be directed at the nature of diagnosis, at the use of indices of disorder, and at possible sources of data such that the indices might be applied to a general population.

The clinical study is concerned with how sociocultural factors actually enter into and affect the lives of those who develop psychiatric disorder. Attention will be given to the opportunities and problems in this kind of investigation at the end of the chapter.

I WHAT IS A CASE?

A case is a particular instance of malfunctioning personality from any of the several families of such patterns outlined in Chapters III and IV. It is a specimen from one of a variety of bundles of qualities to which such names are applied as: brain disorder, mental deficiency, psychosis, psychophysiological disorder, psychoneurosis, personality disorder, and sociopathic disorder. Under each of these are numbers of subvarieties for which a host of terms also exist.

When the meanings of all such names are considered, it is evident that they present certain problems for epidemiological work. Some of the difficulties are general and constitute perennial questions of psychiatric nomenclature, while others are more special to our interests. The general problems derive mainly from lack of sufficiently accepted standardization, with the result that there are overlapping and multiple meanings. This is not to say that the nomenclature is all chaos or that it is without value. On the contrary, it has much utility, but it does reflect the history of its emergence and the effects of a number of different influences and purposes. Some examples of the several influences are: the model of taxonomy in natural history, and especially disease naming in general medicine, the demands of record keeping in hospitals and clinics, and the impact of various and often competing theories of etiology as exemplified in Kraepelin, Freud, Bleuler, and Meyer.

A notable feature of psychiatry as compared to other branches of medicine is the not uncommon practice of making a diagnosis without attaching one of the conventional names. There can be a dynamic appraisal without labeling. From the viewpoint of psychotherapy it is sometimes said that classification by existing names is not only useless but misleading: on the one hand, any term selected may carry implications which do not apply to a particular case, while on the other, the term may fail to imply aspects of major importance. Furthermore, some names such as "schizophrenia" impute for many people a gloomy prognosis which is not justified in numbers of instances, but which may interfere with sufficient effort in treatment. Related to this is the fact that naming sometimes gives a false sense of knowing and so limits investigation. It can be claimed, therefore, that diagnosis—a formulation of the main factors involved in a given disorder of personality—is, for the purpose of treatment, better done without resort to general names.

Although I share these views where it is a question of psychotherapy and feel the importance of realizing in all clinical work the uniqueness of the individual case, the fact remains that this approach is not appropriate for some types of research, and is impossible when it comes to epidemiology. If one is going to count instances of a phenomenon, or a group of somewhat similar or related phenomena, then it is elementary that some concepts for identifying and differentiating these phenomena are necessary and that terms have to be used.

This leads to considering the codified systems that have been developed and widely employed, as by the World Health Organization and by the American Psychiatric Association. These systems have the advantage of providing structured reference points for diagnostic criteria and the use of names. On the other hand, their orientation is in terms of hospital and clinical records and this brings a number of disadvantages so far as our purposes are concerned. The criteria are mainly a mixture of symptom patterns and etiological factors and predicated on the opportunity for prolonged and thorough investigation, taking as many months per case as may be necessary—conditions not likely to be met in any epidemiological survey of communities. The definition of the terms and the organization of the relevant concepts, furthermore, include little attention to aspects of the phenomena which would be most easily seen in their natural setting, as contrasted to the more convenient but artificial setting of the clinic.

Nevertheless, it is necessary to begin somewhere and the codified systems appear to offer an opportunity. As mentioned in Note 1, Chapter IV, the 1952 *Manual* of the American Psychiatric Association has been our choice. It is hoped that by starting with this base we shall be able to introduce whatever modifications the epidemiological task may require. Through specifications and recording of these modifications it should be possible to keep track of what our terms, and hence our findings, mean with reference to other usages of the terms and other specifications regarding the nature of cases of psychiatric disorder. We are thus alerted and prepared for understanding that cases as specified for epidemiological purposes and as specified for clinical usage, while related, may not be identical. These considerations suggest some discussion of the process of diagnosis.

II WHAT IS A DIAGNOSIS?

As just mentioned there are two main aspects to diagnosis in psychiatry: one has to do with formulating the nature of and the main factors in a particular instance of personality malfunctioning, while the other is concerned with differentiating the phenomenon with reference to attaching an appropriate name. It is possible to carry out the first without the second, but the naming cannot be adequately done without some measure of formulation. This measure need not be as thorough and detailed as is desirable for a proper understanding of the malfunctioning personality in order to conduct treatment, but it has in broad terms the same components. These can be considered under five headings:

1. Symptom patterns,
2. Signs,
3. Underlying psychic malfunction,
4. Noxious life experiences,
5. Family history (indications of hereditary tendencies).

Considering symptoms and signs together, we may observe that "symptoms" as commonly employed in medicine refer to disturbances which are both noticed by the patient and recognized as probably significant by the physician. "Signs" on the other hand commonly refer to phenomena of which the patient is unaware but which are elicited on medical examination, such as failure of the pupil to contract when a light is flashed in the eye. The distinction between the two is not always sharp and is particularly apt to be blurred in psychiatry. In Tom Young's case, his anxiety attack in which he broke the window could be regarded as a symptom pattern, while the pulsating artery noted by Dr. Coindreau when Tom was pressed with questions could be considered a sign. Generally, in psychiatry the patient's complaints (and the complaints of others who are close to him) may be thought of as symptoms, whereas signs consist in data of an indicative nature brought out in examination and by psychological tests.

"Pattern" is to be mentioned in connection with symptoms because of the differential importance of arrangements and configurations. This is a matter not only of clustering at any given time but also of development, sequence, and period on the life-arc. The brief sketches of various types of psychiatric disorder given in Chapters III and IV are primarily in terms of symptom patterns.

Underlying psychic malfunction involves conflict and hence continuing disturbance of the essential psychical condition together with partial restorations and defenses against awareness of the disturbance, leading to the formation of symptoms. This is the core of the malfunctioning of the personality. Some examples have been outlined in Chapter III in connection with Tom Young, as for instance unconscious homosexual tendencies, murderous jealousy of his brother-in-law, and fear of being abandoned by his wife.

Noxious life experiences include both the physiological and the psychological, and the question is one of evidence regarding events which could with a high degree of probability have been etiological in their influence. An example of what is meant is seen on the physiological side in the case of the woodsman with violent temper and uncontrolled behavior due to encephalitis. On the psychological side are Tom Young's battle experience, his growing up as an only child on an isolated farm, his father treating him with distance, the overprotection and hostility of his mother, and other patterns of intrafamily relationship.

It may seem strange that the life experiences of a patient which are only suspected of being contributory should be incorporated in diagnosis. After all, one might say that in other areas of medicine a fracture is a fracture and measles is measles, each diagnosable on the basis of present examination, observation, and the developmental history of the symptoms. The causes of the fracture and the source of the measles are important items of information, but they are not, one might assert, part of the data upon which diagnosis should be based. Cannot the same be applied to the phenomena of psychosis, psychoneurosis, personality disorder, and the rest?

This question brings to the fore the fact of a difference between the use of diagnosis for research and for therapy. In the main, as already noted, diagnoses are made in order to plan treatment, and hence practice and orientation are very much under the influence of requirements in this situation. Speed is usually a matter of consequence and so all kinds of evidence, clues, probabilities, and hints are taken into account, including life experiences that might have etiological significance.

As a matter of fact, a fracture is not always clear to examination, even by X-ray, and in such circumstances knowledge regarding the nature of the blow may tip the balance of judgment. The reasoning is something like this: since such and such a type of blow would very likely cause a fracture, and since other evidence is not clear-cut but points in this direction, this probably is a fracture, and we had better call it that and treat it as one. In measles the case is similar; a history of exposure to the disease will weigh very heavily, especially in the preliminary diagnosis.

In psychiatric diagnosis there is a parallel or even stronger inclination to pay attention to theoretically noxious life experiences. Indeed, it can be said that as a rule a diagnosis is not considered satisfactory unless the interrelationships of symptoms, underlying psychic malfunction, and life experience (particularly very early life experience) have been worked out, at least in terms of a plausible set of inferences.

When, however, it is a matter of research directed at the discovery or verification of etiological relationships, the incorporation of causal propositions in the diagnosis is no longer appropriate. This means, however, that such research specifications of a case are not the same as the therapeutic. The point is a matter of considerable importance and suggests some caution and discrimination in the quantitative use of hospital and clinical diagnoses for research concerned with many kinds of etiological factors.

Family history comes into the diagnostic process in a similar way and for similar reasons. If there is indication of numerous instances of psychiatric disorder in a person's family, this may be taken as indica-

Case Finding and Case Study

tive of an hereditary tendency and hence as contributory evidence in favor of his having a psychiatric disorder. In some instances it may influence decision between a psychosis and a psychoneurosis. This could happen if for example the clinical picture were unclear but there was a marked family history of schizophrenia.

In considering these five major components, or areas of attention commonly employed in making a diagnosis, it is evident that a number of them are inappropriate or too difficult for epidemiological purposes. The hereditary interpretation is too uncertain and speculative. In addition to this it involves a factor which it is hoped can ultimately be explored for its influence, and hence should not be incorporated in the definition.

The same applies to life experiences, since these are so intimately related to sociocultural factors. What appears in a diagnostic study as a particular occurrence in a person's life-story may in fact be, directly or indirectly, the expression of sociocultural patterns as these are manifest in that person, family, or other group. Such events cannot be used as criteria for diagnosis without risk of establishing by definition etiological correlations of a sociocultural character. As noted earlier in this frame of reference, correlations with sociocultural factors that are derived mainly from the way the phenomena are defined cannot be altogether escaped, and part of the research aim is to clarify such points. It remains, nevertheless, desirable to avoid those instances that can be anticipated, and hence all aspects of the diagnostic process which are based on theories of life experience as causal factors must be eliminated.

With underlying psychic malfunction, the question is one of difficulty in securing information, rather than of concept. There are serious practical problems in getting the necessary data with which to make responsible judgments, except in the case of people who are or have been under psychiatric treatment.

These points will be developed further in Section IV on sources of data. To be noted now is that numbers of factors conspire to place symptoms and signs in the foreground when one is considering an epidemiological survey. It would seem appropriate, therefore, to examine these a little more fully, particularly with reference to conceptions of their interconnection with underlying psychic malfunction and etiological events in life experience.

III SYMPTOM PATTERNS AND SIGNS

The relationship of underlying psychic malfunction to symptom patterns is sometimes considered in terms of linear cause and effect. The underlying malfunction is thought to cause symptoms in much the same way that an inflamed appendix can be thought to cause abdominal pain and vomiting. Although this is a naïve view, it is not uncommon, even among those professionally active in psychiatry. It goes with picturing therapy as a kind of psychological surgery that finds and removes *the* unconscious cause. The essentials of the idea can be represented as in Figure 7.

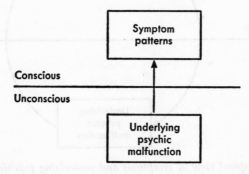

FIGURE 7: *The linear view of symptoms and underlying psychic malfunction.*

A more valid orientation is one that recognizes that by the time a psychiatric disorder is established, symptoms and underlying psychic malfunction have a concurrent, interdependent relationship. This is inherent in what has been said about upset essential psychical condition and symptom formation. The symptoms not only arise from the underlying psychic process but, by virtue of their being part of an incomplete or unsuccessful adaptation, they contribute to the ongoing of the disturbance rather than to its resolution. The symptoms have effects on the rest of the personality, both directly, and indirectly through the reactions elicited from other people. This double effect can be illustrated by considering the consequences of paranoid conditions, hysterical paralyses, and alcoholism. It may also be seen in anxiety attacks as in the case of Tom Young. Here invalidism focused on a supposedly weak heart could well foster the repetition of the

Case Finding and Case Study

crisis due to added worries about the heart and possibly to some relief from difficulties that are germane to the underlying psychic malfunction. The latter could have a number of different forms, but one example might be that of binding his wife more closely to him and reducing an unconscious fear of losing her. Due to these considerations it is thought that the diagram shown in Figure 8 is a closer approximation of the relationships.

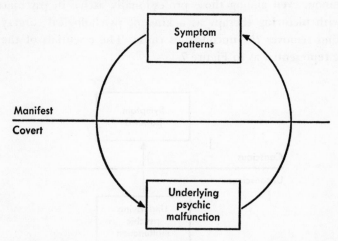

FIGURE 8: *The spiral view of symptoms and underlying psychic malfunction.*

In this diagram time is visualized as at right angles to the paper and the whole is a forward moving process. The arrows of influence should therefore have a corkscrew form rather than lie flatly in the plane of the paper. "Covert" is used to refer to all the psychic processes hidden from the observer. They may in turn be considered as divisible into conscious and more or less unconscious aspects.

A case is, therefore, at any particular moment a cross-section of life-story, not just the residue of a past history; it is a concurrent interactive pattern composed of both symptoms and underlying psychic malfunction. It may be noted, incidentally, that the term "psychopathology" is sometimes applied to what is designated above as underlying psychic malfunction. I prefer to follow Diethelm and use psychopathology to refer to the larger pattern consisting of both symptoms and underlying malfunction, that is, to the total malfunctioning of personality rather than the covert or unconscious aspects only.[1]

Turning now to noxious life experiences, there is again encountered a too simple view of causal relationships. This is sketched in Figure 9.

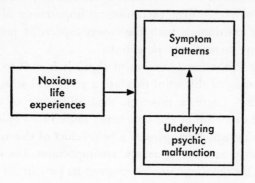

FIGURE 9: *The linear view of noxious life experiences.*

Heredity is omitted from this diagram, but it is understood as setting the stage for susceptibility or resistance to noxious life experiences.

In this frame of reference the etiological significance of early life experiences is not minimized, but there is insistence on the importance of later events, including those going on at the time on the life-arc when the psychopathology has been established and when a diagnosis is apt to be in process. Noxious experiences, in short, amount to more than a shove given to a personality at some point in early life.[2] They can and commonly do have a part in the maintenance of the condition. This is represented in Figure 10.

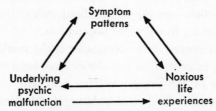

FIGURE 10: *The spiral view of noxious life experiences.*

Again, time is at right angles to the paper, and the arrows of influence should have a corkscrew form. The whole is an ongoing process and occurrences at any one of the apices of the triangle can affect each of the other two.

From this it can be seen that symptoms are conceived to be an integral part of the phenomenon of malfunctioning personality. They

Case Finding and Case Study

are more than "froth on the surface of deep currents." [3] Although they are on the surface in the sense of being visible, they are not superficial in the sense of having little psychological importance; although manifest, they are continuous with the covert aspects of personality malfunction, past, current, and potential.

In turning to the consideration of signs, it is well to be reminded that the meaning of this word overlaps a good deal with the meaning of "symptoms." There is, however, some difference of emphasis and this is in the direction of the sign being more of an epiphenomenon, more something which happens as a by-product of the malfunctioning personality than as a major aspect. Its importance lies in the indication it holds for the diagnostician and not its part in the malfunctioning process. A sign could be something quite trivial and peripheral as far as function is concerned, provided it tended to occur as a regular accompaniment of the disorder and thus serve as a flag to attention. Signs, therefore, can bear a relationship to underlying malfunction that could be roughly represented in a linear diagram such as Figure 7.

IV SOURCES OF DATA

Having discussed, in however limited a manner, the nature of psychiatric cases and some of the components in the diagnostic process, it is appropriate now to give thought to the types of data that are apt to be available. From these two sets of considerations conclusions may then be reached as to how one might go about estimating the prevalence of psychiatric disorder in a general population.

Our point of reference in the Northeast is the small town and rural area. The factors entering into this choice have been mentioned briefly at the beginning of the present volume and will be reviewed more completely in the introduction of Volume II. Of relevance here is the fact of opportunity for multiple types of observation bearing on the same population.

The first and most obvious source of data are the mental hospitals, private sanitaria, and similar institutions which care for those with psychiatric disorders. To these may be added psychiatric out-patient clinics and psychiatrists in private practice. The list derived from all sources of this type would constitute those persons formally recognized as psychiatric patients in the region selected for study.

It is evident that this would not encompass all persons in a state of psychiatric disorder. On the contrary, it would be a group whose selection was influenced by many sociocultural factors that impel certain kinds of cases and people from certain kinds of background toward diagnosis and care, while at the same time diverting other types of cases and persons from such formal recognition. In small-town and rural areas, matters of distance to where services are available contribute an example of an important differential influence. Hence any study of such a population of psychiatric cases would inevitably be a study of the sociology of recognition and care rather than true prevalence and the sociocultural factors contributing thereto.

Investigation, given our purpose, must therefore reach further. One step in this direction would be to adapt or create a psychiatric clinic as a research instrument in the region of study. This would help in the matter of distance and, if the cost to the patient were nominal, it would also reduce economic barriers. More than this, the staff of the clinic through local acquaintance and educational efforts could find many ways in which to diminish fears and prejudice regarding psychiatric treatment and thus facilitate the coming of persons who might otherwise stay home.

It would be unrealistic, however, to expect such a clinic, no matter how adroitly managed, to succeed in drawing to itself all the instances of psychiatric disorder in the population of the area it served. There would remain, one could be sure, many people with clinically definable illness who would not, due to sociocultural as well as individual factors, come to the clinic. In particular, those living in disintegrated groups would by this very condition be inhibited from seeking and accepting help.

One way in which there might be still further reaching out would be through the development of indirect sources of information. The doctors in practice in the area could be interviewed with regard to their patients and in this manner additional individuals discovered as showing evidence of psychiatric disorder. The small-town and rural context would be of particular help since the doctors in such areas generally have a long-term, intimate acquaintance with their patients and know them in many situations besides the office.

In addition to the doctors there are a number of other secondary sources through which evidence regarding the existence of cases of psychiatric disorder could be secured. Careful and systematic interviewing of teachers, clergy, lawyers, and police should be worth while, and one might go beyond this to seeking help from all the formal and informal leaders of the community. These could be expected to have knowledge of the people among whom they live based on seeing them in many different tests of life. There would also be merit in searching the records of general hospitals, almshouses, welfare agencies, and similar organizations. Finally, it would be possible to have a number of field workers who, through a period of residence and participation in various segments of the community, could, under psychiatric supervision, conduct extensive observations and so pick up additional evidence of cases.

These sources of information have been described as if the estimate of prevalence could only be achieved through total count of all instances of psychiatric disorder in the chosen population. Such an approach is one alternative and would capitalize on the small group character and lack of anonymity in small-town and rural areas. One could expect much duplication of information from different sources and by this gain confidence in certain aspects of validity. One would not, however, escape completely from sociocultural bias. On the other hand, this effect should be mitigated, and, by the very intensive and extensive character of the investigation, its nature and force should be fairly well understood. One would be, therefore, in a position to devise compensations, or to make allowances in estimates. Although not eliminated, the total area of doubt in this regard would be reduced and there would be increased opportunity for discrimination.

This conglomerate of sources could be treated as a selective device, somewhat as data gathering according to Set B of the Disintegration Indices (pages 320-323) was suggested as a means of preliminary selection. When, from the various sources, individuals emerged presumed to be or to have been in a state of psychiatric disorder, then the final step could be direct interviews. The aim might be twofold, diagnosis by a psychiatrist and assessment through psychological tests.

There are obvious problems of feasibility in all this, particularly with regard to the last step. Insufficient cooperation could render the diagnostic interviews and psychological tests of little value. There is also the matter of the need to gather during interviews considerable information of a sociocultural sort from each individual so that he or she can be studied in relation to the sociocultural forces which have bearing on his or her present life and previous development. This total of needed information points to long interviews, and hence the larger the number of cases, the more difficult and unmanageable the project would be.

A point of particular importance to be noted involves both ethics and health. As indicated in the previous section, diagnosis is based in part on inferences regarding underlying psychic processes. Information adequate for making judgment in this regard cannot be obtained as a rule except by searching questions which are apt to be disturbing and which in some instances, through upsetting precarious control, might actually be damaging. Hence one cannot feel free to conduct research of this sort outside a therapeutic context, without consent of the subject and without full resources for dealing with any upheaval that might occur. This means that the final interviews, whether done by a psychiatrist or a trained worker gathering information for a psychiatrist, must be limited to data regarding symptoms and signs and to psychological tests that are neutral in their impact.

The alternative to a total count is an estimate based on some kind of probability sample. This does not avoid many of the difficulties mentioned above and it introduces some that are new, but it has certain marked advantages. Notably, data are gathered on each individual in the sample whether or not he gives evidence of psychiatric symptoms, and this is enormously helpful in analysis and statistical treatment. A critical question with sampling, however, is the percentage of cases of psychiatric disorder to be expected. If this is small, then the sample must be large. Since everyone in the sample has to be studied, this can result either in superficial work with insufficient data, or in a task far larger and more cumbersome than the successive approach to the total count.

Whether total count or sampling is used, it is evident that some method is necessary for evaluating the raw data gathered on each person. A series of folders can be anticipated, each containing information on one individual derived from a variety of sources and of varying degrees of reliability and specificity. In some instances there would be actual psychiatric diagnoses obtained from the records of hospitals, in other cases there would be no more than oddities of behavior reported by friends and neighbors.

One approach to evaluation in the face of this range would be to say, "We shall just do the best we can to make the diagnosis. After all, even in a clinic, the information available from case to case is very uneven and on this basis there is always ground for questioning the comparability of diagnoses. The problem before us is one of degree, not kind, in relation to ordinary clinical work. The important thing will be to establish some sort of scale of confidence in our diagnoses so that this can be taken into account in the analysis later."

Anticipating a little what will be described in Volume III, I may say that when an attempt was made to do this, it became apparent that the common denominator in virtually all types of data was the symptom pattern. Hence efforts at making a diagnosis were in fact guesses based on symptoms. The only exceptions to this were the relatively few recognized psychiatric cases from clinics and hospitals where the diagnosis had been made for us. Even here there was some doubt as to how many were based on complete diagnostic work-up that took etiology and underlying psychic malfunction into account, and how many were based on symptom patterns only.

Since we were implicitly leaning so heavily on symptoms as indices, it seemed wise to recognize this and so lean explicitly. Hence diagnosis as such was abandoned and attention turned to the assessment of symptom patterns and signs.

V SYMPTOM PATTERNS AS INDICES OF PSYCHIATRIC DISORDER

If one looks at the descriptions under the names of disorders in the *Manual,* or in other systems, it is evident that these are phrased in part as etiology and underlying psychic malfunction and in part as symptom patterns. The relative emphasis varies from one category to another, but there are symptoms in all. It would seem possible and convenient, therefore, to use these names as labels for symptoms, even though we are not making diagnoses. This is important since there are no other codified names available for symptoms and the alternatives would lie in the direction of very long descriptions or in the invention of a system.

One would have to understand, however, that in this usage the names refer only to patterns of behavior and that the etiological criteria and those pertaining to underlying psychic malfunction ordinarily included in much of the codified system are deliberately excluded. When words like "psychoneurosis" and "psychophysiologic respiratory reaction" are used, they would have to be considered as standing for a full statement which would read, "behavior like that of a person who has been clinically studied and diagnosed as psychoneurotic," "behavior like that of a person who has been clinically studied and diagnosed as having a psychophysiologic respiratory reaction," and so on.

Such naming of symptom patterns, while not diagnosis, would nevertheless be an approximation of diagnosis. It would be concerned with patterns of behavior that are commonly seen in the patients in psychiatric hospitals, those who attend out-patient clinics, or those who are treated by psychiatrists in private practice. The phenomenon could be designated as "behavioral areas of psychiatric interest" and would correspond to what is commonly assessed by clinicians in deciding whether an individual should or should not be accepted for psychiatric study and treatment.

We are here again dealing with parts of a phenomenon used as indices for the whole, an approach which has similarity to that outlined in the previous chapter with regard to social disintegration, and the procedure is hung about with some of the same qualifications and considerations. A major point is the need for understanding the relationship of appraisal based on symptoms to diagnosis based on fuller information. Such is not, however, a matter of validity in any narrow sense. "Validity" would be more properly applied to the question of whether or not the method used for gathering data did correctly register symptoms. The latter are valid by definition.

Rather than validity, the problem of the relationship of symptom pattern appraisals to diagnoses is the problem of understanding the meaning of one body of data in relation to the other. In our particular case, there is the obvious need to know how the behavorial areas of psychiatric significance resemble and differ from the ordinary run of psychiatric diagnoses. Put another way, what would be the result if after making the appraisal the same psychiatrist were then to conduct an intensive clinical study of the same individuals? Perspective along these lines would be essential for interpreting the findings of the epidemiological study in terms that are clinically familiar and comprehensible. It is therefore evident that when it comes to research operations it would be important to devise some means of comparing appraisals of symptom pattern with the results of diagnostic procedures. Only on such a basis would one be in a position to say what the findings might signify in clinical terms. Only in this way can two

Case Finding and Case Study

undesirable extremes be avoided: rejecting the epidemiological survey because it is not the same as a diagnosis and so missing what it has to offer, or accepting it as identical with diagnosis and so drawing unwarranted conclusions.

Bending attention now more specifically to the naming system offered in the *Manual,* let it be observed that this does not provide a direct means for identifying symptom patterns in a given person. It is not designed to permit an intelligent layman to inspect somebody's behavior and then look up his type, as one might identify a specimen with a flower book. Even when it is only a question of symptom patterns and not etiology or treatment, there has to be training and experience in conducting the examination and in the evaluation of the results. What the *Manual* provides is a method for ordering these evaluations and a consistent set of terms for their designation. The clinician remains an essential instrument for the registering of symptom patterns. The principles in terms of which he acts may, however, be sketched, since they are germane to understanding the nature of the results.

Most fundamentally, the clinician makes judgments on the basis of custom and familiarity. In the course of being instructed, and in learning from his own experience in diagnosis, treatment, and follow-up, he develops acquaintance through multiple sensory impressions with symptom patterns. They become part of his world of customary perceptions. The behavior of a newly encountered or studied person is therefore recognized as symptomatic or not according to perceived resemblance to the complex of already perceived patterns stored in the clinician's memory. He acts and reacts in terms of both intellectual grasp and intuitive feel.

Giving attention to the behavior which we are calling symptom patterns is not, however, limited to psychiatrists and clinical psychologists. The shared sentiments of culture constitute standards as to how people can, ought, and might wish to behave. If a person is seen to differ markedly from these cultural expectations he will be noticed and will be tagged as odd, crazy, delinquent or by some other term which highlights deviance.

The cultural definitions of deviance are not, of course, coincidental with clinical symptoms, but there is considerable overlap. Not all forms of cultural deviance are psychiatric symptoms, and, on the other hand, the clinician may perceive symptoms where the layman would not. The former is, like any specialist, on the whole more differentiating in his observations. At the same time, he incorporates the cultural view both as a bearer of the general culture himself and as a specialist in the lore of a particular subarea, namely, psychiatry. This means that even when we set the etiological factors of life experience aside and concentrate on an empirical specification of symptoms, there is a cultural component in the specification. Symptoms are perceived in terms of individual behavior in relation to culturally defined expectations. To be depressed, suspicious, angry, elated, worried or disorganized by apprehension may not be considered illness under some conditions by clinician and layman alike. More than this, *not* to have such feelings and *not* to show such behavior under some conditions would be considered symptomatic. Hence any interpretation of results in which sociocultural factors and symptoms are associated in what might be a causal relationship, must take into account the component of cultural specification in symptom patterns.

It will be appreciated that this point becomes of particular importance where it is a question of counting and comparing numbers of people with symptom patterns in communities that have different cultures. If symptom patterns are to some extent relative to each culture, then a serious problem may arise as to whether, in terms of phenomena, one can actually identify and count the same thing in the two different settings. If the cultures are different, must not the "thing" be different, and so not the "same"? Parallel problems exist in making prevalence comparisons of symptom patterns between different levels of socioeconomic class.

As with many previous points, these matters are not to be settled *a priori* with "yes" or "no" but require careful assessment and examination in actual research operations. The closer two cultures are to each other—as with the French and English in the Northeast—the less of a problem there is apt to be. Unfortunately, it also holds that the closer they are, the less difference there is apt to be so far as cultural effects on psychiatric disorder are concerned. The problem is proportional to cultural contrast and hence looms largest where inquiry would be of most interest.

There remains, however, the possibility and even probability that some kinds of behavior are symptomatic in all cultures. Kluckhohn has suggested a number of patterns such as inaccessibility to communication and lack of control over aggressive impulses as universals in

Case Finding and Case Study

369

this respect.[4] Possibly other universals of this sort could be found, including those of a more subtle character, were careful comparative studies carried out.

Having noted that symptom recognition is an empirical act within the orientation of cultural and professional tradition, we may now look more closely at some components. These include the use of four main bases for distinguishing behavior that is symptomatic from that which is not: pattern quality, intensity, frequency, and duration.

Pattern quality refers to the impact of the pattern as such on the observer. Hallucinations, as for instance hearing a voice when no one is speaking and this in a culturally inappropriate context, may be taken as an example. This kind of behavior, if it occurs at all in a given person, can be considered symptomatic—Joan of Arc notwithstanding.

It is unfortunate for our research purposes, however, that relatively few symptoms are distinguishable by pattern quality and only pattern quality. Most behavioral events must be judged in addition with regard to one or more of the other aspects: intensity, frequency, and duration.[5] Complaints about and appearance of low spirits, for instance, are not necessarily a symptom pattern with psychiatric significance. In order to decide whether or not such behavior has implications of psychiatric disorder, intensity, frequency, and duration in relation to culture and situation have to be evaluated.

The meaning of frequency and duration is fairly evident. Intensity is a subjective matter and concerns degree of feeling, such as the "depth" of low spirits. There is obviously no direct method of measuring this and the observer has to infer it from many facets of overt behavior. One common basis is the relationship of the low spirits to other aspects of personality, as for example whether the mood seems to dominate and pervade so there is difficulty in such functions as concentration and thinking about ordinary daily problems and in the maintenance of customary interpersonal relations. Clinical judgment is also made in terms of the person as he now is compared to how, so far as one can tell, he used to be, and in comparison to the psychiatrist's conception of the behavior of "most other people."

While the recognition of pattern quality is, as the words imply, a qualitative judgment, intensity, frequency, and duration involve ideas of quantity. There are, however, no clear measures or criteria that can be readily specified with regard to cutting point. Each clinician has sentiments which govern his perceptions of "too much," and these derive for the most part from his training, from his experience, and from the expectations of the culture of which he and the patient are a part.

Although definitive criteria are lacking, it is possible to point to some alternatives in a broad framework. Because psychiatric disorder is not an all-or-none affair, the clinician appraising symptoms could decide to select only those persons whose behavior parallels that of hospital cases, or that of patients who come for out-patient and office treatment or whose behavior suggests there may be some personality problems even if a sort too mild or occasional to warrant the time and expense of therapy.

Since our goal is to assess the prevalence of psychiatric disorder, and since this has been defined as that order of phenomena which psychiatrists commonly treat, it is evident that the first and second alternatives combined are most in harmony with the general purpose and orientation. One might therefore say to a clinician about to embark on appraisal: "Make your cutting point one that excludes all except those individuals whose degree of symptom patterning is such as to lead you to think that further investigation would, with a high degree of probability, lead to a diagnosis. Ask yourself, 'If this person came to me with such symptoms would I, as a psychiatrist, think it appropriate to accept him as a patient?'"

The foregoing discussion of symptom patterns as indices of psychiatric disorder gives some general idea of inherent weaknesses as well as opportunities. It is appropriate, however, to go further and point up more definitively certain of the problems, since undertaking them continues to have direct bearing on understanding the use of the indices and the results derived therefrom.

One question has to do with the problem of consensus among clinicians. We may be sure that there are many behavioral events and sequences about which there would be agreement, but we can be equally sure that there are others where expert opinions would differ. Behaviors where this occurs constitute the marginal areas between symptom patterns, and between symptom pattern and not-symptom pattern. If this margin is wide, that is, if there is little consensus, then we obviously have to deal with poorly defined phenomena and will have proportional difficulties in research and the interpretation of results. Conversely, the better the consensus, the better (other things equal) we shall be able to explore the nature of symptom patterns and to search out their relationships to events and circumstances. It therefore becomes a matter of considerable importance to investigate consensus with regard to the evaluation of symptom patterns. This would appear to be a necessary part of the projected epidemiological survey.

A further matter is the clinician's ability to distinguish between the ill and the well, even when consensus between several evaluators is achieved. This has its roots in the nature of diagnosis. Although the psychiatrist has more training and experience than any other category of person in distinguishing between those who show psychiatric disorder and those who do not, this is not the core of his work and his practice in this regard is, as a rule, limited. For the most part the patient is already defined as such by the situation at the time the clinician sees him. Diagnosis therefore runs to assessing the nature of the problem and to finding remedy rather than to sorting the ill from the well. It would seem evident that the psychiatrist must have the ability to make such distinctions, but in actuality its explicit use is not often required. This is perhaps a difference from practice in other branches of medicine. On the occasions where exceptions occur for the psychiatrist, as in court cases or screening for military services, his difficulty in these matters is sometimes rather sharply evident.

What pertains to diagnosis of psychiatric disorder most likely pertains also to the evaluation of behavior with regard to symptom patterns as indices of psychiatric disorder. In other words, it may be more difficult for a psychiatrist to say which behavior is symptomatic and which is not than to say, "Assuming such behavior is symptomatic, then this is what it probably means."

Another point is that the clinician's experience with symptom patterns is almost exclusively in the context of a personality that is disordered. He does not have a comparable experience in the study of the same or related types of behavior in people who on the whole are functioning adequately. This is part of the general problem mentioned several times, namely, that psychiatry, unlike other branches of medicine, is built almost exclusively on the study of pathology and does not have the counterpart of physiology, the study of healthy functioning. As a result the clinician has little knowledge as to the extent to which behavior similar to or identical with what he calls symptoms may be found among people who are not ill. There is some chance therefore that as an instrument for making surveys of people with symptoms he would be too sensitive and register as symptomatic behavior which in fact does not have this significance.

In essence, the above amounts to saying that symptoms as indices may yield a good many "false positives." The converse will also occur, namely, false negatives, or failure to register as ill people who are in fact suffering from a psychiatric disorder. From some points of view, particularly with regard to psychoneurosis, this may be the most serious limitation of all. Both psychic defenses and masking circumstances of sociocultural environment can result in a person who has a major personality malfunction not manifesting this in terms of symptoms, particularly symptoms as described in the *Manual* and which are the basis of the proposal here. This is a most important consideration and the need for some way of dealing with it, at least in exploratory terms, lies before us in planning operations. Some suggestions will be introduced in the next section and also again at the end of the chapter.

The troubles and questions that pervade the use of symptom patterns as indices of psychiatric disorder are counterbalanced by other considerations. Outstanding is the possibility that such behavioral areas of psychiatric interest can be handled more objectively and systematically than can diagnoses—that they are, actually, more definable as phenomena than are the diagnostic entities. The advantages of such relative objectivity are not to be brushed aside by the assertion that symptoms are of little significance compared to the dynamic formulations of diagnoses. The point is that they are of some not fully understood significance, and hence, if they can be defined in terms that lead to valid and reliable methods of detection and classification, the way is opened for investigating their causes and determinants. This in turn has promise of being a portal of entry into problem areas that lie within the dynamic formulation of diagnoses.

The implications and research possibilities lying in the conceptual separation of symptoms and psychiatric disorders was not encompassed in the original draft of this frame of reference. Our horizons widened as a result of touching the phenomena of our problem and trying to plan research. As we have lived with the idea, and tried it out through observing, data collecting, analysis and otherwise prodding nature, perspectives new to us have emerged. These have particular bearing on the character and interrelationships of psychiatric disorder, psychiatric health, diagnosis, and the sociocultural environment.

Case Finding and Case Study

Since these considerations are more part of the results of our research than of the initial frame of reference, they will be discussed in Volume III. It may be noted, however, that a presentation of some aspects can be found in *Explorations in Social Psychiatry*.[6]

VI SIGNS AS INDICES

Although signs can be considered somewhat separately from symptoms, their part in clinical psychiatric evaluations of behavior is very similar; hence much of what has been said in the previous section applies here also. Signs can, however, be used in a manner different from that characteristic of direct psychiatric evaluation; they may be systematically sought and the results combined so as to constitute psychological tests. Some examples are the Rorschach, the T.A.T., the Minnesota Multiphasic, the Army's Neuropsychiatric Screening Adjunct, and the Cornell Index. It would seem appropriate to consider using one or more of these as an instrument for estimating the number of people with personality malfunction in a population.

Since this is a different approach from the clinical evaluation of symptoms and signs, discussion is in order concerning the difficulties and opportunities to be anticipated. With regard to the difficulties, some are obviously peculiar to this or that test, or to this or that type of test, while others are more general, applying to virtually all tests. The assessment of particulars bearing on every relevant test would be a volume in itself, but some of the general problems can be outlined.

First there is the question as to what the tests mean as diagnostic indices. Although often very useful adjuncts to diagnosis and capable of providing information and insight regarding relevant aspects of personality, there is ground for questioning as to whether tests can by themselves be used to make diagnoses. The problem is very similar to one aspect of the employment of symptom patterns alone, namely, do the diagnostic entities defined by such indices coincide sufficiently well with the entities derived from a full-fledged clinical study that extends through time?

In other words, do the diagnostic terms employed in connection with psychological tests refer to the same phenomena as do these terms when employed after psychiatric diagnosis? One sometimes hears discussion in case conference between psychiatrist and psychologist in which the former will insist that a given patient is one thing (e.g., neurotic) while the latter will say the tests show him to be something else (e.g., schizophrenic). Of course, the same kind of difference of opinion can occur between two psychiatrists, but there are times when general agreement among psychiatrists on the one hand and among psychologists on the other inclines one to think that the nub of the matter is a difference in the meaning of terms. For the psychiatrist, the clinical picture may be psychoneurosis and not the clinical picture of schizophrenia. The psychologist, on the other hand, can be correct in his insistence that the pattern of test response is that pattern which he is accustomed to calling schizophrenic. This, however, need not be the same thing as the psychiatrist's schizophrenia. The two patterns of behavior (test response and schizophrenia) may often be associated (and hence the selection of the term for the test response), but it may also be possible for other psychiatrically defined types of personality malfunction such as neurosis to yield at times this "schizophrenic" test pattern. The question then is not, as it is apt to be argued, who is right and who is wrong, but rather what the results of two different methods of assessment mean. The fact of this kind of problem, however, gives pause when it comes to reliance on tests alone as an instrument of survey.

A second problem is test variability with differences in culture and type of education. That such differences do occur is well known, and there is obvious and serious implication with regard to conclusions about correlations of psychiatric disorder and sociocultural environment. This may be no worse than the same problem with clinical evaluations, but it is not necessarily any better either.

The general nature and content of psychological tests are such that one could anticipate difficulty in securing cooperation and there might again be a sociocultural difference here. For example, those with some knowledge of such tests might more often refuse or be more guarded in their response than others. One could also argue the converse, but the point is that any consistent trend associated with a particular sociocultural configuration could lead to apparent correlations that actually had little to do with differences in prevalence of psychiatric disorder. Furthermore, a high rate of refusal in any sample would obviously limit the statistical generalizations that could be made.

If, however, a test could be found in which such difficulties were minimal, a number of advantages would recommend it highly for attention. In the first place, and most ideally, the test might be used instead of symptom evaluation as a procedure. One would look to the advantages of speed, objectivity, standardization of method, and the possibility of tapping, through projective techniques, covert personality malfunction—that is, difficulties not immediately manifest in symptoms. Large probability samples might be used and the way opened for the application of highly discriminating statistics.

A second and, at the present stage of knowledge, more realistic possibility would be the employment of both symptom evaluation and one or more psychological tests. Based on the same individuals, each technique could be used to cross-check and supplement the other. Where one does not have a first-class index for a given purpose, the employment of two or more that are markedly different may provide opportunity for increasing confidence in the results. This is a principle which underlies the use of multiple tests in medical diagnosis as in percussion, auscultation, inspection, measurement, and X-ray of the chest. To the extent that two systems of indices for detecting psychiatric disorder would point to the same conclusions about a particular individual, to that extent confidence would be directly strengthened.

Where the two systems of indices point to different, though not conflicting, conclusions, there may be enlargement of understanding by supplementation and a kind of indirect confirmation through "goodness of fit" with theoretical expectation. An example of supplementation would be finding indications in the psychological tests of some pattern of psychic malfunction not revealed through evaluation of symptoms. If, in addition, this finding were in harmony with theoretical expectations derived from the symptoms, it would be an instance of indirect confirmation through "goodness of fit." A specific illustration of this would be seen if a psychological test suggested that Tom Young had deep-seated fears of desertion by his wife or extreme hostility toward his brother-in-law. Although such underlying psychic problems could emerge without tests in the course of clinical study and treatment, that is, diagnosis, they would not be demonstrated by the evaluation of symptom patterns alone.

Finally, in those instances in which the two systems of indices would conflict, the investigator would be warned to use caution in his interpretations. He could take this as a signal that the matter requires some further investigation and assessment.

In considering this confirmatory use, it is important to keep in mind that, although the symptom evaluation and the psychological test may be employed independently of each other with regard to a particular individual, or population of individuals, the two systems are not independent with regard to their origin. Were this the case, both would have been established independently against a common standard of diagnosed cases. Appropriate psychological tests have, at least as an ideal, this kind of standardization, but the symptom patterns are components of diagnosis. It follows therefore that the psychological test indices are indirectly standardized against the symptom indices.

Despite all these problems it would seem worth while to pick over the available tests in order to find one or more in which such difficulties would be minimal. Even though indirectly standardized against clinical judgment, such tests would not be standardized against the judgment of the particular psychiatrists doing the appraisal and evaluation of the symptom patterns. Thus, some measure of independence could be achieved and one might hope to select tests such that, whatever the limitations and areas of doubt, these would be to a large extent different from the limitations and areas of doubt inherent in the symptom evaluation.

The reference to standardization above suggests a parenthetical comment which may be helpful in visualizing the nature of estimating —and hence in some sense measuring—the prevalence of psychiatric disorder in a population. Suppose you had the problem of measuring the range of height in a group of individuals, but the only instruments available were the span of your hand and a piece of string. In such a case you would be in a better position than is one who attempts to assess people for psychiatric disorder, either through symptom patterns or psychological tests. For you could check the hand and the string against a foot rule and the foot rule against a physical standard. If anyone were to ask, "But what do you really mean by a foot or a yard or a meter?" you could take him to the Bureau of Standards in Washington and, pointing to the platinum-iridium bar, say, "That is what I mean."

The same is true with regard to the complex patterns of the higher organisms called species. For every known species in the world there is somewhere in a museum one or more "type specimens" which are the source of the basic description. Hence if someone presses the question, "What do you mean by *Sylvilagus transitionalis?*" you can take him to the type specimen and say, "That is what I mean."

For disease syndromes and psychiatric disorders, there are no preserved standard specimens. Instead there are generalized descriptions in books which vary a little from text to text; and there is a population of diagnosed patients in clinics and hospitals, no one of whom conforms exactly to the general descriptions. More than this, there is a considerable range of pattern under any particular name and the range of one named pattern overlaps with the ranges of others. Finally, there is the fact of turnover in the population of patients as well as of psychiatrists, so that shifts in usage with time and circumstances are inevitable. Hence, if you press me regarding what I mean by a person with a psychoneurosis, I can take you to a clinic and, pointing to a patient, say, "That is what I mean." But another psychiatrist could easily take you to a different individual who has somewhat different patterns, and I myself might do the same at a later date.

It is important to emphasize that the net result of all this is not chaos but a level of approximation. There is a certain consistency of core in most of the recognized patterns of psychiatric disorder. Nevertheless, the margins are unstable and, so far as differentiating various categories is concerned, one must recognize the relative crudeness of our work. It is also noteworthy that, insofar as we are trying to identify these same kinds of personality malfunction in a population at large, our results cannot be more refined than the categories upon which they are based.

On the other hand, there is room to hope that, through the attempt to assess personality malfunction in its natural setting and to refine conceptualization regarding the influence of sociocultural factors, redefinitions of psychiatric disorder and related phenomena may emerge which will make it possible to move to more discriminating levels of approximation and hence open the way to a greater valid use of quantitative methods.

VII CASE STUDIES

A case study takes a given person for attention and, viewing him as a system, attempts to explain a selected aspect of that system in terms of other aspects, in terms of the functioning whole, and in terms of the history of both. Cross-section of the moment and life-story are thus taken into account together with such components as cognition, affect, basic urges, and sentiments. Analysis of the whole is of course conducted in terms of both conscious and unconscious processes.

Tom Young provides an illustration. If his story, which has been unfolded in various parts of this book, were drawn together and the alternative interpretations reworked into a statement of probabilities, it would constitute an outline of a case study. A full study would, of course, be far more detailed, both with regard to reported facts and with regard to evaluative interpretation.

Case studies are in short personality studies conducted for the particular purpose of diagnosis and treatment, and this kind of investigation may be compared with the epidemiological approach on a number of counts. Both are dynamic in orientation, both can make contributions to theory, and, so far as this book is concerned, both are set in the same frame of reference. One may also say that both involve comparisons and utilize qualitative and quantitative methods, but here there is a difference in emphasis. The case studies are on the whole qualitative and concerned with describing complex patterns, while the central operations of the epidemiological studies are quantitative. Where the former emphasizes descriptions of process, much as an historian or a naturalist would, the latter emphasizes correlations. The most fundamental contrast, however, lies in the fact that the case study is an intensive investigation while the epidemiological is extensive. Thus they complement and supplement each other as means of getting answers to questions about nature.[7]

In order to explain this last statement, let us first take up a brief discussion of methods, and, as a locus for these methods, let us visualize the establishment of a psychiatric service in the area in which the epidemiological and sociocultural studies are to be carried out. Such a unit could serve a number of purposes, one of the most important being to provide a *quid pro quo* to the community for help in the research. This, however, is a different aspect from that which concerns the frame of reference, and the emphasis here will be on the clinic as a source of case material.

The center of the activities of a psychiatric clinic is the interaction between patient and psychiatrist. For each patient, a description of this is ideally precipitated into a case record, and has the form of a cumulative account of the development and current nature of the patient's personality, with, of course, a problem orientation. The account is based on what the patient says and does during the interviews, as interpreted and formulated by the psychiatrist. A good record will have coverage of such topics as the nature and duration of the patient's symptoms, his situation with regard to health, education, and financial resources, and his interpersonal relations as manifest in family, social life, work, and recreation. Whether or not the term itself is used, there will be attention to his sentiments, especially those which may involve conflict and expectations out of keeping with the psychiatrist's estimate of reality and of maturity appropriate to the patient's age. Of particular moment are the patient's sentiments and motives in relation to the psychiatrist, especially transference. Developmental history is reconstructed as accurately as possible and underlying psychic processes may be evaluated through interpretations of dreams, free associations, and the patient's use of symbols.

The psychiatric study is often supplemented by a number of other investigations. These may include a physical examination by a general practitioner or internist, social histories and home visit reports by a social worker, and the results of tests as administered and interpreted by a psychologist. Each of these studies and many of the various steps within each method of study constitute different viewpoints on one or another aspect of the personality system of the patient.

It is worth pausing here to consider by what means the clinician achieves a sense of confidence in the inferences he makes and hence in the validity of the case study. The procedure is not in principle different from that employed in other forms of medical diagnosis, although it has its own particular subject matter and techniques. Nor does it differ greatly from other attempts to feel out and describe a system from multiple types of evidence as in studies of natural history, linguistics, culture, and communities. Perhaps the best known example of this kind of thinking is to be found in Darwin's use of evidence in connection with the theory of the origin of species.

The clinician accumulates confidence in his inferences from a number of different sources. There is a certain background that is taken for granted as part of the psychic process in virtually all human beings, with modifications according to age and sex of the patient. On top of this we may note evidence derived from multiple observations in which each item either checks others or supplements and enlarges the picture by fitting with the rest. This latter type of appraisal, termed "pattern congruity" by linguists, may be visualized as similar to putting together a jig-saw puzzle from a pile of pieces, many of which do not belong to the picture with which you are concerned.[8] These spurious pieces, analogous to spurious inferences, may be rejected when they do not fit. On the other hand, the pieces that do fit into what has already been assembled inspire a certain measure of assurance that one is on the right track. This acceptance must be tentative, of course, since the logic of fit speaks only in terms of relative probability, but it can be allowed to endure for a time and be taken into account along with other items of partial evidence as they are accumulated.

Another type of limited verification lies in the procedures connected with treatment. Certain acts by the therapist appear to work, and this suggests some, though by no means conclusive, support for the theories and expectations that lead to these acts. A related type of evidence is available in predicting the course of a patient's disorder and in anticipating the way he will respond to things the therapist does, or to events taking place outside the therapeutic situation.

A still different source of confidence is that which arises from familiarity. Although each case is unique and it is most important to approach each with very little taken for granted, the fact remains that certain constellations of process with minor variations do turn up over and over again. Hence, when the picture that emerges in the course of study has familiar features one is inclined to rely on the types of inferences that have worked out successfully in the past.

Finally, there is the matter of agreement among observers. This comes into operation particularly at case conferences when there are several staff members who have had contact with the patient. It may include more than one psychiatrist as well as psychologists and the social workers.

As explained earlier, this brief outline of the character of case study has been introduced in order to make as clear as possible the kind of analysis and system description it is, and the particular kinds of verification that are involved. While most anthropologists would recognize a similarity to their orientation and methods, the matter is different for much of sociology and social psychology, where there is reliance on certain kinds of statistical testing and the model of the controlled experiment. The case study looks less to the laboratory

Case Finding and Case Study

381

for a model than to those sciences which have been concerned with life in its natural setting. This is not a question of excluding experimental and statistical testing in favor of observation and interpretation but one of emphasis.

Be it noted that no judgment is implied here as to relative merit with regard to these emphases. Merit and scientific value are matters of appropriateness to problem and context. Case study as a type of pattern analysis and system description, with its particular way of accumulating and handling evidence, is one kind of scientific activity.

This last remark arises from the observation that many of those whose skill and experience is with statistical tests and controlled experiments are inclined to see science only in these latter terms. Hence they banish the kind of thing that is represented by the case study, the cultural study, the community study, and linguistics, without, I feel, understanding what it is they banish. The matter is of immediate importance here because it is only through an understanding of the character of the case study and the composite of partial validations upon which it stands that one can see its potential in relation to the extensive studies.

Before developing this topic further, it is necessary to note that case studies as performed in a service clinic are usually not adequate for the kind of research under discussion here. Case studies are kept for the benefit of the patient and for the protection of the clinic in case it is challenged with regard to what it has been doing; as a rule, each extends no further than is required for these purposes. Not everyone who comes to a clinic, for instance, needs a thorough investigation. For some, indeed, it is contraindicated by the nature of the disorder. Added to this is the fact that as a result of pressures to spend time with patients rather than on paperwork, the psychiatrist and his coworkers may not be able to record more than a small part of their knowledge of each person. Very often what gets put down is no more than an outline. Hence, if a clinic is to be used as a source of case history studies for research, one of the essentials of the arrangement must be a staff-to-patient ratio that will permit sufficient time for a systematic study of each case where this is therapeutically permissible and for a full and careful recording of the results. One can anticipate that this would be no small matter and that the staff time of the clinic should be budgeted as at least half for research and half for service.

With these explanations, the ground is prepared for pointing out that a case study as an intensive investigation and analysis of a particular personality must cover to some extent the relationships, past and present, of that personality to others. *In this lies the link to sociocultural phenomena.* Ordinarily one asks what part the relationships with others played in strengthening the personality system and in fostering the development of disorder. For our purposes the need is to emphasize study of the interplay of factors arising in the sociocultural environment and the psychic processes of the individual.

One cannot, naturally, generalize from a single case. One cannot generalize with regard to either sociocultural patterns affecting personality or the intrapsychic patterns. On the other hand, cases can raise important questions, the generality of which may become a matter for further investigation. How common are such and such symptoms? Are they always related to the same underlying psychic processes? If not, to what varieties of psychic processes are they related? Are the contributing patterns of interpersonal relationships common in the society and culture? Is this kind of mother–child, or peer group, or husband-and-wife pattern a frequent occurrence? Is it tied to larger configurations in the sociocultural system such as the family pattern in a particular culture or subculture, or in an integrated as compared to a disintegrated society?

All this amounts to saying that case studies provide the material from which general questions of process can be developed. These in turn may constitute the basis of a frame of reference consisting in part of general orientation and in part in propositions which lead toward hypotheses of a researchable nature. Chapter V of this book is an example of such orientation and propositions derived directly or indirectly from case studies.

What is to be suggested now is that case studies should not be left as frozen recollections in the background, but continue in the particular communities and culture in which the sociocultural and epidemiological studies are being conducted. This is because of the expectation that the results would have at least two major uses. One is in the interpretation of the epidemiological investigations. These are conceived as proceeding concomitantly with the case studies, but based of necessity on prior studies mostly of different people in other communities. It is a truism that correlations and other quantitative findings have no meaning until interpreted, and it would seem worth while to have case material derived from the same communities and culture as a source of reference and orientation in making such interpretations.

The second use is to constitute a basis for framing new propositions and researchable questions for a later wave of studies which would include further extensive techniques. One can think of this as exploring for significant phenomena relevant to our interest in the effects of sociocultural factors, and the development of indices whereby questions of prevalence and distribution can be ascertained.

Some illustrations with particular topics may help to make this suggestion clearer. For one thing, the range and types of symptom patterns used as indices could be revised through case studies focused on this question, and criteria improved, particularly criteria bearing on impairment. Below the symptom level the patterns of underlying psychic malfunction could be examined. As pointed out earlier, surveys of symptoms yield no data of this type, and it would be most advantageous to know something about these processes in relation to prevalence and the kinds of contexts in which they appear. Out of such investigations might come eventually the development of indices for the underlying processes themselves.

At another level is a possibility already touched upon in the discussion of sentiments as a bridging concept in Chapter VII, namely, that of defining certain patterns of sentiment, particularly shared sentiments, as of major relevance to psychiatric disorder. This would include sentiments as symptoms and as contributors to symptoms. The latter consideration would lead one to the heart of the question regarding what sentiments and conflicts of sentiments play a major part in the malfunctioning of personality. Implicated here are not only sentiments that are components of a given patient's personality system but also the sentiments held by others which have had or are having a detrimental effect on him. Using saliency in relation to psychiatric disorder as the point of reference, the aim could be to distill from case studies those sentiments and categories of sentiments of major importance and to mark them for investigation by other procedures.

Through such an approach the propositions of Chapter V could be modified and new, more specific and testable hypotheses laid out. At the same time the larger realms of general theory might also be illuminated and brought closer to nature.

Finally, the indices of social disintegration could be examined in terms of the case studies. That is, one could seek to find out if such factors play a part, significant so far as psychiatric disorder is concerned, in the life-story and cross-section of the moment of patients, and, if so, what are the sequences and processes concerned. The question here would be, in what ways does the disintegration of a group actually reach and affect the personality system of an individual?

It is worth stating again that, of and by themselves, the case studies contribute little that is conclusive in these matters, but they can be a source of leads and estimated probabilities. Employed in conjunction with the extensive studies, they can add to the meaning of the latter. Both, taken together in a leap-frog fashion through time, will supplement, complement, and check one other. Moreover, they can do so cumulatively, resulting in a combined yield that is considerably greater than that derivable from either alone. Both inevitably fade out in margins of speculation, but when brought together some of these areas of haziness can be reduced.

Having pointed out potentialities of intensive and extensive studies in relation to each other, it now remains to say that case studies as they emanate from a psychiatric service, even under the most ideal conditions, are deficient in one major respect. Whereas the epidemiological studies through probability sampling attempt to deal with both the symptomatic and the asymptomatic, the case studies in a clinic are exclusively samples of malfunction. Outside the clientele of the clinic is a population of unknown character so far as patterns of personality functioning are concerned. It seems likely, however, that there are some patterns in this group, particularly those which are expressive of successful functioning, which never come under the intensive scrutiny of a case study.

For the case study method to reach its full potential of usefulness and to escape from what is in fact a marked systematic distortion, it must be applied to people who are not patients. The practical difficulties in this are considerable and there are in addition some ethical problems as noted previously. I think, however, that these are soluble to a degree that would yield some useful results even though they might not be altogether comparable with those derived from thorough studies in a clinic. The basis for this opinion is in some trials of personality study that I have attempted in a variety of different contexts.[9] The selection of the subjects could be in part through random methods and in part in terms of deliberate choice guided by the epidemiological and sociocultural studies. Thus one might select instances of such categories as people who have always been without symptoms, people who are heavily laden with symptoms but who nevertheless function without psychiatric treatment, people who had many symptoms in the past but who recovered without psychiatric treatment and have no symptoms now.

Each of the above types might be further grouped in terms of age and sex, and those with symptoms might be considered in terms of several categories of patterns such as brain syndrome, psychosis, various types of psychoneurosis, psychophysiological disorder, and so on. There should also be sampling according to such categories as socioeconomic class, role, culture, and social integration and disintegration of milieu. With regard to role, one might think in terms of leadership, followership, conflicting, and nonconflicting roles. The above list is intended only to indicate the possibilities. The various combinations of factors that one could study are enormous, and hence there would have to be discriminating decisions to permit feasibility.

The primary consideration remains that of designating some patterns of well-functioning personality. We would be concerned to examine the people whom the epidemiological methods point out as lacking symptoms in order to see what kinds of psychic processes could underlie this surface condition. Here there would be hope of finally getting at the problem of compensation and masking and related forms of psychic malfunction. One would also be interested in persons with mild symptoms as possibly representing a basically resilient system of personality functioning. From such analyses of surface and depth and from comparison with case studies of patients, it might then become possible to move into the area of positive mental health. One could look forward to establishing criteria for a variety of mental healths and so creating a basis for identifying factors in the sociocultural environment. Taking the long view, the time might come when prevention in psychiatry would mean more than early treatment, and more than putting a stop to conditions that foster psychiatric disorder. It could come to mean developing certain kinds of environmental conditions which have been demonstrated as favorable to mental health.

CHAPTER NOTES

1. There are at least three current uses of "psychopathology." In addition to the two noted in the text, a third refers to "the branch of science which deals with morbidity or pathology of the psyche or mind." *See* L. E. HINSIE and JACOB SHATZKY, *Psychiatric Dictionary, With Encyclopedia Treatment of Modern Terms* (2nd ed.; New York: Oxford Univ. Press, 1953).

The American Psychiatric Association Glossary, 1952, gives psychopathology as "Morbid processes of the psyche or mind in terms of their development."

Diethelm says "Psychopathology includes the subjective, objective and psychodynamic aspects of each individual person. Through Kraepelin, experimental procedures and clear description of the phenomena observed were brought to psychopathology; through Freud, a psychodynamic-genetic approach; and through A. Meyer, the relationship to environment and physiologic manifestation. Modern psychopathology has combined these three historical contributions and developed steadily further, offering a sound basis for the treatment of all types and intensities of personality disorders." *See* OSKAR DIETHELM, *Treatment in Psychiatry* (Springfield, Ill.: Thomas, 1955), p. 9.

2. See pp. 122-123, for an outline of concepts of etiology.

3. *See* BERTRAND RUSSELL, *A History of Western Philosophy* (New York: Simon and Schuster, 1945), p. 596.

4. For some further notes on Kluckhohn's suggestion, *see* ALEXANDER H. LEIGHTON, JOHN A. CLAUSEN, and ROBERT N. WILSON, (Eds.), *Explorations in Social Psychiatry* (New York: Basic Books, 1957), p. 404.

5. *See* JOHN CUMMING and ELAINE CUMMING, "Affective Symbolism, Social Norms, and Mental Illness," *Psychiatry*, Vol. 19, no. 1, 1956, pp. 77-85.

6. *See* ALEXANDER H. LEIGHTON, JOHN A. CLAUSEN, and ROBERT N. WILSON, (Eds.), *Explorations in Social Psychiatry*, pp. 396-402.

7. This complemental and supplemental relationship has been discussed previously in *The Governing of Men.* I am indebted to the late John Dean for pointing out the parallel to the historian. *See:* ALEXANDER H. LEIGHTON, *The Governing of Men* (Princeton: Princeton Univ. Press, 1946), pp. 390-391; JOHN P. DEAN, co-author of Chapters VIII and IX in JOHN T. DOBY (Ed.), *An Introduction to Social Research* (Harrisburg, Pa.: Stackpole, 1954).

8. For a description of pattern congruity, *see* CHARLES F. HOCKETT, *A Manual of Phonology,* Publication 11, Indiana University Publications in Anthropology and Linguistics, 1955, pp. 158-159.

9. An indication of what is meant may be seen in the following: ALEXANDER H. LEIGHTON and DOROTHEA C. LEIGHTON, *Gregorio, The Hand-Trembler, A Psychobiological Personality Study of a Navaho Indian* (Cambridge: Papers of the Peabody Museum of American Archaeology and Ethnology, Harvard University, 1949); WILLIAM C. SAYRES, *Sammy Louis, The Life History of a Young Micmac* (New Haven: Compass, 1956).

In addition, similar personality studies are in unpublished materials of my own and of a number of students who have worked with me. Among the latter are Manet Fowler, Seymour Parker, Charles Hughes, and Jane Hughes.

Chapter XI

Concluding Notes

THE LATTER PART of this book has brought to a head a research idea that had been unfolding in the course of presenting the rest of the frame of reference. It is possible, however, that the numerous qualifications introduced may have so overlaid the scheme as to obscure it. Hence some trenchant recapitulation may be desirable in order to summarize and clarify.

What follows is an attempt to fulfill this need. For the sake of sharpness in the presentation of essentials, it is written as a set of directions.

Choose a population in the Northeast such that there are distinctive geographic boundaries and marked contrasts of community characteristics within these boundaries. The latter should include the presence of both French and English cultural groups.

Determine the main demographic, economic, sociocultural, and historical features.

Using the B set of disintegration indices, select a number of communities which contrast in this dimension. See to it that there are both French and English units at each extreme.

Further assess the communities with regard to disintegration by means of the A set of indices. Provide a descriptive account of these communities which will depict their functioning as self-integrating units. This should include as a focal point a statement of the sentiments most salient with regard to this functioning.

Estimate the number of psychiatric cases in the geographic areas as a whole. Employ symptom patterns as indices and psychiatrists as evaluators. Make the estimate total—that is true prevalence, not just those known to a psychiatrist or an agency that handles psychiatric cases.

Cross-check the estimate of the psychiatrists with a psychological screening device.

Analyze the total count in terms of the main demographic features of the population. Compare true and treated prevalence.

Compare the communities selected as integrated and disintegrated with regard to the frequency and types of estimated cases, thus gathering evidence to bear on the integration–disintegration hypothesis.

Compare French and English communities at both the integrated and disintegrated levels in order to discover differences in case estimates that are associated with cultural differences.

In all of the above comparisons, take into account the type of symptom pattern as well as totals of all types considered in the estimates of disorder prevalence.

Using the A and B disintegration indices as stress factors, assess the relationship of individual stress to frequency of psychiatric disorder.

Endeavor to determine to what extent culture and/or degree of integration of a community makes a difference.

Formulate the results in terms of probable relationships between sociocultural factors and psychiatric disorder.

Operate a psychiatric clinic in the area and utilize the case studies so derived as a basis for interpreting the above results. Extend this with parallel studies of people without symptoms, and of people who appear to be outstandingly successful in their ability to enjoy life and contribute to the enjoyment of others.

Recommend further, more discriminating investigation.

Determine whether or not any practical lines of endeavor are feasible and desirable as products of the research, and make recommendations accordingly.

Revise this frame of reference.

We have been through and around many considerations in the pages of this book, some of them highly abstract. What in the meantime has happened to human beings? Has interest in the happiness and suffering of humanity disappeared in intellectual puzzles, in a sludge of words?

We have left Tom Young dangling with the noose of his anxiety still about his neck. Helen Chauncey and her mother rankle in their unhappinesses, Bernie Chiason remains a drunken bum. Dr. Coindreau lives under the threat of his blood pressure and Dr. Hopkins of his asthma. Where is the end of the story? Only Gordon Chauncey and Willie Smallie seem completed, the one because he was dead before our moment in mid-century began, the other because he is irrevocably withdrawn from life.

And what, too, about the Harbor Town itself, quiet in appearance, yet all the while spinning with change piled on change, tearing the damask of life patterns, stirring with spirals of opportunity and disaster? It too has been left a story picked up and then abandoned uncompleted.

We have seen something of the town's functioning and parts, and something of a few specimen members who suffer from disorder. But what of the well people? Who are these shadowy characters that move in the background as part of the world of interpersonal relations in which the disordered live? What is John, Tom's brother-in-law, really

Concluding Notes

like, and what about Marguerite, Tom's wife? Are they well people? Do they have intrapsychic problems? And if so, how do they handle them? How many are the well—the outstanding in terms of mental health, however you choose to define this—and how do they participate in the flow of community life?

Thus, our men and women, each by each, and taken all together as a community, are left so many dangling questions. But then, life dangles; only conundrums have answers. Life flows in its arcs and streamers of multicolors, but it is not pulled together for us, it is not explained, and neither misery nor happiness are guaranteed. Lines are fixed only in death, madness, and fiction.

Questions of, "What happened then?" "How did it come out?" "Why was it?" and "Did he get all right?" are questions we have to answer for ourselves, or find satisfaction in the search. It is by search and research that we can feed the promptings of the intellect, secure the means to make Tom Young's story come out happily, the means to rescue still others, and the means to rescue ourselves.

To take action, then, is the issue, the solution, and the object. It is not enough to fly over the Northeast in imagination and contemplate the sociocultural fabric lying below. We should alight now and try to take a firm hold of a specific place. Let us have done with "for instance" and begin with "instance."

PART THREE / A PLAN FOR RESEARCH

Appendices

Appendices

APPENDIX A.

Notes on the Concept of Sentiment

JANE M. HUGHES, CHARLES C. HUGHES, AND ALEXANDER H. LEIGHTON

*"It is not actions, but opinions concerning actions,
which disturb men."*—EPICTETUS

CONDUCT WAS RELATED to sentiment long before the idea of sentiment received sufficient intellectual attention to be called a concept. We sense this intuitively, although we do not know the particular way in which it was realized. We speculate that it must have happened much like Whitehead's description of the history of ideas when he tells of the dawning and gradual definition of concepts like "individual," "duty," and "mind" (79). Conjecture as to how the concept of sentiment may have emerged thus underscores the fact that what will be presented here is a brief sketch taken from modern history rather than antiquity and that many of the possible paths of exploration have not been traveled.

Three aspects of the history of sentiment will be discussed. First is the usage in English of the word itself. Second is a tracing of the idea of sentiment in history, philosophy, and literature. Third is a short account of the use in a variety of social sciences of the idea of sentiment and comparison with such kindred notions as "attitude," "opinion," "complex," "habit," "personal construct," "wish," "interest," "norm," "theme," "belief," "value," and "ideology."

It is assumed that the reader now has an idea of sentiment as used in this frame of reference. In order to avoid repetition of the various aspects crucial to this formulation as it is compared with other conceptions, it may be well to begin with a brief summary. Sentiments as Leighton defines them are relatively stable and recurrent compounds of thought, feeling, and striving which relate a person to the objects in his environment. They are the emotionally-toned "templates" through which he defines "what is," "what ought to be," and "what is desirable." The concept of sentiment as an analytic tool rests on the assumption that personalities operate as wholes, that both conscious and unconscious factors may be significant, that sentiments can have both constructive and destructive effects in personalities, and that they tend to be organized into systems. Sentiments can be both individual and cultural; the latter are designated as shared sentiments.

I ETYMOLOGICAL HISTORY

The word sentiment goes back in English parlance to the period when our language was changing from its middle to the modern form. Chaucer used it to signify a person's feelings, a person's intellectual or emotional perceptions, and a person's physical sensations (such as to be "cold and without sentiment"). The second usage, "intellectual or emotional perceptions," is consonant with our definition. A number of special and restricted meanings, however, have also been attached to the word through the years. For example, it has been employed as a synonym for the flavor of something; it has been a toast in "I give you a sentiment"; it has been equated in some periods with the sense of right and wrong as in "moral sentiments"; it has signified amorous feelings and love in "tender sentiments"; and it has had an invidious meaning as in "sentimental" (58).

Despite these variations, the central idea of thought–feeling has continued to be embodied by the word. It has appeared in literature, philosophy, and common language since the fourteenth century. It has been used in the social sciences since the nineteenth century.

II SENTIMENT IN HISTORY, PHILOSOPHY, AND LITERATURE

The idea of sentiment has not always been in style. From the vantage point of the mid-twentieth century it is possible to look back and see when the concept influenced the philosophy of human nature and when it was distinctly out of joint with the main intellectual concerns.

Among the foremost minds of the seventeenth century were those of Newton and Locke (81). They set the stage for the kind of thinking and the points of focus which characterized most of the following two centuries. In textbooks of literature and philosophy, their era is called the Age of Reason. Rationalism and mechanism were its cynosures, and feeling was notably absent as a matter of interest. In his attempt to explore human understanding, Locke pictured the mind as a *tabula rasa,* an empty cabinet which gradually, lawfully, and by certain reasonable principles became filled with the data provided by sense perception. There was no room in this rational closet for the emotional processes, for innate ideas, or for intuitions of which the mind itself was not aware. Although this represented a remarkable advancement beyond the earlier view that ideas were planted in the mind by God, it stirred men's imaginations primarily in one direction. Many years passed before it again became fashionable to observe that it was not only reason and perception which govern the mind.

Three aspects of Locke's philosophy touch on areas of mental activity which sentiment also encompasses. Sentiments include the rational and conscious factors to which Locke and those in his tradition have paid attention. The second is a force which Locke called "prejudice" and defined as the madness of the wrong "association of ideas." It was just this force which he admonished should be overcome and replaced by reasonable judgment. Obviously "prejudice" and all that it implies as to emotional involvement is an aspect of sentiment. The third is religious belief. Locke placed this in an order by itself. It was entirely beyond the "tether" of reason, and in this realm he advocated faith (44). The concept of sentiment, embedded as it is in ideas about how a person acts and feels, resists the division between "faith" and "reason." More than that, it is incompatible with the classic separations of "rational" and "nonrational," of "body" and "mind" (15). The unity of the behaving organism is the underlying assumption for the abstraction "thought–feeling."

Although David Hume in the succeeding century followed generally in the direction which Locke had mapped, some of the side-roads which he explored have relevance to sentiment. The basic units in his system were impressions and ideas. Hume felt that emotions play a part in the vividness and forcefulness with which impressions are to be distinguished from abstract ideas. As a positivist, he believed that all knowledge is based on experience. He recognized, however, that there are things in the mind which cannot be called knowledge and which appear without counterparts in empirical experience. In sleep, in fever, and in madness, the mind becomes aware of things which cannot be understood by principles of association (33). In his social philosophy emotion is also significant. His doctrine of sympathy contributed to a tradition which later had more affinity to that of sentiment than his theory of association. Imagination as one of the mental processes was pivotal to sympathy. It is by imagining what is in the mind and feelings of another person that sympathy arises. The main dissimilarity between Hume's view of the mind and that underlying the concept of sentiment is his denial that the individual can have a conception of himself as a whole or that perception is performed as an integration of many facets in the personality. Hume as a thinker of his own time was an elementarist. The idea of a whole personality acting through the parts and units of mental activity remained almost entirely foreign to the philosophy of human nature from the times of Locke and Hume until the nineteenth century.

On the other hand, a few literary wedges were driven into this *Zeitgeist* during the eighteenth century. Satirists listened to the talk about reasonableness and laughed. In *Gulliver's Travels,* Swift asks the reader to look about the land of Houyhnhnms to see if he can find reasonable men or only Yahoos (73). Sterne's *Life and Opinions of Tristram Shandy Gentleman* can be viewed as an experiment in Lockean psychology (71). All the mechanisms which Locke described as the ways in which the mind operates, Sterne tried to fit into the ordinary thoughts and actions of the Shandys and found that they did not work without the assistance of *sentimentalism* (76).

Sentimentalism as Sterne originally conceived it did not have the same maudlin tone which dominated the literary cult of sentimentalism. It had more in common with Hume's "sympathy," that is, it defined a way in which people relate to one another by the perception of their mutual feelings. Nonetheless, Sterne's *The Sentimental Journey* gave its name if not its meaning to an aspect of eighteenth century literature which *is* noted for its indulgence in "the luxury of grief" and the "sadly pleasing tear" (2). The cult reached its highest absurdity in Henry Mackenzie's *The Man of Feeling* and its most biting attack in Jane Austen's *Sense and Sensibility*. By the nineteenth century it had, for the most part, died out, and the modern psychological novel undertook a more substantial and realistic analysis of feelings and sentiments.

Turning back to philosophy, Adam Smith's "The Theory of Moral Sentiments" is especially to be noted for its use of the term sentiment in a philosophical treatise (68). Although the same idea was then and has continued to be designated by a variety of terms, from Smith's day onward sentiment has had a place in the philosophical and psychological vocabulary concerning motivation and conduct. It is also noteworthy that the term "moral" is used in conjunction with sentiments. It was a time when ethics and psychology had not been disentangled and morals as belief systems which contain strong affect frequently appeared in writings where now one might find sentiments, values, opinions, ideologies. The proximity of morals and sentiment, however, indicates that, beginning with this early period, the idea has referred to a social dimension of opinion and behavior. Like Hume's sympathy, Smith believed that the social sentiments arise in the human capacity for imagination. The concords of sentiment shared between two people are built on the ability to imagine (a function of cognition) and to feel (a function of affect). Smith's "concords of sentiment" differ from the "shared sentiments" discussed here in that the former were thought to be ingredients of moral behavior and social harmony. Shared sentiments of aggression or hostility would be included in our analysis as much as love and altruism.

One of the major intellectual revolutions of the nineteenth century was an awakening to natural science as a source for the generation of new ideas. By this time there had been numerous achievements in natural history and medicine, but the impact on philosophy and literature and the incipient social sciences did not come until human thought was loosened from the security which Newtonian physics had provided (8). When the loosening was achieved, the study of biological organisms and vegetable growth brought to prominence a wholly new set of considerations. The focus shifted from elementarism to holism, from particle to field (25). This had important repercussions in many areas of human thought—literature, philosophy, sociology, and psychology.

For example, the poet-philosopher of the Romantic Movement, Samuel Coleridge, used the notion of biological growth as the basis for his "dynamic philosophy." Here again it is perhaps necessary to

Notes on the Concept of Sentiment

399

restrain the inclination to equate romantic with sentimental and thus miss the contribution which the Romantic Movement made to the history of thought. One of its accomplishments was to balance the emphasis between emotional and rational processes. And Coleridge in particular tried to direct attention away from perception to the perceiver as a participant in the act of perception (11). Two centuries earlier the mind was thought of as a receptor or reflector (to *mirror* nature), whereas Coleridge began to think of the mind as a projector (or *lamp*), shooting its illumination into perception, directing light upon certain areas for special notice, and infusing the percepta with the feelings and emotions of the person (1). Coleridge believed that perception functioned in a way analogous to the growth of a plant which unfolds from an internal urgency of its own as a counterpart to its dependence upon the environment. This view has resemblances to that upon which our concept of sentiment is built. It recognizes that mental activity is not only reactive but also spontaneous and projective. As a mental process, projection, although variously defined, is now commonplace in psychology. Thus sentiments like Coleridge's mental projectors take liberties with reality; they determine the categories, shades, and colorings of "what is" quite apart from what can be objectively agreed upon as existential.

The concept of organism is also essential to Herbert Spencer's philosophy. It was not a dominant theme in England until later, however. The much more influential psychology of James Mills was associationistic and elementaristic, two qualities which characterized British psychology when it was first formalized as a social science. Nonetheless, Spencer comes into this survey of sentiment not only because he used sentiment *per se* but also because he was concerned with the nature of organism and its relevance for understanding society—issues which are also fundamental background for our discussion of sentiments. It must be stated at once that the areas of interest between Spencer and Leighton have more in common than the principles which each derived. This is especially true with regard to the idea of evolution. Thinking about organisms led Spencer to a series of social stages to match organic evolution and to a set of hierarchically arranged sentiments which would reflect these stages of social evolution.

Conscience, which has always concerned philosophers and psychologists, is conceived in this book as a part of the sentiment system which defines "what ought to be." Today no psychology of personality disregards the normative element in behavior. In Spencer's time, however, conscience was approached somewhat differently. Hume and Smith had said that it was constructed out of the sympathetic imagination. The intuitionalists had said that the affectively toned beliefs were stamped into human nature by some mysterious extra-experiential procedure or by God. The utilitarians such as Bentham and Mill said that it was acquired by "rational calculus." It was thought by them that each individual could empirically test his own acts and those of others against the formula of the "Greatest happiness of the greatest number." Spencer rejected the intuitionalist's "moral sense"; he agreed with the utilitarians that reason was an aspect of conscience; but he went further. To him sentiments are founded upon rational observation and then suffused with emotional meaning. But the evolutionary point of view instigated the belief that civilized people are capable of a different order of sentiment than are primitives (32). He distinguishes between presentative feelings which are immediate–reflexive and representative feelings which are conscious–reflective, between sensations and sentiments, and between pre-ethical sentiments and ethical sentiments. Thus the most highly intellectualized, complex, and abstract sentiments ("sentiments of ought") are re-representative feelings (70).

In the next section we shall examine sentiment and a variety of similar concepts which are used in modern social science. In modern philosophy and literature the idea of sentiment is so pervasive that it is impossible to be specific.

The psychological tenor of modern literature is a case in point. Literature has always sought to describe and analyze man's inner nature. Taking the long view, however, it is possible to see one pertinent movement. There has been a gradual turning away from straight reporting—from objective accounts of events, tales of action, and descriptions of exploits. If anything characterizes modern literature it is the attempt to break through the façade of action and behavior and to discover what lies behind: meaning, motivation, feeling, sentiment. For example, the attempt to unravel symbols and capture their quintessence indicates the interior quality of the literature of our period.

Likewise philosophy. In the twentieth century few unitary trends are discernible (78). For every group of philosophers who stress any one aspect there is another group who emphasize its opposite. In many ways, modern thought has tended to steer the middle course and to

Notes on the Concept of Sentiment

401

free itself from the bind of "either–or." This is shown in the growing inclination to use hyphenated concepts, to compound terminology, and to develop hybrid disciplines (7). In this book, sentiment is called thought–feeling. We talk of the continuum of integration–disintegration. We have grown accustomed to such linkages as "social psychology," "the philosophy of science," and "the sociology of knowledge." Thus, most strict dichotomizations are artifacts used to make a point and are not entirely reflective of the actual situation. Yet for purposes of illustration we could align together those who uphold the standard of cognitive certainty—the positivists; we could group those philosophies in which sentiment is a tacit assumption; and then, finally, those such as Bradley, Bergson, and Whitehead who have made emotion a central emphasis. To Whitehead, for example, "Knowledge is always accompanied with accessories of emotion and purpose" (79 p. 12).

III SENTIMENT AND KINDRED CONCEPTS IN SOCIAL SCIENCE

Psychiatry. In psychiatric literature, Bernard Hart is the main exponent of the point of view represented in this volume by the term sentiment. Following Jung, however, he called his concept "complex." That was in 1912 when he wrote *The Psychology of Insanity* (26). In 1922, when he contributed to the Manchester Symposium on the "Relations of Complex and Sentiment," he stated that were he to rewrite the book he would call what he had in mind sentiment (27). He felt that his early definition of complex, prototypic of which are the political bias and the hobby, was more akin to the idea of sentiment as developed by Shand and McDougall than the latter-day emphasis on the unconscious, pathological, and repressed elements of complex.

Thinking of sentiment as feelings for objects, it is possible to see Freud's "object-cathexis" and "identification" in like terms (24). Cathexis and identification emphasize affect focused on valued objects. Neither concept, however, has the social dimension or shared quality characteristic of sentiment

Of the concepts Sullivan employed as major foci, "dynamism" is comparable in a limited sense to sentiment. A dynamism is any habitual reaction toward people. It can be a feeling, an attitude, or an act (72). This meets the criterion of including both thought and feeling.

People are the main objects of interest to Sullivan, while the idea of sentiment is not restricted to the interpersonal field. Inherent in our use of sentiment is the thesis that objects of any variety—parents, acts, abstract ideas—can be suffused with interest and emotional commitment.

As mentioned above, Jung's original use of complex was close to the meaning of Hart's sentiment. In view of the general association of complex with Jung, it is interesting to find that neither this term nor sentiment is given in the glossary he provided for *Psychological Types*. It is, rather, "attitude" which he selects for elaboration. The duality of conscious and unconscious objects is one of the prime characteristics, and he views attitude as a "direction towards a definite thing, whether this be present in consciousness or not" (35, p. 526). He also sees attitude as capable of being expressed in more than one individual —"typical attitudes" or "collective attitudes."

The concept of sentiment was employed by Adolf Meyer in teaching personality study and as part of the psychobiological orientation. In doing this, he acknowledged the influence of the British psychologists, particularly McDougall. As a student of Meyer, Leighton was directed toward a concept which would fuse thought and feeling, and later when searching for a framework in terms of which to conduct personality studies of people who were not patients and who came from different cultural backgrounds, sentiments appeared to be a suitable conceptual tool. It seemed possible on such a basis to have an organizing principle which was not overcommitted to any particular theory and yet which closed the door to no reasonable theory. At the same time it is doubtless true that the concept of sentiment employed here has been carried into areas not necessarily in line with Meyer's thinking. Because sentiment was important in his teaching, it is paradoxical to find that in the four volumes of Meyer's collected works, the word is not indexed (50). In his Salmon Lectures, the concept appears in only a few instances (51). We may conclude, therefore, that for him sentiment as a term was not a way to organize observations of human behavior, although the point of view it represents was.

Among present psychiatrists, John C. Whitehorn is perhaps the strongest advocate of sentiment. He defines personality as "the organized system of sentiments or attitudes by which one establishes relationships with others and negotiates interpersonal transactions" (80, p. 212).

Few other psychiatrists appear to have made explicit use of either

Notes on the Concept of Sentiment

the term or the underlying idea as such. Nevertheless, the recognition of thought–feeling as a reference point for observation and as part of analysis is exceedingly widespread at the implicit level. For instance Horney's consideration of personality in terms of "toward," "against," and "away from" other people, and her emphasis on the conflict between the wish to succeed and the wish to be loved, are largely ways of analyzing and describing particular clusters of sentiment (30, 31). It would require a book in itself, however, to trace psychiatric ideas which, in such an amorphous way, relate to the notion of sentiments. It should be pointed out, nonetheless, that diagnosis and therapeutic procedures are rarely if ever carried out without sentiments, even if under some other name, being an aspect of the thinking.

Psychology. In Britain, G. F. Stout, A. F. Shand, and William McDougall have used sentiment as a basic concept. In 1896 the term was proposed by Shand, who stressed that sentiments are not merely rudimentary feelings but complex and organized systems (66). McDougall defined sentiment as "a system in which a cognitive disposition is linked with one or more emotional or affective dispositions to form a structural unit that functions as one whole system" (49, p. 437). Sentiment is thus a coordinating phenomenon which unites the tripartition of cognition, affect, and conation. The congruence between McDougall's sentiment and Leighton's is not, however, unequivocal. Since in this country sentiment is often thought of as primarily McDougall's concept, it seems worth while to pause here and make the comparison more explicit. The areas of greatest similarity are:

1. Sentiments or sentiment systems although located in individuals must be viewed in a social context. While both suggest that sentiments are products of environment and socialization, equally mutual is the cognizance given to innate endowment and heredity.

2. Sentiments are factors closely related to the stability and predictability of the personality system.

3. The life history approach is used in conjunction with sentiment. This gives leeway for the recognition of factors entering later life which are sometimes neglected by an overweening emphasis on childhood.

4. Sentiments combine both conscious and unconscious components.

5. Conation is emphasized as fundamental to the development of

sentiments. Both stress that the organism is characterized by a constant state of striving. Sentiments are the organization and differentiation of these striving impulses around certain objects.

Important aspects of divergence between McDougall and Leighton seem to be:

1. McDougall's view of instinct is different from Leighton's "basic urge."

2. McDougall conceived of hierarchy and a master sentiment as essential to the integration of the system. The organization of the sentiment system according to Leighton is chiefly characterized by the interdependence of constituent elements or sometimes by a "predominant constellation of sentiments" prevailing over the rest. Although many similar modes of articulation and interrelationship are specified, gradation is not the key concept in our analysis that it was in McDougall's.

3. The "self-regarding sentiment" is McDougall's sovereign entity. According to him, moral or social behavior is possible only when the self-regarding sentiment governs from the top of the hierarchically organized system of subsentiments. This permits the substitution of self-imposed sanctions for either parental or social sanctions. In our frame of reference, no one sentiment is isolated as primarily accountable for optimal functioning of the personality system, although it is suggested that ten essential striving sentiments, interrelated rather than unidominated, are important for maintaining the essential psychical condition.

Comparison between complex and sentiment was the central theme of a Symposium of the British Psychological Society held in Manchester in 1922 to which McDougall, Hart, and a number of contemporaries contributed. Some comments from these discussions indicate how the concept of sentiment fared during the early part of the twentieth century. W. H. R. Rivers, for example, favored the continued use of the two terms on the basis that there are two different phenomena to be described—and thus the need for terminological distinction. In contrast to the morbid and repressed quality of complex, sentiment is an emotionally toned system of ideas, more capable of modification and, on the whole, more available to consciousness than is complex (64). A. G. Tansley, on the other hand, criticized sentiment as a term. He saw it as "the attempt to give scientific precision to a word borrowed out of ordinary language" (74, p. 120). For him the term overemphasized emotion and neglected cognition, although he realized that the specific definition of the term by McDougall and others attempted to overcome this. He favored a term which would emphasize the two-way character of ideas organizing about emotions and emotions organizing about ideas. Shand felt that one of the main distinctions between complex and sentiment was the type of autonomy achieved. A sentiment is noted for its ability to organize and control the component parts. A complex, on the other hand, achieves its consistency by exclusion of wayward components or by a unidimensional preoccupation with one element. Thus a phobia could not be a sentiment (67). Leighton's sentiments in contrast are conceived to be fundamental to both pathological functioning and normal functioning. T. H. Pear's contribution was further exploration of repression as an identifying criterion for complex as compared to sentiment. He said that "the development of some powerful and important sentiments, at least in society as we know it here and now, implies not a little repression" (62, p. 134).

In this country the concept of sentiment was introduced mainly through McDougall. His influence on American *psychiatry* has already been mentioned. In *psychology* his influence has been more sporadic. For a time it looked as though his point of view would become an integral part of psychological thought and research. The reaction against his instinct theory, however, brought also a disaffection with sentiment. But in more recent times there has been a recrudescence. Murray, Morgan, French, Asch, and Cattell have made specific use of the idea of sentiment, and MacLeod has expressed indebtedness to McDougall in his phenomenological approach (46). Whereas in Europe sentiment was compared to "complex," its chief rival in this country has been "attitude." Also distinctive of the American scene have been attempts to use sentiment as a focus in research problems rather than solely as a theoretical orientation.

In his study of fifty Harvard undergraduates, Murray used sentiment and later elaborated the concept in conjunction with Morgan in the monograph, *A Clinical Study of Sentiments*. There he states his preference for sentiment as opposed to attitude because it connotes a deeper-lying and more affectively significant level of personality. Murray defined sentiment as "a more or less enduring disposition (predilection or readiness) in personality to respond with a positive or negative affect to a specified entity," and he outlined a number of categories by which sentiments can be classified (52, 53, p. 11).

Vera French used sentiment in two observational studies of students at Swarthmore College. Her monographs include not only a research report but an historical review of sentiment in psychology which gives considerably more depth than is attempted here. Her definition of sentiments states that they are "highly organized cognitive-affective dispositions characterized by (a) differentiation, (b) clarity and intensity, (c) conscious univalence and unitendency or conscious ambivalence and ambitendency, (d) hierarchic integration, and (e) unconscious component" (21, p. 271, 22, 23). Her view stresses the functioning of sentiments within the personality and is less concerned with the nature of objects to which sentiment becomes attached, the latter consideration being of significance in this frame of reference.

In a comprehensive outline of personality, Cattell uses sentiments, designating that they stem primarily from an environmental as opposed to physiological base. He calls them "the major acquired dynamic trait structures which cause their possessors to pay attention to certain objects or classes of objects and to feel and react in a certain way with regard to them" (10, p. 161). He distinguishes sentiments from attitudes, and attitudes in turn from opinions. He postulates that sentiments are more important for personality analysis because they appear earlier in the individual's development and are more permanent than are the transient opinions and attitudes which arise during adulthood or on the basis of exigency.

Both attitude and sentiment as two phases of the same general phenomenon are used by Asch. He attributes to sentiment a greater degree of centrality, personal significance and transcendent importance—such as the love of one person for another or the devotion of a person to his craft or occupation. Attitudes, on the other hand, are sentiments shared by many people and refer to issues of general concern such as education and political organization (5).

In industrial psychology, Elton Mayo and F. A. Roethlisberger use the specific term sentiment (48, 65). Beyond these two, however, the main agreement has been conceptual rather than terminological.

Equivalent rather than identical terms and units of study have been employed by numerous psychologists, both academic and applied. Of the kindred terms used in psychology, "habit" for a time had prominence. William James, for example, conceived of habit as a tendency derived from experience, founded on an instinctive base, which is characterized by a capacity to pay attention to certain objects (34). In search for a similar unit of analysis, Dewey felt that attitude or disposition would almost equally approximate the concept he had in mind, although he also elected to use habit (14).

Neither habit nor sentiment, however, seems to have fit the predilection of American psychology. In "The Historical Background of Modern Social Psychology," Gordon Allport indicates that attitude is the "most distinctive and indispensable concept in American social psychology" (3, p. 43). Allport himself has made attitude a central factor in his study of functional autonomy (4); Krech and Crutchfield use the concept, footnoting that it bears resemblance to McDougall's sentiment (41); and Newcomb also makes attitude the prime focus of analysis (55). This is to mention but a few.

Allport defines attitude as a "neuropsychic state of readiness for mental and physical activity" (3, p. 43). Attitudes are always directed toward an object or value. The attitude is the state of mind within the individual and the value is a quality outside the individual. The compound, "value–attitude" thus stands for the relationship of person to objects which Leighton denotes by the single term "sentiment." Moreover, Allport favors attitude because it is sufficiently expansive to apply either to the dispositions of individuals or to the broad patterns of culture which he calls "common attitudes." Such plasticity has a parallel in sentiment. Shared sentiments and common attitudes obviously mean the same thing. In comparing attitude and sentiment (the latter primarily as defined by McDougall), Allport says that they differ on four accounts: sentiment suggests the underlying base of motivation whereas attitude is a disposition without regard to its origin or source of energy; sentiments center about specific objects, whereas attitudes can be diffuse; sentiments are considered lasting and hierarchical, whereas attitudes may be transitory; and sentiments are conscious and benign whereas attitudes can be both conscious or morbidly repressed. It is apparent from this summary that Leighton's use of sentiment overlaps in part with attitude and in part with the classical view of sentiment. The main point, however, is that the two concepts refer essentially to the same thing. Differences are largely concerns of preference, habits of thought, or desired emphasis. Smith, Bruner, and White make the same point. They suggest that the boundaries between attitude, sentiment, and opinion are extremely vague, and that in most respects a single idea is in mind (69).

In recent years there has been a growing interest in cognitive structures. The problems of meaning, symbolization, and thinking have attracted much psychological notice. Representative of this trend is George Kelly. For purposes of comparison, it may seem that such an inclination stresses cognition to the slight of the emotional correlates. Although not the main focus, the emotional base of meaning and thinking is considered integral to the present day analyses of cognition, or, to use Kelly's term, "personal constructs" (36).

Sociology. A comparison of the sociological and anthropological use of sentiment and related concepts involves one basic difference in orientation. Our use of sentiment, as well as the various psychological and psychiatric concepts reviewed thus far, takes the individual as the point of departure. Shared sentiments are a ramification which include both persons and groups. The concepts we will now discuss begin, for the most part, at the group level, although group phenomena are inferred from the action of individuals.

A number of European sociologists used terms which have been translated as "sentiment." The meanings, however, are somewhat different from ours. Translators of Emile Durkheim have equated the French term "sentiment" with its English cognate. Durkheim did not specifically define his meaning and it appears more subtle and variable than the straightforward equivalence suggests. Quite often sentiment is a synonym for affect or emotion in the plural mode, but at other times it denotes complexes of affect centered about ideas or objects. Also Durkheim emphasizes symbolism and the mutually reinforcing relationship between a symbol and a sentiment (as between the totem animal and the sentiments of group identification). He makes a division between "general sentiments" (such as religion or nation) and "individual sentiments" (such as ideas about one's person and goods). Durkheim's reference to the "collective sentiments" or "collective conscience" is similar to the shared sentiments of a group, although in his hands they became so important that individual perceptions and emotions were neglected (16, 17).

The German sociologist, Ferdinand Tönnies, used a series of terms which have been translated as "sentiment" only part of which coincide with our meaning. In some instances, he speaks of "sentiments and motives which draw people to each other, keep them together, and induce them to joint action" which is like our usage (75, p. 3). But for the most part sentiment is employed more loosely as signifying "passion," "conscience," "urge to live," and "sensuality."

In Vilfredo Pareto's work three terms are crucial—"sentiment," "residue," and "derivative." With regard to "sentiment," the translators indicate that it is synonymous with "instinct, sensation, preconception, and inclination" (59, p. 2016). The central themes of Pareto's analysis are "logical" and "nonlogical" action. For him nonlogical conduct is rooted in sentiment and becomes rationalized by a series of verbal assertions or "theories." From many such variable assertions (called "derivatives") one can abstract a generic principle or regularity (called a "residue"). For analytic purposes Pareto draws a clear distinction between the sentiment and the residue; however, he recognized that for general exposition this separation is unimportant and spoke of residues including the sentiments which they manifest (29). Leighton's sentiment, in comparison, is considered a unitary concept subsuming Pareto's discrete units of analysis as well as the broader division of logical and nonlogical.

In this country, by the turn of the century when Charles Cooley employed the word, it had already been accepted from the vernacular into the vocabulary of sociologists. It has continued to be used with sufficient frequency to be found in a recent *Dictionary of Sociology and Related Social Sciences* (18). Cooley's definition lacks the explicit idea of orientation toward objects or classes of objects which is an important feature in most usages. By sentiment he meant "socialized feeling" which had been raised out of its instinctive state. Following the tradition of Hume, Sterne, Smith, and the Scottish philosophers, he linked sentiment with sympathy and pointed out that imagination is one of its components, and "sympathetic contact with the minds of others" its medium (12, p. 177). Like others who have used sentiments, he saw them as motivations combined into permanent dispositions which are less changeable than rational thought.

Kingsley Davis utilizes sentiment as one segment of a continuum which includes "value" and "end." He states that sentiments are the "broad backgrounds of feeling which make some things seem valuable, others not valuable" (13, p. 124). His sentiment, like ours, embraces both organic and derived needs. Sentiments, however, lie in the range of general orientation, whereas "value" and "ends" are more specific, a separation which Leighton does not make.

In the work of George C. Homans, sentiment is the mobilization of affect for objects regardless of their "ought" or "desirable" qualities. He is interested in the "internal states of the human body" and he has chosen to call them sentiments "largely because that word has been used in a less specialized sense than some of the others" such as drives, emotions, feelings, affective states, and attitudes (28, p. 38).

For a generation, Talcott Parsons has considered "sentiment," "values," and "attitudes" as those imperatives to action which are not solely reflexive. Commenting on the need for a term to cover the generalized system of normative standards, Parsons suggested "value–attitude" to take the place of sentiment (61). Later he defined sentiment as "culturally organized cathectic and/or evaluative modes or patterns of orientation toward particular objects or classes of objects. A sentiment thus involves the internalization of cultural patterns" (60, p. 41n). Parsons uses the term "value" as the normative and collective aspect abstracted from its motivational base in sentiments. By this means sentiments or value-attitudes or need-dispositions (all referring essentially to the same phenomenon) are conceived as the individual manifestations of cultural values.

The concept of "norm," which has received much more sociological elaboration than sentiment yet is related in a number of ways, seems universally to hinge on a division between existential and desirable realms. Parsons draws "norm" out of the more embracing concept of sentiment, saying that aspects of behavior are normative when they "involve a sentiment attributable to one or more actors that something is an end in itself" (61, p. 75). Sentiments as defined by Leighton point to the mobilization of affect and cognition around either existential propositions or normative end-statements.

Robin M. Williams, Jr., uses "belief" as a working concept, and differentiates it from "value." Belief is related to the existential mode of thought rather than preferential or end-to-be-desired mode. Thus belief lies in the cognitive charting of the universe, but it also implies an affective base, for "belief is a conviction that something is real" (82, p. 379). Value also implies such emotional involvement but refers analytically to desired states of affairs. Both belief and value would be implied by sentiment in our usage.

"Ideology" as elaborated by Karl Mannheim is similar to sentiment in referring to ideas which are firmly linked to an emotional base and which develop as the products of psychological, social, and cultural determinants. On the other hand, ideology defined as the "opinions, statements, propositions, and systems of ideas interpreted in the light of the life-situation of the one who expresses them" is more restricted than sentiment (47, p. 56). Moreover, Mannheim denies that ideology is merely the rationalizer of error and suggests for a more comprehensive parallel term "perspective," meaning "the subject's whole mode of conceiving things as determined by his historical and social setting" (47, p. 266). This enlarged meaning is more like sentiment or systems of sentiment. The concept of shared sentiment is implied in Mannheim's "total ideology" which is essentially the cultural context of an individual which he distinguishes from a "particular ideology," the individual's own elaboration of meaning.

Anthropology. In anthropology, one searches long for any self-conscious use of the specific term sentiment. For the most part it is employed in a matter-of-fact manner which does not far differentiate it from "emotion." Indicative of its use at the level of assumption, or not at all, is the fact that the term is not indexed in those books where one finds a résumé of anthropological thought (6, 42, 45, 83).

Notwithstanding its lack of standardization as an anthropological idea, sentiment appears in the writings of some anthropologists, especially the British scholars Radcliffe-Brown, Firth, and Nadel. Radcliffe-Brown's focus regarding sentiments is the social system rather than the individual. Following Durkheim, "society" for him "depends for its existence on the presence in the minds of its members of a certain system of sentiments by which the conduct of the individual is regulated in conformity with the needs of society" (63, p. 233). Sentiments are divorced from innate individual development and appear rather in the process of the society acting upon the individual. Obviously when Radcliffe-Brown speaks of the "collective expression" of sentiments he is closer to shared sentiments than to the personally significant relationship between individual and objects.

In at least two of his publications, Raymond Firth used sentiment. In *We, the Tikopia*, he employs sentiment to indicate informal behavior between people, not patterned by culture. Sentiments refer to the idiosyncratic processes of interaction among people which transcend formal role requirements. He also draws a distinction between "psychological reality" and "cultural reality," stating that in his view sentiments describe a type of overt behavior rather than a "state of mind which must be inferred" (20, p. 160). In comparison, our use of sentiment is explicitly psychological, and it assumes that systems of sentiments can be inferred which not only have relevance for one individual but can be seen in a social dimension. In a more recent book Firth uses sentiment to designate a variety of phenomena. In general his use is closer to "affect" than our complex of thought-feeling. The implication, however, of recurrent ideas centering about objects and inextricably involved with emotional investment is present in his description of the "sentimental" attachment of the peasants to the soil or of "family sentiments." Even closer to the idea of sentiment are his "belief" and "emotional attitude" (19).

S. F. Nadel's concept of sentiment is more in the psychological tradition of McDougall. He applies the term to the "common denominator" or "over-riding impulse in a variety of contexts" (54, p. 69). This common denominator, like the psychological "disposition" or "readiness," refers to a direction of consciousness, rendered visible in choice of action. Further, he suggests that there is a relatively permanent association of motivation with an object, although he reserves the term "sentiment" for the feeling-tone of such motivation and the term "interest" for the cognitive aspect. This separates terminologically what is believed to be mutually involved in any act of thought-feeling as described by Leighton.

An American anthropologist, the late Edwin G. Burrows, analyzed behavior by an integration of the concepts "value," "sentiment," "dynamic system," and "ethos" (9). His use of sentiment was derived from Murray and Morgan, although he was primarily interested in what they had called "compound sentiments," those in which several different values combine into one interconnected motivational unit.

For the most part, however, American anthropologists have used such related concepts as "configuration," "theme," "enthymeme," "premise," "postulate," "interest," "value," and "value orientation."

The orientation toward sentiments which stresses that they are salient features of individual personality and group interaction compares with Ralph Linton's concept of interest. For Linton, a "cultural interest" is "anything which has meaning for two or more of society's component members" (43, p. 422). Although vague as a definition, the instances he cites imply recognition of cognitive elements, an affective base, an existential as well as a normative perception of experience, and reference to objects or classes of objects. Finally, only those complexes of meaningful associations about an object which persist in a group are called cultural interests. This is reminiscent of Leighton's phrase "tending to recur" in the definition of sentiment.

Kluckhohn has used the term "configuration" to describe regularities or principles which involve covert aspects of culture. The confluence with shared sentiment is thus only partial. Although a person may not be aware of all aspects of his sentiments—shared or private—it would be a rare individual, indeed, who could verbalize almost any configuration. Thus configuration is pre-eminently an analytic concept based on inference. Kluckhohn has also used the term "premise" in much the same way, and more recently "enthymeme." A cultural enthymeme is a tacit premise and thus is equally removed from the overt level (38, 37, 39).

In writing about "themes," Morris Opler has rejected a division of culture into implicit and explicit, ideal or real. He defines theme as "a postulate or position, declared or implied, and usually controlling behavior or stimulating activity, which is tacitly approved or openly promoted in society" (56, 57, p. 120). Although both theme and enthymeme in specific instances describe the same data as do sentiments, they take root in the group aspects and dynamics of human behavior; they are abstractions from the patterning of group data and do not necessarily have any standing in the personality dynamics of given individuals. Insofar, however, as personality partakes of its cultural background, both theme and enthymeme enter as constituents. This is especially true with regard to the affective core outstanding in the concept of sentiment. Affect is vital to sentiment, whereas affect is only implied as a function of the empirical situation in which themes and enthymemes are found, not as part of the abstracted concepts themselves.

The concept of "value" in sociology and anthropology is related to that of sentiment on many accounts. To begin with, Kluckhohn has distinguished values from "sentiments, emotions, drives, and needs," implying that in sentiment there is less a cognitive–normative element than in value. He goes on to say, however, that the definition of sentiment given by McDougall and carried out in this book ("a combination of affective disposition with cognitive disposition, the centering of a system of emotions about the idea of some object") has marked similarity to the key concept used in the Harvard Values Studies. McDougall's sentiment, he says, coincides with their use of "personal value" (40, p. 396).

Value, like sentiment, has numerous variations, depending upon whose framework of analysis is being employed. The meanings of value now becoming standardized, however, indicate that, like norm, it derives from a division between existential and normative modes of human apprehension of experience. Values refer to the desirable as contrasted to cognitive–affective propositions relating to the facts of experience as such. More like our concept of sentiment is the "value-orientation" used by the Kluckhohns and associates. Such orientations are general, organized, and include "definitely existential judgments." A value-orientation is a "profile" of a particular group (or individual) constructed from the salient interests of the motivational life as these have been formed through the interaction of value elements with existential reality (40). For example, in his study of a modern Texan community in the Southwest, E. Z. Vogt speaks of value-orientations as "meaningful clusters of associated values and not just lists of things" (77, p. 7). He emphasizes that they attach to important foci in the life of the group. An example of a major value-orientation inferred from the behavior of the Texas Homesteaders is such a themal statement as "living for the future" which is buttressed by associated values like "be progressive," "be optimistic," "try to be successful." A sentiment used for illustrative purposes in Leighton's description of the Harbor Town is "virtue is rewarded." The resemblance between the concepts is obvious. The major area of difference is reflected in the fact that *a* value-orientation is a synthetic product, formed from analytically separate units of affect and cognition; whereas *a* sentiment is, from the start, a unit of thought–feeling which may be directed toward "what is," "what ought to be," or "what is desired."

BIBLIOGRAPHY

1. ABRAMS, M. H., *The Mirror and the Lamp: Romantic Theory and the Critical Tradition* (New York: Oxford Univ. Press, 1953).
2. ———, "Sensibility and Sentimentalism," *A Glossary of Literary Terms* (New York: Rinehart, 1957), pp 87-88.

Notes on the Concept of Sentiment

415

3. ALLPORT, GORDON W., "The Historical Background of Modern Social Psychology," in Gardner Lindzey (Ed.), *Handbook of Social Psychology* (Cambridge: Addison-Wesley, 1954), pp. 3-56.

4. ———, Personality, *A Psychological Interpretation* (New York: Holt, 1937).

5. ASCH, SOLOMON E., *Social Psychology* (New York: Prentice-Hall, 1952), p. 569.

6. BIDNEY, DAVID H., *Theoretical Anthropology* (New York: Columbia Univ. Press, 1952).

7. BOULDING, KENNETH, "General Systems Theory—The Skeleton of Science," in Ludwig von Bertalanffy and Anatol Rapoport (Eds.), *General Systems, Yearbook of the Society for the Advancement of General Systems Theory,* (Ann Arbor: Braun-Brumfield, 1956), Vol. 1, pp. 11-17.

8. BRONOWSKI, J., *The Common Sense of Science* (Cambridge: Harvard Univ. Press, 1955).

9. BURROWS, E. G., "From Value to Ethos on Ifaluk Atoll," *Southwestern Journal of Anthropology,* Vol. 8, 1952, pp. 13-35.

10. CATTELL, R. B., *Personality: A Systematic, Theoretical, and Factual Study* (New York: McGraw, 1950).

11. COLERIDGE, S. T., *Biographia Literaria* (J. Shawcross, Ed.), (London: Oxford Univ. Press, 1954).

12. COOLEY, CHARLES H., *Social Organization* (Glencoe, Ill.: Free Press, 1956).

13. DAVIS, KINGSLEY, *Human Society* (New York: Macmillan, 1949).

14. DEWEY, JOHN, *Human Nature and Conduct: An Introduction to Social Psychology* (New York: Holt, 1922).

15. ———, *Intelligence In the Modern World* (Joseph Ratner, Ed.) (New York: Modern Library, 1939), pp. 811-812. Gives a definition of "mind" which surmounts the old body-mind controversy and which matches in many respects our use of sentiment.

16. DURKHEIM, EMILE, *Division of Labor in Society* (George Simpson, trans.) (New York: Macmillan, 1933), for example, p. 79.

17. ———, *The Elementary Forms of the Religious Life* (Joseph W. Swain, trans.) (London: Allen and Unwin, 1954), especially, for example, pp. 16, 73, 375, 393.

18. FAIRCHILD, HENRY P., et. al., *Dictionary of Sociology and Relation Science* (Ames, Iowa: Littlefield, Adams, 1957), p. 270.

19. FIRTH, RAYMOND, *Elements of Social Organization* (London: Watts, 1952), for example, pp. 98, 209, 237.

20. ———, *We, The Tikopia* (London: Allen and Unwin, 1957), for example, p. 128.

APPENDIX A

21. FRENCH, VERA V., "The Structure of Sentiments. I. A Restatement of the Theory of Sentiments," *Journal of Personality*, Vol. 15, no. 4, 1947, pp. 247-282.

22. ——, "The Structure of Sentiments. II. A Preliminary Study of Sentiments," *Journal of Personality*, Vol. 16, no. 1, 1947, pp. 78-108.

23. ——, "The Structure of Sentiments, III. A Study of Philosophico-religious Sentiments," *Journal of Personality*, Vol. 16, no. 2, 1947, pp. 209-244.

24. FREUD, SIGMUND, *The Basic Writings of Sigmund Freud* (A. A. Brill, Ed.), (New York: Modern Library, 1938).

25. HALDANE, J. B. S., *The Philosophy of a Biologist* (Oxford: Clarendon Press, 1935).

26. HART, BERNARD, *The Psychology of Insanity* (New York: Macmillan, 1912).

27. ——, "The Relations of Complex and Sentiment," *British Journal of Psychology*, Vol. 13, October 1922, pp. 141-145.

28. HOMANS, GEORGE C., *The Human Group* (New York: Harcourt Brace, 1950).

29. —— and CURTIS, CHARLES P. JR., *An Introduction to Pareto: His Sociology* (New York: Knopf, 1934), for example, p. 88.

30. HORNEY, KAREN, *The Neurotic Personality of Our Time* (New York: Norton, 1937).

31. ——, *Our Inner Conflicts, A Constructive Theory of Neurosis* (New York: Norton, 1945).

32. HUDSON, WILLIAM HENRY, *An Introduction to the Philosophy of Herbert Spencer* (New York: Appleton, 1894).

33. HUME, DAVID, *A Treatise of Human Nature* (reprinted from the original edition, L. A. Selby-Bigge, Ed.), (Oxford: Clarendon, 1896).

34. JAMES, WILLIAM, *The Principles of Psychology* (New York: Holt, 1890).

35. JUNG, CARL G., *Psychological Types* (New York: Harcourt, 1933), especially pp. 526-530.

36. KELLY, GEORGE A., *The Psychology of Personal Constructs* (New York: W. W. Norton, 1955).

37. KLUCKHOHN, CLYDE, "The Philosophy of the Navaho Indians," in F. S. C. Northrop, Ed., *Ideological Differences and World Order* (New Haven: Yale Univ. Press, 1949).

38. ——, "Patterning as Exemplified in Navaho Culture," in Leslie Spier, *et al.*, Eds., *Language, Culture and Personality* (Menasha, Wisc., Sapir Publications Memorial Fund, 1941).

39. ——, "The Study of Culture," in Daniel Lerner and Harold D. Lasswell, Eds., *The Policy Sciences: Recent Developments in Scope and Method* (Stanford: Stanford Univ. Press, 1951), pp. 86-101.

40. —— et al., "Values and Value-Orientations in the Theory of Action: An Exploration in Definition and Classification," in Talcott Parsons and Edward H. Shils, Eds., *Toward a General Theory of Action* (Cambridge: Harvard Univ. Press, 1951), pp. 388-433.

41. KRECH, DAVID, and CRUTCHFIELD, RICHARD, *Theory and Problems of Social Psychology* (New York: McGraw-Hill, 1948), p. 184*n*.

42. KROEBER, ALFRED L., (Ed.), *Anthropology Today* (Chicago: Univ. Chicago Press, 1951).

43. LINTON, RALPH, *The Study of Man* (New York: Appleton-Century, 1956), especially pp. 422-438.

44. LOCKE, JOHN, *As Essay Concerning Human Understanding* (Alexander Fraser, Ed.), (Oxford: Clarendon, 1894), for example, p. 28.

45. LOWIE, ROBERT H., *History of Ethnological Theory* (New York: Farrar and Rinehart, 1937).

46. MACLEOD, R. B., "The Place of Phenomenological Analysis in Social Psychological Theory," in John H. Rohrer and Muzafer Sherif, Eds., *Social Psychology at the Crossroads* (New York: Harper, 1951), pp. 215-241.

47. MANNHEIM, KARL, *Ideology and Utopia* (New York: Harcourt Brace, 1936).

48. MAYO, ELTON, *The Human Problems of an Industrial Civilization* (New York: Macmillan, 1933).

49. McDOUGALL, W., *An Introduction to Social Psychology* (23rd ed.; London: Methuen, 1936), especially pp. 104-110, 137, 140, 150-196, 305, 308, 431-433.

50. MEYER, ADOLF, *The Collected Papers of Adolf Meyer* (Eunice E. Winters, Ed.) (Baltimore: Johns Hopkins Press, 1951).

51. ——, *Psychobiology, A Science of Man* (compiled and edited by Eunice E. Winters and Anna Mae Bowers) (Springfield, Ill.: Thomas, 1957), for example, p. 85.

52. MURRAY, HENRY A., *Explorations in Personality* (New York: Oxford Univ. Press, 1938).

53. —— and MORGAN, CHRISTIANA D., "A Clinical Study of Sentiments: I and II," *Genetic Psychological Monographs*, Vol. 32, 1945, pp. 3-149, 153-311.

54. NADEL, S. F., *The Foundations of Social Anthropology* (Glencoe, Ill.: Free Press, 1951), especially pp. 68-72, 305.

55. NEWCOMB, THEODORE, *Social Psychology* (New York: Dryden, 1950).

56. OPLER, MORRIS E., "Themes as Dynamic Forces in Culture," *American Journal of Sociology*, Vol. 56, 1945, pp. 198-206.
57. ———, "Some Recently Developed Concepts Relating to Culture," *Southwestern Journal of Anthropology*, Vol. 4, 1948, pp. 107-122.
58. *The Oxford English Dictionary* (Oxford: Clarendon Press, 1933), Vol. IX, pp. 470-471.
59. PARETO, VILFREDO, *The Mind and Society* (Arthur Livingston trans. and ed.) (New York: Harcourt Brace, 1935), especially Vol. II, p. 511 and Vol. III, pp. 885, 1126.
60. PARSONS, TALCOTT, *The Social System* (Glencoe, Ill.: Free Press, 1951), especially pp. 41-42.
61. ———, *The Structure of Social Action* (Glencoe, Ill.: Free Press, 1949), especially pp. 255, 672.
62. PEAR, T. H., "The Relations of Complex and Sentiment," *British Journal of Psychology*, Vol. 13, October 1922, pp. 130-140.
63. RADCLIFFE-BROWN, A. R., *The Andaman Islanders* (Glencoe, Ill.: Free Press, 1948), pp. 233-234, and 234n.
64. RIVERS, W. H. R., "The Relations of Complex and Sentiment," *British Journal of Psychology*, Vol. 13, October 1922, pp. 107-112.
65. ROETHLISBERGER, F. A., *Management and Morale* (Cambridge: Harvard Univ. Press, 1944).
66. SHAND, ALEXANDER F., "Character and Emotions," *Mind, A Quarterly Review of Psychology and Philosophy*, Vol. 5, 1896, pp. 203-226.
67. ———, "The Relations of Complex and Sentiment," *British Journal of Psychology*, Vol. 13, October 1922, pp. 123-129.
68. SMITH, ADAM, "The Theory of Moral Sentiments," *Essays, Philosophical and Literary* (London: Ward, Lock, [n.d.]).
69. SMITH, M. B., BRUNER, J. S., and WHITE, R. W., *Opinions and Personality* (New York: Wiley, 1956), especially p. 34.
70. SPENCER, HERBERT, *The Principles of Ethics* (New York: Appleton, Vol. 1, 1896, pp. 102-131, and 325-339.
71. STERNE, LAWRENCE, *Life and Opinions of Tristram Shandy Gentleman* (New York: Modern Library, 1950).
72. SULLIVAN, HARRY STACK, *The Interpersonal Theory of Psychiatry* (New York: Norton, 1953), especially pp. 62-109.
73. SWIFT, JONATHAN, *Gulliver's Travels* (New York: Rinehart, 1950).
74. TANSLEY, A. G., "The Relations of Complex and Sentiment," *British Journal of Psychology*, Vol. 13, October 1922, pp. 113-122.
75. TÖNNIES, FERDINAND, *Gemeinschaft and Gesellschaft* (trans., Charles P. Loomis as *Community and Association*) (London: Routledge and Kegan Paul, 1955), for example, pp. 53, 135, 163, 278.

Notes on the Concept of Sentiment

76. TRAUGOTT, JOHN, *Tristram Shandy's World, Sterne's Philosophical Rhetoric* (California: Univ. of California Press, 1954).

77. VOGT, E. Z., JR., *Modern Homesteaders: The Life of a Twentieth-Century Frontier Community* (Cambridge: Belknap of Harvard Univ. Press, 1955), pp. 7, 201-203.

78. WHITE, MORTON, (Ed.), *The Age of Analysis, 20th Century Philosophers* (New York: Houghton Mifflin, 1955).

79. WHITEHEAD, ALFRED NORTH, *Adventures of Ideas* (New York: Mentor, 1955), for example, pp. 17-18.

80. WHITEHORN, JOHN C., "Guide to Interviewing and Clinical Personality Study," *Archives of Neurology and Psychiatry,* Vol. 52, No. 3, September 1944.

81. WILLEY, BASIL, *The Seventeenth Century Background* (Garden City: Doubleday Anchor, 1953).

82. WILLIAMS, ROBIN M., JR., *American Society* (New York: Knopf, 1951).

83. WINICK, CHARLES, *Dictionary of Anthropology* (Ames, Iowa: Littlefield, Adams, 1958).

APPENDIX B.

Propositions

SERIES A. THE FUNDAMENTAL PROPOSITIONS
(pages 146, 160)

A1. All human beings exist in a state of psychological striving.

A2. Striving plays a part in the maintenance of an essential psychical condition.

A3. Interference with striving leads to a disturbance of the essential psychical condition.

A4. Disturbance of the essential psychical condition gives rise to disagreeable feelings.

SERIES B. PROPOSITIONS CONCERNED WITH THE EVOLUTION OF PSYCHIATRIC DISORDER *(pages 168, 177)*

B1. Given a disturbance of the essential psychical condition, a personality may adopt patterns of sentiment and action which lead to some relief from the resultant disagreeable feelings (A4), but which fail to restore adequately the essential psychical condition.

B2. Because of the relief, each response facilitates its repetition: hence there is a tendency for a personality to persist in a maladaptive direction (B1) once this has been started, leading ultimately to the occurrence of psychiatric disorders.

B3. Given a disturbance of the essential psychical conditions (A4), physiological symptoms may appear as part of a general disturbance of dynamic equilibrium in the organism.

B4. Given a disturbance of the essential psychical condition (A4), pre-existing defect in personality may contribute toward the development of psychiatric disorder and/or the appearance of physiological symptoms.

B5. Given a disturbance of the essential psychical condition (A4), sociocultural conditions have a selective influence on the emergence and persistence of malfunctional patterns of personality leading to psychiatric disorder (B1, B2, and B3).

SERIES C. PROPOSITIONS CONCERNED WITH THE NONOCCURRENCE OF PSYCHIATRIC DISORDER *(pages 169, 170, 177)*

C1. Given a disturbance of the essential psychical condition a personality may adopt patterns of sentiment which lead to relief of the resultant disagreeable feelings (A4) by means of restoration of the essential psychical condition.

C2. Because of the relief, each response facilitates its repetition, hence there is a tendency for a personality system to persist in the constructive direction (C1) once this has been started, leading to adequate, or even superior functioning.

C3. Given a resolution of the disturbance to the essential psychical condition, and a consequent improvement in dynamic equilibrium of the organism, the nonoccurrence or disappearance of psychophysiological disorders will take place.

C4. Given a disturbance of the essential psychical condition (A4), pre-existing resources of the personality may contribute toward the development of adequate or superior functioning.

C5. Given a disturbance of the essential psychical condition (A4), sociocultural conditions have a selective influence on the emergence and persistence of personality patterns which do not lead to psychiatric disorder and which may lead to superior functioning (C1, C2, and C3).

SERIES BC. COMBINED PROPOSITION *(page 170)*

BC1. The trends indicated for the development of psychiatric disorder (B1, B2, B3, and B4) and for the maintenance of health or increasing capabilities (C1, C2, C3 and C4), can occur simultaneously in the same personality.

APPENDIX B

422

SERIES D. PROPOSITIONS CONCERNING INTER-FERENCE WITH THE ESSENTIAL STRIVING SENTIMENTS *(page 157)*

D1. Given Proposition A2 certain striving sentiments may be designated as essential because maximally concerned with the maintenance of the "essential" psychical condition.

D2. Essential striving sentiments may fail in this function due to interference imposed by the environment.

D3. Essential striving sentiments may fail in this function due to defects inherent in the objects of striving.

D4. Essential striving sentiments may fail in this function due to defect, inborn or acquired, in the personality.

SERIES E. PROPOSITIONS RELATING ESSENTIAL STRIVING SENTIMENTS AND SOCIOCULTURAL ENVIRONMENT *(pages 158, 159)*

E1. Sociocultural situations which interfere with sentiments of physical security foster psychiatric disorder.

E2. Sociocultural situations which interfere with sentiments of securing sexual satisfaction foster psychiatric disorder.

E3. Sociocultural situations which interfere with sentiments bearing on the expression of hostility foster psychiatric disorder.

E4. Sociocultural situations which interfere with sentiments of giving love foster psychiatric disorder.

E5. Sociocultural situations which interfere with sentiments of securing love foster psychiatric disorder.

E6. Sociocultural situations which interfere with sentiments bearing on obtaining recognition foster psychiatric disorder.

E7. Sociocultural situations which interfere with sentiments bearing on the expression of spontaneity (positive force, creativity, volition) foster psychiatric disorder.

E8. Sociocultural situations which interfere with sentiments of orientation in the person regarding his place in society and the place of others foster psychiatric disorder.

E9. Sociocultural situations which interfere with the person's sentiments of membership in a definite human group foster psychiatric disorder.

Propositions

E10. Sociocultural situations which interfere with sentiments of belonging to a moral order and of being right in what one does foster psychiatric disorder.

SERIES F. PROPOSITION RELATING INTERPERSONAL PATTERNS AND SOCIOCULTURAL ENVIRONMENT *(page 159)*

F1. Sociocultural situations which expose a growing personality to defective role relationships foster psychiatric disorder.

SERIES G. PROPOSITIONS REGARDING THE NATURE OF SOCIETY AND CULTURE *(pages 216, 217)*

G1. Human society is composed of a network of interrelated sociocultural self-integrating units.
G2. Each self-integrating unit is an energy system and is in a constant state of performing functions upon which its existence depends.
G3. The functioning of the unit as a unit (G2) proceeds through patterns of interpersonal relationships based on the communication of shared symbols and coordinating sentiments.

SERIES H. PROPOSITIONS RELATING SOCIOCULTURAL PATTERNS TO PSYCHIATRIC DISORDER *(pages 289, 290)*

H1. Given that human society is composed of functioning self-integrating units based on patterns of interpersonal relationships which include communications, symbols, and sentiments (G series), it follows that the different functional parts of a particular unit such as associations, socioeconomic classes, and roles may have differential effects on personalities exposed to them and hence on mental health (B5, C5, D3, E series, and F).
H2. Given that human society is composed of functioning self-integrating units based on patterns of interpersonal relationships which include communication, symbols, and sentiments (G series), it follows that different units with different patterns of organization

(culture) may have differential effects on personalities exposed to them and hence on mental health (B5, C5, D2, D3, E series, and F).

H3. Given that human society is composed of functioning self-integrating units based on patterns of interpersonal relationships which include communications, symbols, and sentiments (G series), it follows that social disintegration will affect personalities in such a manner as to foster psychiatric disorder (B5, C5, D2, D3, E series, and F).

APPENDIX C.

Acknowledgements

I N GENERAL, it is our intention to make acknowledgements as these become relevant in each of the three volumes. There are, however, certain over-arching sources of debt that should be mentioned as such.

First of all is the endless patience, good temper, and cooperation that have been shown us by the people of Stirling County. Their willingness to take time and trouble to assist in the work, often at considerable personal sacrifice, has made a deep impression. It is our belief that these actions spring not so much from politeness, or friendliness to ourselves, as from a desire to contribute to the welfare of mankind, and the hope that this might in some measure be accomplished by helping in this piece of research.

The funds to carry out the work have come from four primary sources, the Milbank Memorial Fund, the Carnegie Corporation of New York, the Department of National Health and Welfare of Canada, and the Department of Public Health of the Province of Nova Scotia. To all of these we wish to express a keen sense of appreciation for the opportunity given us, and for the freedom to go ahead and do what we wanted, in the way that we wanted. We are particularly sensible of the prolonged and sustained nature of the support as well as its extent. These sources are not, however, the authors, owners, publishers, or proprietors of the volumes, and are not to be understood as approving by virtue of their grants any of the statements made or views expressed therein.

In addition to the four main grants, we also received, in the early, pilot study phase, a number of short-term grants that were most helpful in enabling us to meet special needs. Appreciation is therefore expressed to the American Philosophical Society, Cornell University, the Rockefeller Foundation, and the Wenner-Gren Foundation for Anthropological Research.

The study has been carried out in collaboration with Dalhousie and Acadia Universities whose continuous assistance in numerous aspects of the research has been a fundamental resource in the accomplishment of many of our endeavors. Invaluable help has also been given by the Faculté des Sciences Sociales of the Université Laval.

During all phases of the work over the last ten years we have leaned heavily on consultants. This was made necessary by the interdisciplinary character of the Study, by the desire to have our ideas evaluated by well-informed residents of Stirling County, and by the need for both guidance and backing from government and university authorities. It is a pleasure, consequently, to take this occasion to express thanks to the following people who have aided us in one or more of the above ways. Our faults should not, of course, be laid at their door.

Vian Andrews,* Basil Belliveau, Pierre Belliveau, Douglas G. Black, Bernard Blackford,* Donald S. Brennen, Urie Bronfenbrenner, Victor Cardoza, Medric Comeau, Oskar Diethelm, J. K. Galbraith, Lawrence Hersey, Robert O. Jones, Watson Kirkconnell, Philippe H. Le Blanc, Georges-Henri Lévesque, O.P., Douglas E. Lewis, Edward Llewellyn-Thomas, J. Cameron MacDonald, Clyde Marshall, John R. McCleave, Herbert J. Melanson, H. J. Pothier, F. C. Purdy, Peter F. Regan, III, Thomas A. C. Rennie,* J. S. Robertson, Edward A. Suchman, Edith M. Wallis, Robin M. Williams, Jr., Theodore P. Wright.

Particular mention should be made of personal interest taken by the late Edmund Ezra Day, President and then Chancellor of Cornell University, and the late Angus MacDonald, Premier of Nova Scotia.

The present volume had its beginnings in a faculty seminar held at Cornell during 1950 and 1951. Many of the ideas presented have been lifted directly from this interchange. The group was composed of:

Urie Bronfenbrenner, John P. Dean,* Walter T. Federer, James J. Gibson, Dorothea C. Leighton, Allister M. Macmillan,* William Magill, Robert B. MacLeod, Charles Mertens de Wilmars, Norman S. Moore, Seymour Parker, Robert N. Rapoport, Stephen A. Richardson,

* Deceased.

Lauriston Sharp, Robert J. Smith, Edward A. Suchman, Marc-Adélard Tremblay, Robin M. Williams, Jr., William F. Whyte.

Since that time there have been repeated revisions in the frame of reference that have benefited from the criticisms of the Stirling County Staff. Comments by Charles C. Hughes, Jane M. Hughes, Dorothea C. Leighton, Allister M. Macmillan,* Robert N. Rapoport, and Marc-Adélard Tremblay have been particularly helpful.

A fellowship at the Center for Advanced Study in the Behavioral Sciences during the academic year of 1957–1958 gave opportunity for making a final revision. Of major importance at the Center was the securing of reactions and thoughts from the other Fellows who were present at that time, and also from the staff. Those who gave generously of their help included:

Ethel M. Albert, John Bowlby, John Clausen, John P. Gilbert, Neal Gross, Ward Goodenough, Clarence Morris, Talcott Parsons, Philip Rieff, Charles Savage, Guy E. Swanson, John W. Tukey, Ralph W. Tyler, Charles Wagley.

For detailed reading of the manuscript and many helpful suggestions appreciation is expressed to Oskar Diethelm and Edmund Volkart.

Jane M. Hughes has carried the main load as research associate in the development of this volume. Many aspects of the relevant literature have also been reviewed by Charles C. Hughes. For all of this I am heavily indebted.

Endpaper photographs are used through the courtesy of John Collier, Jr. (who supplied the photographs for both front endpapers and the right-hand back endpaper) and D. C. MacNutt (who supplied the photograph for the left-hand back endpaper).

Special thanks are also due Blanche McDonald Beeler, Ruth O. Kent, Shirley T. Lueder, Kazuko S. Smith, Jean Vernon, Joan S. Warmbrunn, and Shirley Watkins, who have worked long and painstakingly in the preparation of the manuscript.

Additional acknowledgements with regard to particular points have been made in the course of the book.

In the pages that follow, staff members, full or part time, are listed alphabetically. The nature of their contributions is indicated by the phase numbers, as noted in the Introduction to the Stirling County Study (p. 7). These refer to I. The Pilot Study; II. Planning; III. Field Operations; IV. Analysis; and V. Reporting.

* deceased.

G. A. W. Angus (Psychiatry), Psychiatric Unit, Phase III, Director of the Clinic, 1958 ——.

Roderick A. Armstrong (Psychiatry), Psychiatric Unit, Phase III, Psychiatrist in the Clinic.

Jane Brant (Administration), Administrative Assistant, Phase II, 1951.

Rosalind Dymond Cartwright (Sociology), Phase I, 1948.

Norman A. Chance (Anthropology), Social Science Unit, Phases III and IV, 1954–1957.

Eric J. Cleveland (Psychiatry), Psychiatric Unit, Phases III, IV, and V, Director of the Clinic, 1953–1955.

Regina Buckley Cohen (Mathematics), Psychological Screening Unit, Phase IV, 1957–1958.

Jessie L. Cohen (Sociology), Statistical analysis, Phase IV, 1952–1955.

John Collier, Jr. (Photography), Social Science Unit, Phases I and III, 1950–1952.

Carol Coops (Interviewing), Psychological Screening Unit, Phase III, 1956.

Elaine Cumming (Sociology), Psychiatric Unit, Phase IV, Social Scientist in the Clinic, 1955–1956.

John Cumming (Psychiatry), Psychiatric Unit, Phase III, Psychiatrist in the Clinic, 1955, Director of the Clinic, 1956.

Emmet Currie (Interviewing), Psychiatric Unit, Phase III, 1957.

Herbert N. Davy (Psychiatry), Psychiatric Unit, Phase III, Director of the Clinic, 1957–1958.

Bessie Dalrymple (Interviewing), Psychiatric Unit, Phase III, 1954–1957.

J. Alphonse Deveau (Sociology), Social Science Unit, Phases III and IV, 1952–1956.

Helen Snow Dickson (Interviewing), Psychological Screening Unit, Phase III, 1951.

Bruce P. Dohrenwend (Social Psychology), Social Scientist in charge of statistical analysis, Social Science Unit, statistical advisor, Psychological Screening Unit and Psychiatric Unit, Phases IV and V, 1954–1957.

Charles-F. Dumas (Psychiatry), Psychiatric Unit, Phase III, Psychiatrist in the Clinic, 1952–1953.

William R. Dymond (Economics), Phase I, 1948.

Judith C. Easton (Interviewing), Psychological Screening Unit, Phase III, 1956.

Marjorie Fahrig (Psychology), Psychiatric Unit, Phase III, Psychologist in the Clinic, 1951–1952.

Gerald A. Fortin (Sociology), Social Science Unit, Phase III, 1952, Phase IV, 1954–1955.

TERESE FORTIN (Interviewing), Social Science Unit, Phase III, 1952.

MARION E. GRANT (Psychology), Psychiatric Unit, Phase III, 1955.

JOHN O. GODDEN (Internal Medicine), Psychiatric Unit, Phase IV, 1957.

EMILE GOSSELIN (Sociology), Phase I, 1950; Consultant in Phase II; Social Science Unit, Phase III, 1951, 1952, and 1954; A principal consultant in Phase IV, 1952 ——.

CHRISTOPHER HAFFNER (Psychiatry), Psychiatric Unit, Phase III, Director of the Clinic, 1957.

LUCE JEAN HAFFNER (Social Work), Psychiatric Unit, Phase III, 1952, and Phase IV, 1957, Social worker in the Clinic.

JOHN S. HARDING (Social Psychology), Psychiatric Unit, Consultant in Phase IV, 1956–1958; Phase IV and V, 1958 ——.

BERNARD HEBERT (Psychology), Psychiatric Unit, Phase III, 1953–1957; Psychologist in the Clinic, 1953–1956; Administrator of the Clinic, 1956–1957.

KATHRYN K. HOLLENBACH (Administration), Administrative Assistant, Phase II, 1951.

CHARLES C. HUGHES (Anthropology), Social Science Unit, Phase III, 1952; Phase IV, 1952–1954; Phase V, 1955–1958; Director of the Social Science Unit, 1956–1958; Assistant Director of the Stirling County Study, 1958 ——.

JANE M. HUGHES (Anthropology), Administrative Assistant 1951–1954 and 1955; Social Science Unit, Phase III, 1952, Psychiatric Unit, Phase III, 1952, Phases IV and V, 1956 ——; Assistant to the Director, 1956 ——.

WILLIAM A. JENKINS (Economics), Affiliated with the Social Science Unit, Agricultural consultant in Phases III and IV, 1954 ——.

ALVIN KAPLAN (Sociology), Phase II, 1949.

RUTH O. KENT (Administration), Administrative Assistant, Phase IV and V, 1956 ——.

ELIZABETH KERR-WILSON (Social Work), Psychiatric Unit, Phase III, Social Worker in the Clinic, 1956–1957.

BEATRICE E. LANDMAN (Social Work), Psychiatric Clinic, Phase III, 1952–1953.

GOTTFRIED O. LANG (Anthropology), Phase IV, 1953.

ALEXANDER H. LEIGHTON (Psychiatry and Anthropology), Phases I, II, III, IV and V, Director of the Stirling County Study, 1948.

DOROTHEA C. LEIGHTON (Psychiatry and Anthropology), Phase I, 1948 and 1950, Phase II, 1951–1952; Psychiatric Unit, Phase III, 1952–1953; In charge of Psychiatric epidemiology, Phase IV and V, 1954 ——.

ALICE L. LONGAKER (Anthropology), Administrative Assistant in Psychiatric Clinic, 1955–1956, Psychiatric Unit, Phases III, IV and V, 1956 —.

WILLIAM D. LONGAKER (Psychiatry), Psychiatric Unit, Phase III; Psychiatrist in the Clinic, 1953–1956; Director of the Clinic, 1956; Phases IV and V, 1955 —.

DOROTHY LOWELL (Interviewing), Social Science Unit, Phase III, 1952.

EDGAR LOWELL (Psychology), Social Science Unit, Phase III, 1952; Phase IV, 1953–1955.

SHEILA MacDONALD (Interviewing), Psychological Screening Unit, Phase III, 1951.

ADA MacLEOD (Administration), Administrative Secretary, 1954–1955.

ALLISTER M. MACMILLAN * (Social Psychology), Phase I, 1949–1950; Phase II, 1951–1952; Director of Psychological Screening Unit, 1951–1958; Phases III, IV and V, Deputy Director of the Stirling County Study, 1953–1958.

CORAL MACMILLAN (Registered Nurse), Psychiatric Unit, Phase IV, 1956.

DAVID B. MACKLIN (Social Psychology), Social Science Analyst, Assisted in statistical analysis, Social Science Unit, Psychological Screening Unit and Psychiatric Unit, Phases IV and V, 1957 —.

WILLIAM MAGILL (Sociology), Phase II, 1950–1951; Social Science Unit, Phase III, 1951–1952.

PAULINE MAHAR (Sociology), Psychiatric Unit, Phase IV, 1956–1957.

ANNE McCREARY (Interviewing), Social Science Unit, Phase III, 1952.

GARNET E. McCREARY * (Statistics), Statistical Analyst, Phase II, 1951–1952; Social Science Unit, Phase III, 1952; Social Science Unit, Psychological Screening Unit, and Psychiatric Unit, Phase IV, 1952–1955.

EDGAR B. McKAY (History), Affiliated with Social Science Unit, Phases III and IV, 1954 —.

JOHN VINCENT MARTIN, O.S.B. (Sociology), Social Science Unit, Phase III, 1951.

WILLIAM C. MARTIN * (Anthropology), Phase I, 1950.

GORDON R. MASON (Interviewing), Psychological Screening Unit, Phase III, 1951; Social Science Unit, Phase III, 1952; Psychiatric Unit, Phase III, 1952–1957.

PAULINE G. MELHORN (Interviewing), Psychological Screening Unit, Phase III, 1951.

CHARLES MORRIS (Interviewing), Psychological Screening Unit, Phase III, 1951.

* Deceased.

PATRICIA MORRISON (Interviewing), Psychological Screening Unit, Phase III, 1956.

J. FRASER NICHOLSON (Psychiatry), Psychological Screening Unit, Phase III, 1951, Consultant in Phase IV, 1953.

HELEN OLMSTEAD (Interviewing), Psychiatric Unit, Phase III, 1957.

JAMES OLMSTEAD (Interviewing), Psychiatric Unit, Phase III, 1957.

HILDA PARKER (Interviewing), Social Science Unit, Psychiatric Unit, Phase III, 1952.

SEYMOUR PARKER (Anthropology), Social Science Unit, Phase III, 1951–1952; Phase IV, 1952–1953; Consultant, Phase IV, 1955.

ROBERT N. RAPOPORT (Anthropology), Phase II, 1950–1951; Director of Social Science Unit, Phases III and IV, 1951–1953; A principal consultant in Phases IV and V, 1952 ——.

KENNETH RAWNSLEY (Psychiatry), Psychiatric Unit, Phase III, Psychiatrist in the Clinic, 1956.

LOUISE G. RICHARDS (Social Psychology), Psychiatric Unit, Phase IV, 1957.

STEPHEN A. RICHARDSON (Human Relations), Phase I, 1950; Phase II, 1951.

THERESA A. ROBICHEAU (Interviewing), Psychiatric Unit, Phase III, 1957.

AUDREY ROPER (Administration), Administrative Assistant in the Psychiatric Clinic, 1952–1953.

GEORGE ROPER (Psychology), Psychological Screening Unit, Phase III, 1951; Psychiatric Unit, Phase III, Social Worker in the Clinic, 1952–1953.

JANINE CHAPPAT ROSENZWEIG (Anthropology), Phase I, 1949.

MARK R. ROSENZWEIG (Psychology), Phase I, 1949.

JANICE A. ROSS (Psychology), Social Science Unit, Phase III, 1952; Psychiatric Unit, Phases III and IV, Social Worker in the Clinic, 1953–1956.

WILLIAM C. SAYRES (Anthropology), Phase I, 1950.

RICHARD SCHWARTZ (Statistics), Social Science Unit, Phase IV, 1953–1954.

ARNOLD G. SIMMEL (Sociology), Psychological Screening Unit, Phase IV, 1955–1957.

WILLIAM E. SINCLAIR (Interviewing), Psychological Screening Unit, Phase III, 1951.

ANN HAASE SINGLETON (Social Work), Psychiatric Unit, Phase III, Social Worker in the Clinic, 1953.

PATRICIA AHERN SMITH (Interviewing), Psychological Screening Unit, Phase III, 1951.

NORRIS P. SMITH (Anthropology), Phase I, 1949.

ROBERT J. SMITH (Anthropology), Phase I, 1949–1950, Phase II, 1951.

MARC-ADÉLARD TREMBLAY (Anthropology), Phase I, 1950; Phase II, 1951; Social Science Unit, Phase III, 1951–1956; Director of Social Science Unit, Phase IV, 1953–1956, A principal consultant, Phase V, 1956 ——.

JAMES S. TYHURST (Psychiatry), Phase II, 1951; Psychiatric Unit, Phase III, Director of Psychiatric Clinic, 1951–1953.

LIBUSE TYHURST (Psychiatry), Phase III, Psychiatrist in the Clinic, 1951–1953.

LIONEL VALLÉE (Social Work), Psychiatric Unit, Phase III, Social Worker in the Clinic, 1957 ——.

RENÉE VALLÉE (Social Work), Psychiatric Unit, Phase III, Social Worker in the Clinic, 1957 ——.

JOAN VENNER (Interviewing), Psychological Screening Unit, Phase III, 1957.

JEAN VERNON (Administration), Administrative Assistant in the Psychiatric Clinic, 1953–1955.

W. H. D. VERNON (Psychology), Consultant in Phase I, 1949–1950; Consultant in Phase II, 1951; Social Science Unit, Phase III, 1952; Senior Psychologist and Clinic Administrator, 1953–1955; Consultant in Phase IV, 1952 ——.

ELIZABETH MARSH WANNINKHOF (Child Psychology), Social Science Unit, Phase III, 1951–1952.

MALCOLM WILLISON (Sociology), Social Science Unit, Phase III, 1955; Phase IV, 1956–1957.

CAROLINE WINGET (Interviewing), Social Science Unit, Phase III, 1952.

JOHN A. WINGET (Sociology), Social Science Unit, Phase III, Assistant Social Science Field Director, 1952.

LIONEL WISHNEFF (Sociology), Statistical analysis, Phase IV, 1955–1956.

TOSHIO YATSUSHIRO (Anthropology), Social Science Unit and Psychiatric Unit, Phase IV, 1954–1955 and 1957.

FRANK W. YOUNG (Anthropology), Social Science Unit, Phase III, 1954–1956; Phases IV and V, 1956–1957.

In addition, approximately 123 clerical, stenographic, and statistical assistants have participated in the Study. During a characteristic year such staff have numbered twenty.

APPENDIX D.

Publications Based on the Stirling County Study

The following list is arranged chronologically and alphabetized by author within each year:

ALEXANDER H. LEIGHTON, "A Proposal for Research in the Epidemiology of Psychiatric Disorders," in *Epidemiology of Mental Disorders* (New York: Milbank Memorial Fund, 1950).

ALEXANDER H. LEIGHTON, "The Stirling County Study," in *The Interrelations Between the Social Environment and Psychiatric Disorders* (New York: Milbank Memorial Fund, 1952).

ALLISTER M. MACMILLAN and ALEXANDER H. LEIGHTON, "People of the Hinterland, Community Interrelations in a Maritime Province of Canada," in Edward H. Spicer (Ed.), *Human Problems in Technological Change* (New York: Russell Sage Foundation, 1952).

STEPHEN A. RICHARDSON, "Technological Change: Some Effects on Three Canadian Fishing Villages," *Human Organization*, Vol. 11 no. 3, 1952.

ALEXANDER H. LEIGHTON, "Psychiatric Disorder and Social Environment," *Psychiatry, Journal for the Study of Interpersonal Processes*, Vol. 18, no. 4, 1955.

ALLISTER M. MACMILLAN, "Sub-Cultural Change: Discussion of a Social Problem," *Bulletin, Maritime Psychological Association*, Spring, 1955.

BERNARD HÉBERT, "Facteurs sociaux et santé mentale (Stirling County Study)," *Contributions à l'étude des sciences de l'homme*, No. 3, 1956.

DOROTHEA C. LEIGHTON, "The Distribution of Psychiatric Symptoms in a Small Town," *The American Journal of Psychiatry*, Vol. 112, no. 9, 1956.

WILLIAM C. SAYRES, *Sammy Lewis, The Life History of a Young Micmac*, (New Haven: Compass, 1956).

E. J. CLEVELAND and W. D. LONGAKER, "Neurotic Patterns in the Family," in *Explorations in Social Psychiatry* (New York: Basic Books, 1957).

JOHN COLLIER, JR., "Photography in Anthropology: A Report on Two Experiments," *American Anthropologist,* Vol. 59, no. 5, 1957.

BRUCE P. DOHRENWEND, "The Stirling County Study, A Research Program on Relations Between Sociocultural Factors and Mental Illness, *The American Psychologist,* Vol. 12, no. 2, 1957.

ALEXANDER H. LEIGHTON, "The Annual Dinner" (The Stirling County Study) in *Programs for Community Mental Health* (New York: Milbank Memorial Fund, 1957).

ALEXANDER H. LEIGHTON and ALICE LONGAKER, "The Psychiatric Clinic as a Community Innovation," in *Explorations in Social Psychiatry* (New York: Basic Books, 1957).

DOROTHEA C. LEIGHTON, "Community Study of Mental Health: Preliminary Findings on the Distribution of Persons with Symptoms of Psychiatric Significance in Relation to Social Environment," in *The Nature and Transmission of the Genetic and Cultural Characteristics of Human Populations* (New York: Milbank Memorial Fund, 1957).

ALLISTER M. MACMILLAN, "Field Relations in Community Research," *Bulletin, Maritime Psychological Association,* Spring, 1957.

ALLISTER M. MACMILLAN, "The Health Opinion Survey: Technique for Estimating Prevalence of Psychoneurotic and Related Types of Disorder in Communities," *Psychological Reports,* Monograph Supplement 7, 1957.

MARC-ADÉLARD TREMBLAY, "The Key Informant Technique: A Nonethnographic Application," *American Anthropologist,* Vol. 59, no. 4, 1957.

ALEXANDER H. LEIGHTON, "Mental Illness and Acculturation," in IAGO GALDSTON (Ed.), *Medicine and Anthropology* (New York: Internat. Univ. Press, 1959).

ALEXANDER H. LEIGHTON, "The Stirling County Study, Some Notes on Concepts and Methods," in Paul H. Hoch and Joseph Zubin (Eds.), *Epidemiology of Mental Disorders,* Proceedings of the Annual Symposium of the American Psychopathological Association, February 1959, (New York: Grune and Stratton, in press).

ALLISTER M. MACMILLAN, "A Survey Technique for Estimating the Prevalence of Psychoneurotic and Related Types of Disorders in Communities," in Benjamin Pasamanick (Ed.), *Epidemiology of Mental Disorder* (Washington, D.C.: American Association for the Advancement of Science, 1959).

THESES PRESENTED TO THE FACULTY OF THE
GRADUATE SCHOOL OF CORNELL UNIVERSITY

For the degree of Doctor of Philosophy:

ALLISTER MILES MACMILLAN, "Explorations in Rural Community Health with Particular Reference to Psycho-physiological Symptoms," September, 1954.

MARC-ADÉLARD TREMBLAY, "The Acadians of Portsmouth: A Study in Culture Change," September, 1954.

SEYMOUR PARKER, "Union Participation: A Study in Culture and Personality," February, 1955.

WILLIAM HENRY DALTON VERNON, "A Psychological Study of Thirty Residents of a Small Town," June, 1957.

FRANK WILBUR YOUNG, "Integration and Urban Influence: A Study of Two Canadian Fishing Villages Undergoing a Natural Experiment," June, 1957.

NORMAN ALLEE CHANCE, "Portsmouth: The Study of a Bi-Cultural Community under Stress," September, 1957.

For the degree of Master of Arts:

SYLVIA VERIN MANGALAM, "Multicultural Affiliations and Sentiment Structure in Children," September, 1957.

THESIS PRESENTED TO THE DEPARTMENT OF
PSYCHOLOGY OF ACADIA UNIVERSITY

For the degree of Master of Arts:

GEORGE E. ROPER, "Study of the Use of the Chicago Non-Verbal Examination in a Rural Psychiatric Clinic," August, 1952.

THESIS PRESENTED TO THE DEPARTMENT OF
SOCIAL SCIENCES OF LAVAL UNIVERSITY

For the degree of Master of Arts:

JEAN ALPHONSE DEVEAU, "Patterns of Acculturation of Acadian-Descent People in Bristol," August, 1953.

PERMISSIONS

The author extends grateful acknowledgement to the following publishers and individuals for permission to quote from the material cited:

AMERICAN JOURNAL OF HUMAN GENETICS: Robert M. Stecher, "Identical Twins Discordant for Interventricular Septal Defect and Absent Radius and Thumb," Vol. 9, no. 3, September, 1957.

AMERICAN JOURNAL OF PSYCHIATRY and W. LLOYD WARNER: W. Lloyd Warner, "The Society, The Individual, and His Mental Disorders," *American Journal of Psychiatry*, Vol. 94, no. 2, September, 1937.

AMERICAN PSYCHIATRIC ASSOCIATION: *A Psychiatric Glossary*, 1957.

THE CLARENDON PRESS: Jose Ortega y Gasset, *Toward a Philosophy of History*, W. W. Norton & Company, Inc., 1941.

J. & A. CHURCHILL LTD.: F. R. Winton and L. E. Bayliss, *Human Physiology*, 4th ed., Little, Brown & Co., 1955.

COLUMBIA UNIVERSITY PRESS: Abram Kardiner, *The Psychological Frontiers of Society*, Foreword by Ralph Linton, 1945; Clyde Kluckhohn and William H. Kelly, "The Concept of Culture," in *The Science of Man in the World Crisis*, edited by Ralph Linton, 1945.

THOMAS Y. CROWELL CO.: Stuart A. Queen, Walter B. Bodenhofer, and Ernest B. Harper, *Social Organization and Disorganization*, 1935.

THE GILMARY SOCIETY: *The Catholic Encyclopedia, an International Work of Reference on the Constitution, Doctrine, Discipline, and History of the Catholic Church*, Robert Appleton Co., 1919.

PAUL B. HOEBER, INC., and JAMES S. BROWNING: James S. Browning and John H. Houseworth, "Development of New Symptoms Following Medical and Surgical Treatment for Duodenal Ulcer," *Psychosomatic Medicine*, Vol. XV, no. 4, 1953.

McGraw-Hill Book Company, Inc.: Kurt Lewin, *Principles of Topological Psychology*, translated by Fritz and Grace Heider, 1936.

G. & C. Merriam Company: *Webster's New International Dictionary, Second Edition*, copyright 1934, 1939, 1945, 1950, 1953, 1954, 1957, 1959, by G. & C. Merriam Company, publishers of Merriam-Webster Dictionaries.

Milbank Memorial Fund: Theodosius Dobzhansky, "The Biological Concept of Heredity as Applied to Man," in *The Nature and Transmission of the Genetic and Cultural Characteristics of Human Populations*, 1957.

Oxford University Press, Inc.: David Henderson and R. D. Gillespie, *Text-book of Psychiatry*, 1950.

Peabody Museum of Archaeology and Ethnology: A. L. Kroeber and Clyde Kluckhohn, *Culture, a Critical Review of Concepts and Definitions*, Peabody Museum Papers, Vol. XLVII, no. 1, 1952.

Penguin Books, Inc., and Geoffrey Gorer: Geoffrey Gorer, "The Concept of National Character," in Clyde Kluckhohn and Henry A. Murray, *Personality in Nature, Society, and Culture*, Alfred A. Knopf, Inc., 1956 (originally published in *Science News*, no. 18, copyright 1950).

Random House Inc.: Donald K. Adams, *The Anatomy of Personality*, Doubleday and Company, 1954.

The Ronald Press Company: Amos H. Hawley, *Human Ecology, a Theory of Social Structure*, 1950.

Charles Scribner's Sons: Charles H. Cooley, *Social Process*, 1918.

Charles C Thomas, Publisher, and Oskar Diethelm: Oskar Diethelm, *Treatment in Psychiatry*, 1955; Charles C Thomas, Publisher, and Ralph Linton: Ralph Linton, *Culture and Mental Disorders*, 1956.

C. A. Watts & Company, Ltd.: Ludwig von Bertalanffy, *Problems of Life, an Evaluation of Modern Biological Thought*, 1952.

John Wiley & Sons, Inc.: M. Brewster Smith, Jerome S. Bruner, and Robert W. White, *Opinions and Personality*, 1956.

INDEX

Aberle, D. F., 274
"abnormal" vs. "normal" behavior, 239
abstraction, 231, 234; interference principle in, 137; levels of, 10-11, 297
acculturation, meaning of, 340
Adams, Donald, 269-270
adaptation, 25, 348-349
Adler, Alfred, 179
affect, 20, 23, 26, 73, 252-253, 261; in case studies, 379; defined, 19; mobilization of sentiment and, 411; psychiatric disorders involving, 106, 166; sentiment as synonym for, 409
African tribes, cultural units in, 293-294
age, as factor in psychiatric disorders, 386
age-mates, 72, 156
aggression, 166; in infancy and childhood, 60; love deprivation and, 68; object substitution and, 161; as universal symptom pattern, 369
aging, 83; brain disorder and, 121; in psychiatric disorders, 144-145
alcohol: essential psychical condition and, 164; as "sentiment," 238
alcoholism, 104-105, 143-144, 165, 359; in Model community, 308, 312; psychological stress and, 50-51; unstable sentiments in, 163
Allport, Gordon W., 183, 220, 267, 408
ambivalence, 407
American Psychiatric Association, 125-126, 354-355, 387; Manual of, 368, 373
amnesia, 102-103; in Collection, 312
anabolism, 22, 139
anal stage, 60

Anderson, Walfred A., 296
Angel, Ernest, 180
Angell, Robert C., 345
anger, 101, 165, 334
Angyal, Andras, 217
anthropology: child rearing and, 91; culture defined in, 297
anticipation, 25, 247
anxiety, 75-76, 94, 112, 139, 165, 173; compensation in, 114; defined, 99, 126; vs. fear, 126; "inspiring" of, by mother, 69-70; personality structure and, 231
anxiety attack, 32-33, 35, 37ff., 39-40, 41, 356; vs. anxiety reaction, 93; conflicting sentiments in, 261; defined, 99; heart disease and, 359; patterning of, 173
anxiety neurosis, 65-66; fear as cause of, 69; interpersonal relationships in, 72; sociocultural factors in, 72; substitutability of symptoms and, 51
anxiety reaction, 62, 78; vs. anxiety attack, 93; defined, 99
approximation(s): clarification and, 12; first, 115; level of, in cultural analysis, 286; in psychiatric diagnosis, 378; in social disintegration, 331, 336; successive, 12, 234, 278
Arensberg, Conrad M., 295
arteriosclerosis, 96, 121, 168
Asch, Solomon E., 272, 406-407
association, principle of, 397-398
associations, 291, 293; in community unit, 203, 216; as disintegration indicators, 318; shared sentiments and, 255

Index

asthma, 105-106, 167; factors in, 39
attitude: defined, 408; sentiment and, 395
autism, 166, 312

baldness, 53, 112
barbiturate addiction, 104
Barnes, Harry Elmer, 220
Barton, Walter E., 273
basic urge(s), 23, 27, 61, 166, 238, 252-253, 261; blocking of, 61 (see also blocking; interference); in case studies, 379; in Collection, 311; community system and, 198; community sub-patterns and, 205; conflict in, 63-64, 74; development of, 60, 68; function of, 26; instincts and, 63, 230; inter-ference and (see interference); lack of, 154-155; life-story and, 61; personality and, 19-20, 228; sentiments and, 233; shared sentiments and, 206-207; striv-ing and, 137, 149; "strong" and "weak," 140; variation in, 73
Bayless, L. E., 85, 346
Becker, Howard, 220, 347
Beckner, Morton, 347
behavior: evaluations of through signs and tests, 374; hierarchical organiza-tion of, 270-271; integration levels in, 17; "normal" vs. "abnormal," 239; shared patterns of, 10; systematic theory of, 231
behavior patterns, 148, 366, 371
belief, concept of, 395, 411
Bellak, Leopold, 180, 182
belonging, sense of, 148, 202
Benedict, Paul K., 87
Benedict, Ruth, 90, 344-345
benign environment, 177-178, 191, 278, 285, 307, 329
bereavement, 150
Bergson, Henri, 402
Berreman, Gerald, 337
Bertalanffy, Ludwig von, 219, 224, 295
biological system, vs. psychic energy, 22
birth process, 57, 60
birth trauma, interference principle and, 137 (see also interference; trauma; traumata)
Blake, Robert R., 182
Bleuler, Eugen, 128, 353
Bloch, Herbert A., 343
blocking, in childhood, 137; see also interference; striving
blood vessels, changes in, 167
Blum, Gerald S., 86
Blumer, Herbert, 343
Bodenhafer, B., 341
bodily injury, in psychological life ex-perience, 57
borderline states, 334
Borgotta, Edgar F., 267
Boulding, Kenneth V., 219-220
Bowers, Anna Mae, 219, 269

Bowlby, John, 88
brain, structure of, 222
brain disease, 167-168
brain disorder, 110-111, 121-122, 353
brain syndromes, 94, 386; in Collection, 312; in Model community, 309
Breuer, Joseph, 127
Brinton, Crane, 36
broken homes, 318, 327, 329
Bronfenbrenner, Urie, 182
Broom, Leonard, 267, 343
Brown, Lawrence G., 343
Browning, James S., 81
Bruner, Jerome S., 271, 408
Bryson, L., 219
Bucy, Paul C., 128
Burrows, Edwin G., 413
Burton, Maurice, 186
"busyness," as escape from anxiety, 75-76

Cameron, Norman, 89, 186
case, defined, 353-355
case studies, 352-386; as personality studies, 379; sources of data in, 362-374; statistical testing in, 382; verifi-cation in, 381
Cattell, R. B., 406
causal relationships, 193-194, 304, 332, 359, 361
cell colonies, 199-200
central nervous system, 57, 333
change, capacity for, 198, 216
Chauncey, Gordon F., 33
Chiason, Bernie, 35
child development, psychodynamics of, 68, 191-192
childhood: defective experience in, 159; essential psychical condition in, 166; mental deficiency and, 120; noxious influence in, 283; origin of psychi-atric disorders in, 74, 166; psycholog-ical damage in, 63; psychological factors in, 79
childhood schizophrenia, 110
child rearing, 68
class, sociocultural patterns of, 204, 216, 256, 274; sentiment system and, 210 (see also socioeconomic classes)
Clausen, John A., 5, 126, 129, 187, 219, 271, 273, 387
Cleghorn, R. A., 82, 179, 186
Cleveland, E. J., 274-275
clinic, see psychiatric clinic
clinical psychiatry, 81, 268
clinical psychology, 79; core of, 59-60
clinical study, vs. epidemiological, 352, 367
clusterings, in sociocultural unit, 203
cognition, 23, 140, 252-253, 261; in case studies, 379; in Collection, 311; faulty, and mental retardation, 26; as human characteristic, 19; loss of, in brain damage, 155; modification of uncon-

cognition (cont'd)
scious process by, 241; personality and, 228; psychiatric disorders and, 166; striving as characteristic of, 270; unconscious, 21; variation in, 73
cognitive-affective constructs, 61, 407
Cohen, Albert K., 274, 343
Coindreau, Dr. Auguste, 35 ff.
Colby, Kenneth Mark, 181
Coleridge, Samuel Taylor, 399
colitis, 105
Collection, in community area, 306, 310-312
communication: absence of in Collection, 311; in community unit, 216; forms of, 206; maintenance of, 255; shared sentiments in, 207-210, 253; sociocultural categories and, 289-290; in sociocultural unit, 205-216; symbols and, 206; technological advances in, 215; weak, 319
community, 196-206; organic conception of, 296-297; as sociocultural unit, 251 (see also community unit)
community functioning, psychiatric disorder and, 287
community leaders, case studies with, 364 (see also leadership-followership)
community resources, therapeutic, 177
community studies, 295, 382
community unit, 279-290; as functioning whole, 292; individual experience and, 330; integration in, 200; integration-disintegration balance in, 314-315; "Model" vs. "Collection" in, 306-312; sentiment changes and, 213-215; symptom patterns in, 369
compensation, 112-114, 147
complex, concept of, 395
concepts, frame of reference and, 15-16
conceptualization, 114, 277
conceptual outlook, personality and, 16-28
concreteness, misplaced, 71, 88-89
conditioned reflex, 272
conflict: basic urges and, 68; potential, in personality system, 22; psychic processes and, 230 (see also interference)
congenital defects, 85-86
consciousness: as "mental health," 249; personality and, 20-21; symbols and sentiments in, 237
"consensus," 341, 371-372
conversion reaction, 94, 103
Cooley, Charles H., 89, 268, 410
coordination: in community unit, 216; in sociocultural unit, 205-216
Cornell Index, 374
Cornell University, 6
coronary occlusion, 44, 185
cortex, 222, 273
Cottrell, Leonard S., Jr., 89, 267, 343

creativity: as community need, 198; as striving sentiment, 148
crime, as disintegration indication, 319
cross-section-of-the-moment, in personality development, 25, 232-233, 245, 258-259, 261, 277, 293-295, 326, 379
Crutchfield, Richard, 408
Cuber, John F., 342
cultural analysis, 285
cultural contrast, 283, 293-294
cultural differences, 203-204, 281
cultural disintegration, 288, 321
cultural groups: in community unit, 203; sentiment system and, 210
cultural integrity, 288
cultural systems, in community unit, 204, 216
culture: absence of in Collection, 310; as basis for typing communities, 281; communication and, 206; defined, 297-298; functional effectiveness of, 286; six main groups of, 297
Cumming, Elaine, 387
Cumming, John, 387
"current circumstances," in psychiatric disorder, 49, 62
current environment, reaction to, 51, 62 (see also environment)
Cuvier, Baron Georges Leopold, 23

Davis, A. K., 274
Davis, Kingsley, 267, 295, 410
daydreams, object substitution through, 164-165
Dean, John P., 388
death wishes, rejection and, 70
defense mechanisms, 61, 239
delinquency, 165, 274; as disintegration indicator, 319
delirium, 111, 121
democracy, civil service and, 31
dependency conflict, 74
depression, 165-166, 334; pattern quality and, 370; psychotic, 106-107
depressive reaction, 94, 101 (see also manic-depressive psychoses)
desire, 248
Deutsch, Felix, 186
deviance, cultural definition of, 368
Dewey, John, 408
diagnosis: defined, 355-358; "labeling" in, 354; probability sampling and, 365-366; in psychiatric disorders, 80; supplementation in, 376 (see also symptom patterns; symptoms)
diagnostic interviews, 364 (see also psychiatric interview)
diarrhea, 176; fear and, 50
dietary deficiency, personality disorders and, 57-58, 333
Diethelm, Oskar, 268, 360, 387
diphtheria, 31, 213

disintegration: idea represented by, 337; vs. "disorganization," 339-343; social (see social disintegration)

disorder, psychiatric (see psychiatric disorder)

disorganization: vs. disintegration, 337-343; social meaning of, 340

dissociative reaction, 94, 103

division of labor, 342-343

Doby, John T., 388

Dobzhansky, Theodosius, 83-85, 217

doctors, case study through, 363-364

Dollard, J., 88, 187

dominance-passivity relations, in Model community, 309

Dorland, W. A. Newman, 85

dreams, interpretation of, 380

dream symbolism, 61

drive, vs. instinct, 183

drug addiction, 105, 274

drugs, traumatic effects of, 58

Durkheim, Emile, 409, 412

dynamic equilibrium, 139, 169, 191; in community and town, 197; energy exchange in, 197; of personality system, 228; restoration of, 314

dynamic psychiatry, 60, 65, 125-126; modern era of, 127; multiplicity of objects in, 138

"dynamic system," concept of, 413

Eaton, Joseph, 87

economic depression, 197

economic loss, in anxiety cases, 48

economics, in Model community, 307

education, 31, 307

educational neglect, in mental deficiency, 54

educational programs, advances in, 214

educational system, shared sentiments in, 209

Eggan, Fred, 339

ego, 71; in personality structure, 64; in personality system, 21

elation, 107, 166

electrocardiograms, 40

Ellenberger, Henri F., 180

Elliott, M. A., 341

Emerson, Alfred E., 220

emotional crisis, 43-44, 47, 76

emotional difficulties, physiological disturbance and, 96

emotional instability, 27, 104

empathy, in anxiety neurosis, 69

encephalitis, 356; epidemic, 111; later symptoms of, 128; mental deficiency and, 155; mental disturbances and, 58

endocrine activity, 167

endocrine disturbances, 111

endogenous change, 198-199, 212, 229, 248, 314

energy: environmental, 22; psychic (see psychic energy)

energy exchange, 328; in community unit, 199; in sociocultural unit, 197

energy system, sentiments and, 243

energy utilization, in community unit, 292

English-French interactions, Northeast, 322

"enthymeme," concept of, 413

environment, 72, 98; conditions in, 49, 62; effect of on psychiatric disorders, 5; energy drawn from, 22; vs. heredity, 55-56, 67, 83; interdependence in, 190; noxious and benign, 177-178; physical, 189; reaction to, 51; reification of, 190; sociocultural (see sociocultural environment); striving sentiments and interference in, 149-150

epidemiological studies, 386; vs. case studies, 379; vs. clinical studies, 352, 367; interpretation of, 383

epilepsy, 111; heredity in, 121

Eskimo, cultural activities of, 281

essential psychical condition, 138-141; in Collection, 311; developmental history of, 247; disturbed, 160-162, 168, 356; essential striving sentiments and, 157; interference and, 150; instability in, 156; logical inconsistencies and, 242; in Model community, 308; as multidimensional process, 170-171; psychiatric disorder and, 246-247; striving and, 142; striving sentiments and, 147; unconscious motivation and, 249

"essential shared sentiments," 254-255 (see also shared sentiments)

essential social condition, 255

essential striving sentiments, 146-149, 246-247, 254, 259, 307-308; disagreeable feelings and, 160-161; mental deficiency and, 154; object substitution and, 160-161; pan-human needs and, 282-283; propositions concerning, 157

etiological factors, 354; in psychiatric diagnosis, 111-122, 357; symptom patterns and, 369

exogenous change, 198, 248, 314

Explorations in Social Psychiatry, 5

family, 64-66, 291, 293; in community unit, 216; "extended," 202; feeling-toned specifications in, 210; as functional configuration, 202; impaired relationships in, 97; kinship and, 203; in Model community, 307; overlapping, 202; patterns of, 309

family formation, group function and, 255

family history, in psychiatric diagnosis, 355, 357

fantasy: in Model community, 308; object substitution through, 164-165

Faris, Robert, 341

father, Oedipus complex and, 64-65

father role, sentiment clusters and, 262

fatigue, 102; mental illness and, 57
fear, 166; vs. anxiety, 126; in anxiety
    attack, 40; as cause of personality dis-
    order, 69; excessive, 154; forgetting
    and, 49-50; freedom from, 68; inborn,
    154; physiological symptoms accom-
    panying, 50
feeling: affect and, 20; and sentiment,
    404, 415
feral children, 120, 129
Firth, Raymond, 224, 296, 339, 412-413
fixation, 62
Fodor, Nandor, 86, 125
foetus, congenital diseases and, 85-86
forgetting: in anxiety cases, 49; as es-
    cape mechanism, 165; as psychiatric
    disorder, 102-103; of recent events, 144
    (see also amnesia)
Fowler, Manet, 388
frame of reference, 80, 255, 263, 278, 297,
    305-306, 330-331, 337, 391, 395; cogni-
    tive activity in, 241; development of,
    133; defined, 134; psychic energy in,
    249-250; striving sentiments in, 148-149
Frank, Jerome D., 178
Frank, Lawrence K., 86
fraternal organizations, 203
free associations, 380
free will, vs. determinism, 242
French, Vera, 406
French culture, Northeast, 369; psychiat-
    ric disorders and, 285-286
French language, in Northeast, 29, 162,
    204, 322
Freud, Sigmund, 22, 86, 127, 179-180,
    241, 353
Friedman, Milton, 36
friendship clusters, in sociocultural unit,
    203-204
Fromm, Erich, 86, 179
frustration, in interpersonal relation-
    ships, 64
function: malfunction and, 26, 345;
    personality and, 25; structure and, 222-
    223; theories of, 279, 286
functional configuration, in sociocultural
    unit, 202-203
"functional interdependence," 341
fundamental propositions, in psychical
    life, 141-146

Gantt, W. Horsley, 187
Gaynor, Frank, 125
genetic determinism, 54
genetic factors, 90, 335
genetics, 18, 52-53, 83-84 (see also he-
    redity)
genital stage, 60
Gerard, Ralph W., 220
German measles, pregnancy and, 57
Gillespie, R. D., 268
Gillin, John, 298
Ginsburg, Benson E., 83, 184

gloom, 107
Goldstein, Kurt, 180
Gorer, Geoffrey, 86, 90
Gottschalk, Louis, 36
government: in community unit, 216; in
    Model community, 307; organismic
    view of, 201; shared sentiments in,
    209; in sociocultural unit, 196
government groups, 203-204
gratification, interference with, 137
Greenacre, Phyllis, 86
Grinker, Roy R., 91, 128, 220
Gross, Neal, 90
group behavior: vs. individual, 263; sen-
    timent systems in, 207-210; shared sen-
    timents and symbols in, 206-209; in
    sociocultural environment, 194-195
group membership: broken homes and,
    328; in Collection, 311; in Model com-
    munity, 308; moral order and (see
    moral order); sociocultural categories
    of, 278; as striving sentiment, 148
group patterns, stability of, 252
guilt tendencies, 173
gun(s): phobic fear of, 100; as sexual
    symbol, 63, 66, 143; as symbol of man-
    liness, 70; as symbol of war experience,
    77-78
Gurvitch, Georges, 343

Haldane, J. B. S., 347
Hall, Calvin S., 219, 267
Hallowell, A. I., 86-87, 272
hallucination, 110-111, 370
Harbor Town, 36, 40, 313, 319, 415;
    class groupings in, 290-291; communi-
    cation networks in, 206; main com-
    ponents in, 204; sentiment changes in,
    215; as sociocultural unit, 196, 202-
    204; subsistence activities in, 197; un-
    completed story of, 391; urban-rural
    differences in, 294; "virtue rewarded"
    sentiment in, 257-259
Haring, Douglas G., 87
Harper, Ernest B., 341
Hart, Bernard, 405
Hartley, Eugene L., 89
hate, 166; in interpersonal relationships,
    64; outbursts of, 68
Hawley, Amos H., 296-297, 342
headache, 167, 176; fear and, 50
health: characteristic features of, 346;
    mental (see mental health); in Model
    community, 307; personality and, 28;
    preoccupation with, 165
health system, shared sentiments in, 209
heart failure, anxiety reaction mistaken
    for, 32-33, 35, 39, 78, 173, 240
Heinicke, Christoph, 266
Henderson, David, 268
heredity, 73, 75, 79, 82-83, 90, 97, 116,
    123, 172, 175; brain disorder and, 121;
    control of organism through, 140;
    effect of, vs. environment, 55-56, 67,

336; pathogenesis and, 44; in personality disorder, 117; in psychiatric diagnosis, 355, 358; in psychiatric disorder, 52-56, 120-122, 355; in psychotic disorders, 120, 355; relative weight of, 55
hierarchical integration, 407
Hilgard, Josephine, 81
Hinsie, L. E., 125, 387
Hoch, Paul H., 125, 128
Hockett, Charles F., 388
holism, 219, 337; cultural, 11; personality theory, 11, 231
Hollingshead, August B., 88, 299
Holmberg, Allan R., 298
Homans, George C., 411
homeostasis, personality and, 228
homosexual tendencies, interference in, 137; latent, 62
Honig, Emanuel M., 82
Honigmann, John J., 86-87
hormones, secondary sexual characteristics and, 54
Horney, Karen, 179, 404
hospital: in community unit, 176, 196, 203; mental (see mental hospital); shared sentiments and, 209, 213
hostility, 101, 278; in Collection, 311; as disintegration indicator, 318; in Model community, 308; psychological growth and, 72; as striving sentiment, 148
Houseworth, John H., 81
Hughes, Charles C., 182, 219, 224, 337, 388, 395
Hughes, James W., 90
Hughes, Jane, 337, 388, 395
Hume, David, 397-399, 410
husband-wife conflict, 74
hypertension, 167
hyperthyroidism, 44
hypnotherapy, 81
hypochondriasis, 94; defined, 102; as escape from "disagreeable sensations," 165
hysteria, 127, 359; defined, 104; as escape from "disagreeable sensations," 165

"I," consciousness and, 20-21; meaning of, 269
id, 71; in personality structure, 64; in personality system, 21
ideology, concept of, 395, 411-412
Idols, convention and, 218
incest wish, 64-65
industrial psychology, 407
industrialization, in Northeast, 30-31
industry, in community unit, 216
infancy: mental deficiency and, 120; origin of psychiatric disorders in, 74; psychological factors in, 79; unfolding urges in, 60, 62
inferiority feelings, 75
influenza, 85; encephalitis mistaken for, 58-59
Ingalls, Theodore H., 86

Inkeles, Alex, 87, 267
insecurity: class mobility and, 351; emotional crisis and, 47
instinct(s): concept of, 183; basic urges and, 230, 233; life-arc and, 66; as personality aspect, 19; striving sentiments and, 149; "strong" and "weak," 140
instinct satisfaction, 139; interference with, 137; in prenatal period, 60
institutions, 202-204, 291, 293, 397
integrated unit, 22
integration: components in, 21; concept of, in personality study, 18; idea represented by, 337; levels of, 17; meaning of, 344; personality and, 18; sociocultural, 263
integrity, 61
intelligence tests, social disintegration and, 315 (see also psychological tests)
interdependence: environment and, 190; sentiments and, 240
interest, concept of, 395
interference: defined, 247; elimination of, 168; essential psychical condition and, 146; internal and external, 138; person-centered, 154; "pure," 158; reality conflict as, 248; relation of, to essential psychical condition, 150-151; as sentiment conflict, 247; sociocultural environment and, 157; striving and, 135-138, 142; types of, 149-157 (see also striving)
intergroup differences, 84
interpersonal relationships, 159-160, 231, 279; low spirits and, 370; mental illness and, 54; patterns of, 72-74; psychic processes and, 64; role-taking in, 156; sentiments in, 68; symbols in, 238
intersentiment conflict, 137
intrapersonal behavior, 279
intrapersonal conflict, 138
intrapsychic behavior, 60, 73, 140, 263, 383
intrauterine influence, interference principle and, 137
Itard, J. M. G., 129

Jacks, Irving, 87
Jahoda, Marie, 273
James, William, 186, 269, 408
Japan, disrupted sociocultural groups in, 288
Jung, C. C., 402-403
juvenile delinquency, 165, 274, 319

Kahl, Joseph A., 299
Kallmann, Franz J., 82, 120
Kaplan, Oscar L., 92
Kardiner, Abram, 86, 266
Karpf, Fay B., 220
katabolism, 22, 139
Kelly, George A., 267, 439
Kelly, William H., 125

perception: anticipation and, 149, 247; interference and, 142; in psychological life experience, 57

persecution, delusions of, 105

personality: adaptability in, 242; biochemical aspects of, 16; biological dimensions of, 23; birth-death sequence of, 23-24; cross-section-of-the-moment in, 232-233, 245, 258-259, 277, 293-295, 326, 379; defined, 16-17, 27, 227, 242-243; disintegration of, 61-62; health as factor in, 28; hierarchical organization of behavior in, 270-273; holistic concept of, 231-232; individuality and, 192; integration of, 230; interlocking dimensions of, 24; intrapsychic aspects of, 263; life-story and cross-section, 25; "orchestra" analogy in, 18, 21; patterning concept in, 17-18; psychiatric categories and, 19; psychic energy of, 229; psychological content of, 18-19; self-integrating unit in, 172; sentiments and, 26-27, 149, 227-246; sequential relationship and, 228; social disintegration and, 326; sociocultural factors and, 189-190, 383; stability of, 242; striving and, 230; subpatterns of, 23; as "system," 17-18; threats to, 68; total, 26; "toward" and "against" concepts in (Horney), 404; unconscious factors in, 239; "unit" aspect of, 23

personality defect: in anxiety neurosis, 65-66; essential striving pattern and, 154; "fixing" of, 60; "pure," 158; two concepts of, 74

personality disorder, 104; alternatives to in Model community, 308-309; broader meaning of, 127; "case" of, 353; defined, 103; etiology of, 116; interference and, 137; sentiments as part of, 246; types of, 105-110

person-as-a-whole, 139

phobia, vs. sentiment, 406 (see also fear)

phobic reactions, 94, 99; object in, 100

physiological factors, 73, 75, 97, 116, 172; in brain disease, 121; in life experience, 57-59; in mental deficiency, 120; prenatal and infancy periods, 78-79; in psychiatric disorders, 122; in psychophysiological disorders, 118-119; social density and, 333

population changes, 212; in community unit, 198; in Northeast, 30; social disintegration and, 376

positive mental health, 386 (see also mental health)

prenatal period: instinctual satisfactions in, 60; physiological influences in, 78-79

probability sample, case studies and, 365

projection, 63

psychiatric cases, 94, 352-386 (see also case studies)

psychiatric clinic: case studies in, 362-363, 382; patient-psychiatrist relationships in, 379-380

psychiatric disorder: avoidance of, 168-171; case studies in, 352-386; categories of, 97; causes of, 38-39, 43, 171-175; child rearing and, 68; in Collection, 311; community characteristics and, 326; community functioning and, 287; defined, 16, 122-123; derivations of, 115-116; diagnosis in, 80; differentiation in, 98; distribution of, 304; early treatment in, 386; effect of environment on, 5 (see also environment); essential psychical condition and, 246-247; etiology of, 116, 119-120; faulty memory of motivations and experiences in, 64; "fostering" of, 158, 160; function-malfunction concept and, 26; fundamental propositions in, 146; heredity in, 52-56 (see also heredity); incompatible role-taking and, 72-73; interference and, 142; vs. mental health, 6, 363; in Model community, 309-310; patterns in, 133, 370; personality and, 16-28; physiological factors in (see physiological factors); prevention of, 5; propositions concerned with evolution of, 168, 177; propositions concerned with nonoccurrence of, 169-170, 177; psychological factors in, 59-80; range of, 94; sentiment as core of, 261; signs as indices of, 374-378; social disintegration and, 326, 331-333; sociocultural environment and, 133-179, 188-216, 277, 289-290; sociocultural factors in, 4, 172, 304, 391; striving and, 136, 148-149; symptoms and diagnosis in, 38; symptom patterns as indices of, 366-374; types of, described, 98-115; war neuroses and, 91-92

psychiatric examination, 192, 356-357, 364; symptom patterns and signs in, 359-362 (see also diagnosis)

psychiatric theories, 97

psychiatry: clinical (see clinical psychiatry); diagnosis in (see diagnosis); distinguished from psychoanalysis, 232; dynamic (see dynamic psychiatry); imbalance in, 240; nomenclature of, 124; sentiment in, 402-404; taxonomy in, 96

psychic energy, 229; vs. biological system, 22; concept of, 141, 181; in frame of reference, 249-250

psychic processes, 141-146, 229-230; behavior and, 17; inferences regarding, 365; personality and, 228-229

psychoanalysis: classical, 89, 270; distinguished from psychiatry, 232; evidence in, 66-67; professional rivalry in, 67; understanding of symbolism and symptoms in, 65

psychodynamics, 89, 241

psychological experience: in personality disorder, 117, 122; sociocultural factors and, 136

psychological factors, 75, 97; in brain disease, 121; in infancy and early childhood, 78-79; in mental deficiency, 120; in psychoneurosis, 116; in psychophysiological disorders, 118-119; in psychotic disorders, 119; in sociopathic disorders, 118

psychological tests: behavior evaluation through, 374; diagnostic terms used in, 374-375; lack of cooperation in, 364; standardization of, 377; vs. symptom evaluation, 376

psychology: clinical (see clinical psychology); industrial, 407; sentiment in, 404-409

psychoneurosis, 386; anxiety in, 99; anxiety reaction and, 93-94; "case" of, 353; confused with schizophrenia, 375; derivations of, 45-81; etiological factors in, 116-117; life-arc and, 48; malfunction in, 26; patterns of, 68

psychopathic conditions, sentiments and, 262

psychophysiological disorders, 81, 94, 105, 167-168, 386; "case" of, 353; in Collection, 312; dynamic equilibrium and, 169; etiology of, 118-119; in Model community, 309; symbolic meaning of, 174-175; vitamin deficiency and, 334

psychosis, 94, 386; alternatives to, in Model community, 309; "case" of, 353; in Collection, 312; malfunction in, 26; psychosomatic symptoms and, 81

psychosurgery, 82

psychotherapy, 354; in asthma, 106; interdependence factor in, 240

psychotic depressions, 106

public health services, Northeast, 31

Pueblo Indians: cultural activities of, 281; ritualism of, 315

Pumpian-Mindlin, Eugene, 180

punishment, in child development, 68

quasi-organisms, 212, 251; in community unit, 200, 296; culture in, 281; family as component of, 202; individual approach to, 328, 330; integration of, 339; sentiment systems in, 210, 256; sociocultural categories in, 279-280, 292

Queen, Stuart A., 341

Radcliffe-Brown, A. A., 279, 295, 412

Ramsey, Glenn V., 182

Rank, Otto, 86

Rapoport, Anatol, 219, 295

Rapoport, Robert N., 347

reality testing, 250

recall, anxiety attack and, 40-41

recognition: broken home and, 327-328; in Collection, 311; family and, 202; in

Model community, 308; obtaining of, 278, 287; as striving sentiment, 148

recreation: in community group, 203-204; patterns of, as disintegration indicator, 318

Redfield, Robert, 220, 295, 344, 347

Redlich, Frederick C., 88, 273, 299

reference group behavior, 181-182

rejection: anxiety as form of, 70; striving sentiment vs. interference and, 150

religion: breakdown in, 350; changes in, in Northeast, 31; in community unit, 216; in Model community, 307; vs. science, 350

religious conflicts, 42, 74, 153

religious groups, 202, 204, 210, 291, 293

Rennie, Thomas A. C., 299

research: case histories and, 363-365; plan for, 303-392

residues, 410

response-to-stress complex, 167

Richardson, Stephen A., 347

Rivers, W. H. R., 405

Roethlisberger, F. A., 407

Rogers, Carl, 180

role concept: in community unit, 216; interference and, 137; in sociocultural analysis, 72-73, 293; in sociocultural unit, 204

roles: as bridging concepts between individual and societal patterns, 262; conflicting and nonconflicting, 386; sociocultural categories and, 291

Rorschach Test, 113, 374

Rose, Arnold M., 88

Rosenberg, Morris, 343

Ross, W. Donald, 82

Russell, Bertrand, 217, 387

Russell, E. S., 347

sampling, in psychiatric case studies, 365

Sanders, Irwin T., 296

Sapir, Edward, 86, 272, 274, 344

Sarbin, Theodore R., 90

Sargent, S. Stanfield, 87

Sargent, William, 92

Sayres, William C., 388

schizophrenia, 97, 109, 128, 333; childhood (see childhood schizophrenia); confused with psychoneurosis, 375; described, 107-108; as escape from "disagreeable sensations," 165; heredity in, 120; "labeling" of, 354

school system: in community unit, 196; shared sentiments in, 209; in sociocultural unit, 176-177, 203, 214

Scott, John Paul, 89

secularization, 347; as disintegration indicator, 322

"security," vs. "opportunity," 31

security: broken home as risk to, 327; in Collection, 311; family and, 202; interference and, 150; in Model community, 308; object substitution and,

security (cont'd)
161; physical, 151-152, 162, 235, 278, 287; as striving sentiment, 148
self: concept of, 22, 269; evaluation of, 261; experience of, 271; as "internal community," 156
self-confidence, loss of, 145
self-disparagement, 173, 261
self-effacement, 104
self-integration, 22, 206, 259
"self-regarding sentiment" (McDougall), 405
Selye, Hans, 186
senility, 83, 111; onset of, 168
sentiment(s): abstractions and, 234; as acts, 243; alteration of through object substitution, 160-162; analytic use of, 245; in anthropology, 412-415; as approximation to nature, 245; beliefs as, 264-266; as bridging concept between sociocultural and personality processes, 257-266; in case studies, 379; categories of, 235; concept of, 227-266, 395-414; conflict of with basic urges, 74; as construct in personality, 149; conversion of to motive, 248; in current environmental situation, 52; defined, 396; definitions of, 232-233; distorted, 68; duration of, 236, 260; effect of on psychoanalyst, 67; effect of on unconscious processes, 240-241; etymological history of word, 396; flexibility of, 242; four types of, 260; functional significance of, 258-259; group patterns of, 252; in history of human thought, 264, 397-402; idea of, 26-27; in inductive psychology, 407; inferring of, 244; interdependence of, 242, 253; intrapersonal, 253; "invoking" of by symbols, 257; loss of, 152-153; mental health and, 246-251; nonshared, 211; origin of, 210-211; in patient-psychiatrist relations, 380; personality and, 61, 227-246, 384; as observable "phenomenon," 235; pre-existing, 211; prevalence of, 254; psychiatry and, 384, 402-404; "repertory" of, 265; shared (see shared sentiments); social science and, 402-415; sociocultural groups and, 251-256; of striving, 136 (see also striving sentiments); symbols and, 237, 251, 257; in therapist, 66-67; and thought feelings, 234, 247-248; time-dimension in, 236; unconscious factors in, 238-240
sentiment system, 216; changes in, 212-213, 251-252; disintegration of, 163; foresight in, 173; in sociocultural unit, 207-210; stability of, 255; technological advance and, 214
sex: psychiatric disorder and, 386; in Western culture, 283
sexual behavior: in Collection, 312; deviant, 105; diversion through, 166

sexuality, 60
sexual promiscuity, as defective object, 164
sexual satisfaction, 235, 278; in Collection, 311; in Model community, 308; poverty and, 328; sociocultural categories and, 287; as striving sentiment, 148
sexual symbols, 144-145
sexual urge: absence of, 155; in infancy and childhood, 60; as personality aspect, 19
Shand, A. F., 402, 404
shared sentiments, 206-209, 252, 328, 409; in disintegration studies, 325; healthy vs. unhealthy environment of, 263; in Model community, 308; plasticity of, 211-212; symptom patterns and, 368; typology of, 254-255; variations in, 259
shared symbols, 217; in Model community, 307
Shatzky, Jacob, 125, 387
Sherif, Muzafer, 182
Shull, George Harrison, 84
signs: as indices of psychiatric disorder, 374-378; in psychological tests, 374; vs. symptoms in mental illness, 38-39, 355, 359-362
Simpson, George, 343
slime mold, cell organization in, 200
Smith, Adam, 399, 408, 410
Smith, M. Brewster, 271, 273
Smith, Marian W., 87
Smith, Robert J., 298, 348
social behavior, cultural patterns in, 282
social change, as disintegration indicator, 322
social disintegration, 290; as antecedent to psychiatric disorders, 332; broken homes as indicator of, 318; community comparisons and, 303-336; definition of, 306-315; disaster as indicator of, 320; genetic factors in, 325; heredity vs. environmental factors in, 335-336; indices of, 315-326, 330, 342, 390; in Northeast, 289; noxious and benign climates in, 329; poverty and illness in, 321; psychiatric disorders and, 326, 331-332, 385; relative nature of, 314, 323-324; vitamin deficiency and, 333-334
social health, 255, 263
social pathology: "disorganization" and, 340; vs. psychopathology, 263
social science, sentiment in, 402-415
Social Science Research Council, 5
social structure, 221-223; vs. social organization, 338-339
"socialized feeling," sentiment as, 410
society: abstract implications of, 234; self-integrating units in, 216-217; three functions of, 348
sociocultural components, problems of, 10

sociocultural environment, 68, 123, 188-217; communication and coordination in, 205-216; community in, 196-197; correlations vs. causal relationships in, 193; essential striving sentiments and, 157-160; hereditary factors and, 56; indefinite nature of, 192; individual behavior in, 194; interferences arising in, 149-150; interpersonal relationships and, 159-160; investigator's relation to, 192-193; noxious vs. benign, 177-178; personality in, 189-190; propositions relating to, 158-159; psychiatric disorder and, 4, 135, 172, 175-177 (*see also* psychiatric disorder); self-integrating units in, 216-217; technological change and, 212-214
sociocultural indicators, 315-317
sociocultural patterns: personality and, 383; polar categories and, 278
sociocultural unit, 194-205; basic urges and, 205; communication and coordination in, 205-216; components of, 202-205; family as component of, 202-203; government in, 201; organismic view of, 200-201; status quo in, 198 (*see also* community)
socioeconomic classes, 204, 210, 216, 256, 274, 290-291, 386; in community unit, 204; social mobility and, 351
sociology: culture in, 297; sentiment in, 409-412
sociopathic disturbance, 94; in Collection, 312; defined, 104-105, 127; etiology of, 118; in Model community, 308-309
Spencer, Herbert, 279
Spicer, Edward H., 347
Spiegel, John P., 91
spontaneity, 25, 151; in Collection, 311; as community need, 198; expression of, 287; family and, 202; as striving sentiment, 148, 242, 278, 308, 328
Srole, Leo, 299, 344
Stecher, Robert M., 85
Stern, Marvin, 82
Sterne, Lawrence, 398, 410
Steward, Julian H., 345
Stigler, George, 36
Stirling County Study, 4-7, 357
Stout, G. F., 404
Straus, Anselm, 89
stress: anxiety attack and, 173-174; in Collection, 312; psychiatric disorders and, 330
striving: act of, 136; essential psychical condition in, 138-142; fundamental propositions concerning, 146; interference with, 136, 149-157, 247; object in, 138; personality and, 230, 270; state of, 135
striving sentiments, 136, 235; in community needs, 197-198; essential (*see* essential striving sentiments); factors

in, 146; lack of, 155; loss of, 152-153; mental deficiency and, 154; objects in, 248 (*see also* object); sociocultural sub-patterns and, 205; unconscious process and, 143
structure: concept of, 221-223; vs. function, 223
"substitutability of symptoms," 51-52
Suchman, E. A., 348
suicide, 70, 143-144
Sullivan, Harry Stack, 69, 88-89, 179, 402
superego, 71; in personality structure, 21, 64
supplementation, in diagnoses, 376
suspiciousness, 103, 166; excessive, 155
Sutton, F. X., 274
Swift, Jonathan, 398
symbiotic interdependence, 342
symbolism: in maternal relations, 70; sentiment and, 409; sexual, 65-66
symbolization, 272
symbols, 349-350; in communication, 206; invoking of sentiments by, 257; in patient-psychiatrist relations, 380; in psychiatric diagnosis, 38; sentiments as, 237, 251, 253-254; shared, 207
symptom patterns, 354-355; appraisals vs. diagnosis in, 367; as "common denominator," 366; in community unit, 369; false positives and negatives in, 373; as indices of psychiatric disorder, 366-374; pattern quality in, 370; in psychiatric examination, 359-362
symptoms: as basis for definition of mental illness, 97-98; as constellations of sentiments, 240; in psychiatric diagnosis, 355; in psychiatric disorders, 38 (*see also* symptom patterns); vs. signs, 362; substitutability of, 51
syndromes, classification of, 38 (*see also* brain syndrome)
syphilis: congenital, 85; fear of, 99-100; mental deficiency and, 58
system: concept of, in personality study, 17; self-integrating, 22

tachycardia, paroxysmal, 105
Tansley, A. G., 405
Tax, Sol, 339
technological change, 274, 349; sociocultural environment and, 212-214
Teicher, Morton I., 87
"templates," 396
"temporal thickness," 24
Thematic Apperception Test (TAT), 113, 374
"theme," concept of, 395, 413
therapist, effect of personal experience on, 67
therapy, diagnosis and, 357
Thomas, Alexander, 82
Thomas, W. I., 184, 343

Index

451